Our Angry Hospital

*How Goliath Defeated David
With Misused Power*

Jerry Martin

Our Angry Hospital
How Goliath Defeated David With Misused
Power

Dedication

This book is dedicated with sincere gratitude and admiration to the many physicians, nurses, CNAs, and technicians who lovingly, and with uncommon professional skills, devote their lives, after years of medical study and research, to unglamorous and un-extolled activities that save and significantly improve the lives of many total strangers.

Acknowledgments

I appreciate the loving feedback and generous support offered by Candi Suddjian. Suddjian's proof reading and cooperative collaboration with tasteful opinions were all operative and intelligent. She was partially responsible for bringing this novel out of the forgotten depths of my computer into the light of publication. Her encouragement lit my dormant fire.

Joyce Anastasia's book, *Extraordinary Leadership During Extraordinary Times*, was very helpful in accurately describing the problems with the prevailing destructive leadership that was practiced by many of the managers and administrators in our hospital. Anastasia's accurate description of abusive <u>power over</u> leadership rather than productive <u>power with</u> leadership described the difficulties that destroyed our morale, motivation and daily joy.

The team at AMZ Publishing Pros who helped me prepare this book for self publication were Marshall Salazar, James Horn, Helen Cooper, Antonio Lopez, Walter Krasniqi, and Tammy Z.

Table of Contents

Introduction

This novel is mostly based on events I witnessed during fourteen years of employment. Some events, however, are products of my fertile imagination and are included to add color to a potentially pedestrian storyline. Names have been changed, not to protect the innocent (whatever that means), but rather to avoid lawsuits. Occasionally the order of events has been changed for plot development, and embellishments made for humor.

Being in a unique position, well educated, but working in a corporate controlled manual labor job, I felt compelled to write about a common problem, easily ignored and denied, that exists in many American corporations. The low level worker needs and deserves a voice, mostly silenced until now. Not many janitors with two college degrees and 14 years work experience write novels. I found myself in a disrespected, though very necessary, job. I needed to speak out and represent an important segment of our common work force. More people need to become aware of a very destructive managerial obstacle that requires repairing. I hope this book calls attention to a ruinous flat tire on which we have been driving for far too long.

Chapter 1: Flush

He called himself Flush. "The job ain't over 'til the *flushin's* done," he often proclaimed. It took a while, but over time everyone else called him Flush, too.

He said "Flush" best described his job as a porter, one who removes waste that is a constant in a hospital. The porter moves through all the halls, pulling bags of soiled linen, common trash, bio-med waste, chemo dross, and recyclable materials. He puts most of it into a large wagon, takes it down to the back of the building, and sorts it into different locations.

Flush and I first met five years ago in a mid-size hospital in northern California. I had just been hired, part-time, in the Environmental Services Department (EVS), where Flush had worked for eight years. Flush trained me as a porter when I was hired, overcoming our 46 years difference in ages. He was 70, and I was 24.

Over several years, Flush and I became good friends, talking a lot about many subjects regarding our jobs. I sometimes partied at his modest house, with him drinking red wine, which he did about once a week, and me often drinking beer. Sometimes some of his friends would come with cannabis, which we used sparingly but with great hilarity and imagination. It opened us up and helped us all drop our community-imposed introversion, diving into creative behavior seen mostly by friends. We had fun together, though, in case you're wondering, certainly nothing sexual. We both were attracted to women's bodies, if not the complexities they always brought to every relationship.

During one of many evenings, Flush said he'd been married before to a wonderful wife who died of cancer 15 years ago. They had no kids, intentionally, but were very fortunate for the 22 years they had together. She was a lawyer, very bright, who appreciated his sense of humor and slightly eccentric personality. Her only fault was she liked to argue, which sometimes stretched his patience. He hated arguments and angry people who argued a lot. I'm not sure, but he sort of suggested that she objected to his

4

smoking pot; she thought he could progress further without it.

I could tell by his recounting that he missed her a lot. Replacing her had been unsuccessful, hence he was satisfied being a bachelor. He said he'd like to find another wife, but he had become very particular and knew what he wanted; he wouldn't accept less, so was unlikely to try marriage again.

I'm much younger than Flush, but we became friends starting my first day on the job when he trained me. I was fortunate for his kindness and leadership in a job in which I expected neither. He showed me how to grow in a boring job that I could have resisted and devalued. To me, he was a mentor, the parent I didn't have, who took the time to teach some of the attitudes and capabilities necessary for success in this complex world we have created. I began to admire his picaresque personality, which sometimes brought fun to a usually boring job.

Flush told me that when he first took the job eight years before I came, he thought it would be temporary, filling a gap to pay his bills. He applied for the job with hesitation. It had been mentioned to him by a female friend, Delphus, who had applied but been turned down. He didn't consider it anything for which he was suited, educated, or interested. He figured 3 months max, and he'd find another job better matching his capacities. But now, years later, he was still there, having found things about himself and the job that were more valuable than originally considered.

He taught me that sometimes how you do a job is as important as what the job does. You can make hauling the discarded trash a great contribution if you combine it with a friendly manner towards patients, most of whom are desperate for friends in an unfamiliar place that's uncomfortable when it isn't mind-numbingly boring. Casual friendliness worked well for visitors, who were also uncomfortable and "lost" in these unfamiliar and often overwhelming circumstances.

During his fourteen years of service in the hospital, Flush decided to develop a strong extroverted personality, which he could turn on and off. From a moderately quiet introvert, he became more outgoing and friendly, characteristics that gave him a fuller life. He convinced me to take advantage of this opportunity, which I did. It was like a hands-on college-level course to me, more useful than most courses I took. Following his pattern of casual friendliness, rare and needed in a hospital, I overcame my shyness and learned the value of extroversion.

Flush was way overqualified for his janitor position. He had a PhD in anthropology and, as I could recall, taught many college courses over his 75 years; he also wrote a published textbook that nobody read. But, as he explained, he couldn't survive on the little salary part-time college teaching provided and thought custodial work in a medical context would expand his understanding of how humans work.

He was right. He came to regard his job as a hands-on educational opportunity far beyond any college course he had taken or taught. And it gave him a wonderful chance to develop warmth while interacting with other humans, patients and visitors, needing a friend, and co-workers with friendly attitudes. Flush was one of the most interesting people I ever met. And the only college graduate in Environmental Services until I came.

I had just graduated from Chico State University as an undistinguished journalism major. I had a B average and could have done better had I tried, but I had spent much of my college years chasing women, having bought the middle-class myth that I needed a wife to become complete, a partner who would spark my potential. I didn't find her and am still looking, though now, with a mature realism I lacked before several unsuccessful forays into romance taught me that some women are more trouble than they're worth.

I came to writing through my dad. Before his divorce from my mom, as a kid, I remember seeing him on weekends, between his bureaucratic job, writing longhand on yellow pads of paper. He was usually outside, sitting alone, writing his novel. It never got published, and I'm sure his aspiration was never totally extinguished. I never read it and paid little attention during my youth. I'm sure his example unconsciously formed my penchant for writing, which got me through journalism school doing something I enjoyed. It wasn't really work.

As an undergraduate, I edited the college literary magazine during my senior year. We put out three issues of students' writings. I wrote a couple of short stories and a poem that was printed in my junior year. Editing was fun, more work than I expected, and I realized I was articulate but not eloquent. I hate Shakespeare; can't really understand the original. Not even fond of the synopsis of his plays. I know a guy who named his dog, a Scottie, "Lady Macbeth."

I still think I was wise to choose journalism. Someday, I might get a journalist's job and have a career. Not today. And probably not tomorrow. But writing this novel is close and satisfies, for now, my literary ambitions.

Upon graduation, my job prospects were dismal, not to mention my $33,000 in debt, money borrowed over four years to attend a not-anything-special state college. Eight months after graduation, while searching from the comfort and security of my mother and step-father's home, I was happy to get any job (other than the army), even at a local hospital that didn't employ any of my skills, education, or ambitions. I was still trying to figure out what I wanted to be when I "grow up," hoping for a chance to develop a career of yet undiscovered specifics. Maybe journalism related.

My job search in journalism has proven fruitless so far. In college, they never told us that jobs were slim and might require moving to some small town in rural Alaska. I was offered an intern (unpaid) job for six months at a small weekly news rag in the desert near Death Valley, California; I had enough sense to reject it. Glad I did. The hospital job gave me freedom and an efficiency apartment away from the bickering of my mom and the disapproval of my step-dad. And my two younger step-sisters were annoying, also. I even bought a used car, an old 1986 Pontiac with 226,000 miles. I was glad for the change but visited them, ten miles away, about once a month.

Except for training, Flush and I didn't work side-by-side, but we often crossed paths several times each day. We also sometimes ate and took breaks together in the cafeteria. We also shared strong opinions (his, not mine, as I was too young to have any worth mentioning, but he had plenty for both of us) in his relaxed bachelor house, which was an "oasis from daily turmoil" for me. He influenced me like a close grandfather, and many of my opinions were directly attributed to Flush.

Our custodial jobs didn't fit either of us well but served our separate financial purposes at the time. He convinced me that there were several things about the job that were educational, making it less onerous. Flush also tinkered with songwriting. Here's one of his masterpieces, like his others, going nowhere. It covers the many different aspects of our job as a porter.

"Flush Rules"
(to the tune of "Puff the Magic Dragon")

Flush, the dirty porter
Toils in the halls
hefting bags of poop and such
His orders, they are tall

Flush, the busy porter
Running when he can
Knocking over wheelchairs
With his massive smelly van

Flush, the worried porter
Knows that he is late
Removing trash from everywhere
Smells like last week's bait

You ask why he's so happy
Here's the reason why
The job gives him exercise
His spirit will not die

Flush, the smiling porter
Shining when he works
A beaming smile is all he's got
He has no other perks

Flush, the mean old porter
The devil's next of kin
His wagon's like a bowling ball
The patients are the pins

Flush, the dismal porter
Had an attitude
When things went wrong and not his way
He came across as rude

Flush, the stinky porter
Always has to clean
His rancid hands 'bout 50 times
His clothes about 19

Flush, the stupid porter
Needs a GPS
He gets lost most everyday
But never will confess

Flush, the brilliant porter
Lived by his wits
But when it came to huffin' trash
His performance was the pits

Flush, the timid porter
Runs when he is scared
From anything that isn't bagged
Or anybody bared

Flush, the singing porter
Warbles like a lark
Sing this song and you will see
It gives your job a spark

He also told me of his concern. Three different men, all porters at NCMH, had died from cancer over a period of eight years. This could have been a coincidence, as there was no verified cause and effect between the job and their deaths. Still, that many mortalities of porters in a short time was at the back of his mind. He didn't present it as a warning. It was just something that needed awareness. Was there something about hauling hospital waste that caused cancer?

Over those fourteen years, Flush occasionally saw a problem in the hospital. Sometimes, he'd point it out to a manager, particularly if he had a solution, which was often the case. This might be considered small-time whistleblowing, except he never took it outside hospital walls. He never mentioned our problems to the local newspaper, two radio stations, or a public access TV station, so maybe he wasn't a whistleblower after all. I'm probably the whistleblower with this book since I plan to describe the destructive "war" between us blue-collar workers and an opaque, insensitive, authoritarian administration, probably representing many such in hospitals and other private institutions that devolved into mercenary efforts that penalize their workers. If so, it's a whistle that needs blowing often.

I just saw the movie, *The Hospital*, starring George C. Scott, released in 1971. It took place in a large hospital in New York City. It mostly dealt with doctors, nurses, and patients and had a lot of medical terminology. It also had a complex, fictionalized (I assume) plot with several doctors and a nurse being murdered in such a way as to look like accidents. It had a suicidal doc, a psychotic doc, and a Native American shaman doing a war dance in a patient's room. It also showed some high-level corruption, confusion among professionals, a seduction, a strike, and a community on a warpath protesting housing neglect.

Except for the fictionalized ending, what you're reading has none of these Hollywoodish things. It's mostly from the point of view of a janitor, me, who knows a few medical terms (which are mostly not needed here), and I'm writing about a few docs and nurses. Of course, they're there, but only in peripheral roles. However, almost everything in this novel is based on real events. There's not much fiction (though I'm guilty of a few embellishments), just my interpretation of reality in a mid-size, 21st-century, American hospital in rural northern California. Hollywood will be bored until the ending. I hope you're not. I wasn't, sometimes. And Flush's mentoring gave me insights and growth unavailable elsewhere.

Most of the doctors and nurses are excellent, as near as I could tell. This story in no way intends to criticize them. They work hard in difficult jobs and circumstances and, in my experience, care a lot about patients. Patient survey, a short questionnaire filled out by patients when leaving, showed a high level of satisfaction. I wish the medical staff the best and came to admire them for their conscientious, generous, loving natures and competent professionalism. I wish I could say the same for the administration.

***

We porters used two large wagons, one red and one blue. They were both about five feet tall, three feet wide, and six feet long. They were pushed (one at a time) on four large creaky, never maintained wheels. When empty, they were easy to push. Top empty speed was about 1 MPH. When full, they weighed between 300 and 600 pounds and were hard to maneuver through halls occupied by many other things you didn't want to hit, even at 1/2 MPH. Once there were three wagons, but some administrative fool, without consulting the porters, eliminated one of them. Those kind of decisions were common.

Each of the five kinds of trash is designated by colored plastic bags; blue for linen, clear for common trash, red for bio-meds, yellow for chemo, and green for recyclables. The different colors are very useful for differentiation. The red bio-meds and yellow chemo bags were transported in red "tote" barrels on wheels with large, heavy flip-top lids. The blue, clear, and green bags were transported in the two large aforementioned wagons.

While training me as a porter, Flush employed a self-created acronym: APEAM. It stood for Advanced Porter Evacuating Air Maneuver. This was important, as it allowed us porters to fill the wagon as much as possible before having to take it down to be emptied. It involved squeezing the air out of every bag. He usually did it before tying the bag shut. But sometimes, the bag was already tied shut, so he'd punch a hole in the bag with his thumb and then squeeze the air out. APEAM required setting the air-filled bag on the frame that held the bag and then putting his chest on the bag to squeeze the air out. This looked like a monkey-making whoopee with a football if seen from the back. Without APEAMing, we would haul a lot of air and not much waste. This was inefficient and would require too many trips with the wagon. So APEAMing was a critical skill in every porter's repertoire.

Flush named the blue wagon *Sigmoid.* Sigmoid is the lower section of the large intestine in the human digestive system, a word he had learned in a medical terminology class. Except for color, Sigmoid, the wagon, was analogous to the body part, both serving a holding purpose. However, the wagon held waste contained in pretty, multi-colored plastic bags (possibly compared to a rainbow), while the lower intestine in humans holds waste of a darker, less cheerful hue.

He named the red wagon *RRR,* or *Triple R.* Many people asked him what that stood for. *"Rolling Red Rectum"* always got a chuckle. Most people understand the rectum's role in human waste removal.

In that same medical terminology class, Flush also learned *peristalsis,* which is the muscular contractions of intestines in the digestive system. This action pushes food, while it becomes poop, through and out, as waste. Porters do this with hospital dross. He taught this word to me, which became my elusive description of my hospital title to people I wanted to deceive into thinking I was important. Some girls were impressed when I bragged, "I'm the peristalsis of the hospital," hoping they wouldn't ask for a definition. If they had a medical background, they didn't need to; if they didn't know medicine, they rarely inquired further.

Another medical term, *ileus*, describes the log jam in our bodies when peristalsis fails; "ain't nothin' movin'," as they say in the nurse's lounge. It's an uncomfortable condition which, metaphorically speaking, in a hospital context, with no waste being removed, would affect a powerfully repugnant odor, eventually shutting down the place. Smelling our condition, were ileus ever to occur for the whole hospital for 2 or more days, our patients would become impatient. Flush quickly convinced me of the importance of the porter job to counter ileus.

Those four words, *sigmoid*, *rectum*, *peristalsis*, and *ileus*, comprised the entire necessary medical vocabulary for porters, according to Flush. A teacher by nature, he taught this uncommon vernacular to all newer male employees who learned porter-dom from him. Flush wrote a poem, intended to become a song, a melody for which was never composed. Here it is:

Winnie Ain't the Only Pooh in Town

Winnie ain't the only pooh in town
Winnie's cute and cuddly and he's brown
A legendary teddy bear
But other pooh is not so fair
Winnie's not the only pooh in town

Winnie ain't the only pooh in town
He's happy and he never wears a frown
But porters know there's more
That's <u>not</u> to be adored
Winnie ain't the only pooh that's brown

Winnie ain't the only pooh in town
We porters haul a lot of pooh around
We smell it everywhere
In bags and in the air
No, Winnie's not the only pooh in town

Winnie ain't the only pooh in town
He's second when it comes to gettin 'down
We porters always know
That pooh has got 'ta flow
Winnie's not the only pooh around

Winnie ain't the only pooh in town
Nurses witness pooh when it's unbound
Doctors see it too
For them it's nothing new
No, Winnie's not the only pooh in town

When considering the human digestive system, we immediately conclude that the entrance, known as a mouth, gets a lot more attention and respect than the exit. Food, talking, and kissing all take place at the entrance and are valued intensely, in public, by all humans. But there's no glory at the exit end. We are porters, the bowel bosses, the masters of movement, sometimes cathartic, necessary to make the purging happen smoothly. Sometimes (never intended for the public) Flush would chant: "Purge! Purge! Purge!" as he quietly, professionally, made his appointed rounds.

Porter is at the bottom of all hospital hierarchies. Porter-dom is a sometimes messy (inconsiderate people discarded half-filled paper cups in the trash, sometimes leaking liquids from the bags onto the floor, to be cleaned up by unsuspecting, now irritated, porters), frequently stinky, potentially dangerous, and disrespected job that deserves better public relations. Granted, it's not a high-skilled, prestigious job; almost everyone *could* do it with some training. But how many of us *would* do the job long enough to solve the problem? Wouldn't is just as exclusionary as couldn't.

In his professional defense, Flush eventually persuaded the medical employees that being the peristalsis was important and indispensable for human and hospital survival. In some unfortunate hypothetical situation, if there were nobody doing the job of hospital porter for two days, a hospital would be a very sick, clogged up, stinky, and constipated body. Obstipation (thanks to Dr. Sam Chin for this arcane word) would set in. If this dereliction continued, we could kiss our JCAHO approval and our jobs goodbye as state inspectors would shut the hospital down. Performing 24 hours a day, portering is very important in every hospital, but nobody realizes it except porters.

This could not be said about the high-paid administrators whose offices were on the top (2nd) floor. These folks, all women, took off for two weeks over Christmas and New Year. Two weeks with nobody doing administrators' jobs, the hospital continued to function, and few noticed their absence.

Some employees rendered Flush the respect he and his job deserved. They recognized that, in his case, substance trumped status. Some even liked him, mostly for his open personality, often despite the professional disparity between their occupations.

Others, driven by stereotypes, continued to see him as a low-level manual laborer of common variety, just a trash man. Unaware of his Ph.D., to them, Flush was like the untouchables in old caste India, highly despised men who collected garbage and dead bodies in every community. These co-workers failed to recognize his specialness

and unusual contributions.

Flush's unbridled sense of humor sometimes backfired, though not enough to get him fired or even in serious jeopardy. On my second day, while training with him, he pulled a stunt that was popular with the patients but received a silent rebuke from the director of Cardio Rehab. This was a successful program for older ex-patients, now recovering from heart attacks, who came twice a week for an hour to work out together on a variety of exercise machines. These old timers rode stationary bicycles and treadmills while conversing with others like themselves. This program was as much a socializing occasion as it was for physical exercise. Everyone left sweaty and tired but happy to have recently recovered from near death and on the mend.

Flush and I entered the large exercise room without any interruption, though several patients smiled and greeted him; he was popular and known to them. He came there every day, so they knew each other. He was about their age, in his seventies, so some admired his ability to still do physical work and get paid, with a fair energy level.

Flush tied the blue bag of towels and hoisted it from its stand. He told me to replace it with a new empty bag. He started to carry the full bag towards the hall, holding it in front of him with both hands. Then he faked a trip and fell forward, landing on the bag, which served as a cushion to avoid injury. There was a loud "Thump!" as he landed and groaned on the floor, while most of the patients erupted in laughter. When he stood up, the room showed appreciation with applause. Comedy was rare here, unexpected in a hospital which produced very little humor, and appreciated by old-timers without much to laugh about.

The Cardio Rehab director gave him a dirty look, as was expected by admin, but I suspect she secretly admired his levity and welcomed it, which helped her patients. She knew the power of humor. He did it often, so I knew she didn't report him for punishment. Later, I copied it, too, but never in that room. That was Flush's stage. It always got a laugh and countered a boring and often depressing atmosphere.

***

The hospital officially calls us "attendant," which probably sounds better than janitor, or porter, or even custodian (an attempt at dignity). But "attendant" is pathetically general, so unspecific it says nothing, except we are in attendance. So is the flag pole out front. Our title says we're there, attending. "Attending to what?" a reasonably curious person might ask. "Whatever" would be a reasonable answer. For a title, it's weak, miserably non-descriptive, and marginally respectable. It somehow failed to make me proud of my recent college degree.

Fortunately, there were sub-titles, though "Attendant" appeared on the name badges of the eight full-time and six part-time men in EVS. The sixteen full and part-time EVS women had "House Keeper" on their name badges.

**

One of Flush's many successful attempts to engage patients and their visitors in interesting conversation occurred many times in a small area at the end of a long hall in 2 North. Nearby, Room 200 was reserved for patients (always one at a time) on the fast train to the great beyond and hereafter, and was furnished more comfortably than the other rooms. It was occupied by a different patient, horizontally declining, about once or twice a week. Visits by friends and family were usually emotional, hushed, and restrained; sometimes, Room 200 would have eight or ten grieving kindred spirits. They all expected to see tomorrow, unlike the expiring center of attention. The impending departure of that soul was imminent.

Outside the room were six armchairs arranged against three walls at the end of a long hall. There was a table with a lamp and several pitifully unpopular magazines in one corner. An original painting gifted to the hospital by a very talented artist, Kathleen French, a cancer survivor, hung on one wall. This beautiful work of art was a critical tool that Flush used to make friends while temporarily distracting visitors from their grief.

The picture displayed a winter landscape out in the countryside; a barn at the edge of a forest on a snow-covered hill, two geese in flight over a small stream, and a large hilltop leafless oak casting a long shadow across the frozen winter ground. The sky in the background was colored with pinks and yellows, the kind of sky we see at sunrise and sunset. Behind the barn was a cylindrical, two-story silo with a round roof, half covered with snow. It proved relevant to the mystery.

Sometimes saddened and/or exhausted relatives gathered in the chairs outside Room 200, away from the gloomy, grim darkness that death unavoidably delivered inside the room. It might be three middle-aged children, two brothers and a sister, consoling each other, whose 81-year-old mom was the paying "guest." It might be a 78-year-old younger sister of an 82-year-old dying brother and his 80-year-old wife. It might be family and friends of a young woman dying of cancer.

In addition to these grieving relatives, other recipients of Flush's unique tactic were patients pushing an IV pole, wearing pajamas and patient gowns and yellow socks, accompanied by a nurse or CNA (Certified Nursing Assistant—she's the one who does most of the dirty work), or a family member, shuffling around the 2 North and 2 South hallways. If they were going towards Room 200 and Flush was there, he would politely invite them to be detectives. Flush never asked the seriously impaired patients who wouldn't feel comfortable participating in his challenge. Whether it was strolling patients or grieving sitters in that area outside Room 200, Flush often would make friends, using the painting as a "tool." These people were always receptive, welcoming the diversion from their immediate troubles.

"Can I show you a painting?" he'd start a conversation. After a surprised hesitation (conversations like this rarely happened with hospital staffers), they'd always say, "Sure."

At the painting, he'd say, "This is my favorite painting in the hospital. It was done by a patient here, who was cured of cancer but later died. Her daughter works here now."

This would get their attention, and the patient and medical staff or family members would now be scrutinizing the painting.

Then Flush would ask, "Look at the sky. Look at the colors. Now you have to be a detective. Is it a sunset? Or a sunrise? It's got to be one or the other. I had to look at it many times, but I found a clue that is definitive."

After some reflection, someone might say, "I think its sunrise."

"Why?"

"There's a light on in the barn."

Flush, having heard this many times, would refute, "But the light could be on in the evening, too."

"Yeah, I guess you're right."

Then another visitor might say, "It's sunset because the geese are flying."

"But geese fly in the morning, too." Flush was a hard teacher.

They'd study it more and discuss various theories, but rarely arrive at a definite rise or set decision. Flush would usually tell them, but only if they asked.

"It's a sunrise. Look at the round roof on top of the silo. Half has snow and half doesn't. In the Northern Hemisphere, the sun goes across a southern arc. So the half without snow is to the south, so we must be looking east, so it must be a sunrise."

"Ohhhhhhh, yeah. That makes sense."

These kinds of interactions with the public were typical of Flush. He brought much more to his job than just collecting waste, but the administration never recognized his contributions. In fact, some even complained that he was wasting time. They were good at turning a good thing into a bad thing. This was common at NCMH. And Flush was sometimes the target of narrow-minded people with no imagination. In this case, their complaints failed to curtail Flush's successful distraction from the visitors' unavoidable sorrow.

***

Flush also tried to relate to staff, at least to those who were receptive and friendly. He knew he couldn't offer anything of medical value, but his sense of humor and comradeship motivated him to reach out when appropriate.

Every morning he'd enter the Emergency Department to collect the blue bags of soiled linen from the night before and would cheerfully say to the doctors, nurses, and occasional paramedics, who were usually stressed out, "Good morning, you lifesavers."

Some clever doc, intentionally referring to the candy, might say, "What flavor are we?"

"The flavor of angels on a mission," responded Flush.

***

Several years ago, before NCMH was sold to a large corporation (Diggery Wealth) in 2012, the hospital allowed humor in its monthly newsletter. Flush was a good writer who occasionally wrote humor for the newsletter. Introducing himself as the newest porter, transitioning from his former job as a floorist, Flush wrote the following article.

In my last column in December, I mentioned my formal title ("Minister of Evacuation"), which I once wore proudly, bestowed upon me by Dr. Lance Boil, in a moment of mirth. However, after several frustrating months of trying feebly to convince people that I was of Ministerial caliber, and getting incredulous looks from the skeptics, I've now realized that the title was pretentious, inappropriate and possibly even egotistical. Curse you, Doctor Boil!

Then I thought "Agent of Purgation" sounded good enough to mention at my 50th high school reunion, but then I realized it's not much of an improvement over 'M. of E.' So I have adopted a new nick name, (for use only at work, in this job), which, I think, properly and accurately describes, in a more realistic, down-to-earth tone, my less than glamorous function here.

Call me "Flush."

I'm offering a $5 prize to the person who can best vocally reproduce the sound of a toilet flushing.

He never had to pay this offer; several attempts were pitifully inaccurate, unworthy of any award.

***

Most people imagine a porter's job is slow, repetitive, dull, and uninspiring. They'd be right. But Flush learned how to bring fun, sometimes, to an otherwise dreary, humdrum job. Two "incidents" happened to him, both of which are worth writing (and reading, I hope) about here.

It's not often that porters are called to heroism. They work among heroes, people who, in their varied jobs, save lives as a matter of everyday activities. But saving lives is not in a porter's job description. The most Flush ever saved is a ripped bag of trash that would spill a mess if he didn't notice and tie it up, not exactly the stuff of heroics. Flush never sutured a gushing wound or applied CPR or gave an aspirin to a stroke victim.

But one boring day, he got an excited call: "Stat! Will the porter report to 1 South immediately? There's a dangerous spider on

35

the loose, threatening death and panic. Stat!" "Stat" was hospital vernacular for "drop everything and hurry immediately to this emergency." Without hesitation, Flush dropped his usual chores of huffing soiled linen bags and rushed to the rescue. On his way, he found two women, a nurse and a technician, huddled, in fear, clutching each other for protection as if King Kong were about to break in and ravish them both. They were in the hall that goes from 1 South to the Surgery break room. The pitiful lasses were backed up against the wall opposite a large plate glass window, trembling as they would upon first seeing themselves in a mirror with a new hair coloring job gone horribly bad. There, on the window, menacingly vibrating in a web, was a small brown spider. Each time a small wind blew, the web would pulsate, the spider would shift slightly, and the two women would let out piercing screams of fright, not heard anywhere this side of a roller coaster ride filled with 7th-grade girls.

"Oh, Flush! Flush! Save us," they pleaded. "It's a deadly brown recluse."

Naturally, his masculine juices began to flow at this chance to rescue not one but two fair maidens in distress. Flush approached cautiously, broom (as weapon) firmly grasped, knowing that should he drop it in the impending struggle, he might be overwhelmed by a creature whose size did not represent its perilousness. Upon tense, skittish inspection, like a seasoned diagnostician confronting a mysterious pathogen, Flush determined that the threat was OUTSIDE the thick window. This realization didn't immediately calm the shrieking victims. But eventually, Flush was able to assure them that the threat wasn't, and they went about their usual business of saving lives. Flush returned, out of breath, to his mundane, considerably less dramatic bags of waste.

On another memorable occasion, Flush's bravery was put to a test, which he passed with grace, but without recognition by indifferent colleagues, who failed to acknowledge his gritty pluck. Flush was summoned to the pharmacy (cue the mystery music) to dispose of 2 very unusual, 5-gallon plastic containers of something called RCRA (pronounced "Rikra"), which, he was told, with a hint of tension, was nitro-glycerine. The person handing this canned destruction to Flush looked him over, assessing his steadiness and reliability. Not a chemistry major, Flush only remembered that "Nitro" was highly explosive if jarred or, heaven forbid, dropped. His demeanor, advanced age, and fidgety posture did not suggest confidence. Training had been nil. But he took the unusual "bombs" anyway, for refusal might question his fitness for the job.

The task terrified him, fearing he might innocently bump into someone, drop the dreaded WMD, and be singly responsible for removing the top of our neighborhood, this hospital included. Thousands dead, with Flush as the cause. What if he stubbed his toe? Or got sweaty, slippery palms? Do you remember Mrs. O'Leary's cow? The Great Chicago Fire of 1897? It occurred to Flush that it may be repeated here, caused by his clumsiness.

Several months later, after the annihilation of our dear workplace and the toiling masses therein (that would be everyone), and after investigators from all over the world had combed through the shredded debris, they'd discover the clumsy porter responsible and label Flush as the modern equivalent of that poor innocent cow. She probably didn't mean to kick over that lantern amongst straw in the barn. But for good fortune, Flush might have "mooooed" like Bessie.

Needless to say, the James Bond in Flush aroused into action, and he handled the potentially ticklish episode with assertive aplomb. He didn't often get to perform with aplomb, so this challenge was welcomed, retrospectively. Things could have gone south quickly, but you're here reading this, so by now, you've concluded that Flush Bond completed the assignment without tragedy.

Who says portering is mundane? Have fun sometimes, even on the job. Flush was good at fun.

***

And he learned empathy, contributing to his goal of living a full life. By his admission, he became a nicer person. Almost every time he entered a patient's room, he was able to engage them in a non-medical conversation, often cheering the patient and forming an immediate, though obviously temporary, friendship. The patients benefitted from his boundless sense of humor.

To Flush, these frequent opportunities were a chance to grow into a fuller life. He considered the hospital an educational laboratory to develop a more extroverted personality. He took advantage of these many opportunities to relate to a variety of people, patients, and visitors, all of whom welcomed friendly conversation in a context dominated by medical subjects. Most just wanted a friend, which he became, unlike the professionals who were rolling and prodding bodies and measuring a variety of bodily functions. Not exactly subjects of friendly conversations.

***

Flush was creative, sometimes proposing unusual suggestions for solving unusual problems. One time a CNA accidentally, while changing the sheets and blankets on a bed recently vacated by a leaving patient, lost a telemetry monitor amongst the bedding.

Small, weighing less than a pound, it was unintentionally discarded into a blue bag, rolled up among soiled linens. One of the several common instruments used to monitor a patient's bodily functions, it costs about $300. This didn't happen often but was a big problem when it did.

Flush was asked to find it. But its absence wasn't reported until several hours later when about 85 blue bags of soiled linens had been collected and deposited in large rolling wagons near the San-i-Pack area. It would take hours of messy work to search through these stinky bags. Flush asked if the telemetry monitor had any metal. He was told that "Yes, it did." Flush went to his boss and suggested they rent a metal detector from a local business that rented a variety of tools. The boss, open to original thinking, liked the idea. He went to the business, rented a metal detector, and gave it to Flush. It was still painstaking, searching through many blue bags, but at least they didn't have to open each bag and dump its contents on the ground. Within half an hour, they located the lost monitor, much to the relief of all concerned. No one ever thanked Flush for his imaginative solution. Flush began to realize that was normal at NCMH, where outside-the-box solutions weren't valued, usual omissions of this culture.

***

Flush's job took him into the Emergency Department about three or four times each day. Mostly, he was there to pick up six blue bags partially filled with used sheets and pillowcases. These blue bags were supported inside metal hampers, open on four sides, held rigid by sturdy metal supports, and designed with a flip-top lid that opened by a foot pedal.

Two of the bags were outside the three small patient rooms frequently inhabited by 51-50s, people with mental disorders. Some were suicidal, many were on heavy drugs, and all were guarded and restrained by our team of security guards, all employees of an outside agency. Good guys, these guards, but trained never to give much patient information, which might violate HIPAA restrictions. Whenever there was a patient or two in these rooms, which was almost always, a security guard sat in a chair in the hallway outside. Most of the time, his job was very inactive. They sat reading or texting or doing Sudoku, usually bored.

Flush, ever a jokester, often asked a new, young guard if he'd changed the batteries in the soiled linen hamper located three feet from the guard's chair. This was absurd, as there was nothing electrical about these simple hampers. The guards learned to play along with the joke, though a couple, at first, were perplexed and took him seriously.

Another time, Flush was gathering a blue bag in emergency. Five feet away, lying on a gurney, an old man asked him for a glass of water. Flush went to the nurses' station and told the two nurses who were typing into the computers. One of them got a cup of water which Flush took to the old patient. When Flush returned to the blue bag he was tying, the old man said, "Thanks." They started talking, something which Flush often did with patients and visitors, and Flush realized the man had a good sense of humor. He said, "I have a favor to ask. As long as you're here, watch this empty bag and make sure nobody steals anything out of it. These dirty sheets are in demand in some circles, and I can't be here to guard against evil larceny." The old patient chuckled, realizing silliness was introduced into a serious environment, and appreciated this invitation for laughter. This was a common reaction to Flush encounters.

***

Being single, he never cared about making money. Flush was more interested in making creative contributions, developing himself as a complete human, and learning how people functioned and were happy. He was original and lived, as much as was allowed, a free and full life. I admired him for it and learned a lot from him. Outside the hospital, his creativity was appreciated and occasionally effective. But that's a different novel. This one is about NCMH.

Unfortunately, the corporate hospital administration didn't share my opinion. Flush was too much of an individual to fit in well with the bureaucracy and knew little about medicine, though, in his job that was not needed. He was smart and learned fast, but his style wasn't appropriate at NCMH. He asked too many difficult questions, which shone light on a variety of problems, the kind of problems the corporate administration wanted to bury unaddressed. Administrators, supervisors, and managers regularly swept some problems under the rug, hoping nobody would notice. They also passed the buck on controversial decisions, hiding behind HIPAA and its opacity whenever convenient. Communication was faulty; I hope it's better with medical issues, which I never see. Effective leadership was disappointedly absent. As Flush said, "They couldn't lead fireflies to a flame or diarrhea patients to an outhouse. If *Passing the Buck* were an Olympic event, our administrators would be first stringers, bringing home the gold."

A simple example of neglect: there were many wall clocks in the hospital. But whenever time changed for daylight savings twice a year, it took about a week for all the clocks to be brought up to the correct time. Apparently, nobody was assigned this job, and this problem continued. It was always someone else's job. And typically, with small problems like clock settings, if you pointed out the problem to a manager, the response would be, "You saw the problem, you solve it." That passed for wisdom in our hospital culture. It also discouraged anyone from calling attention to problems. *Pass the buck* was accepted policy. Sweeping most problems under the rug was another.

Flush found himself in trouble often, though not enough to be fired. But he often came damn close. A few people with power appreciated his intelligent candor, though they wouldn't say so publicly. Even so, Flush rarely got honest answers to any questions, fomenting him to conclude that they were almost always hiding something. There was a big trust gap between management and everyone else, including unionized nurses, unionized technicians, and docs, all of whom were independent contractors grouped together in a more powerful bargaining agent. This loss of trust caused low morale among the employees and doctors.

Flush was not a big man. Of average height and build, he was in remarkable shape and health for his age. At 74, he was probably the oldest of 850 employees. He often said one of the best things about his job was its physical demands. The job required moderate exercise, though doable, but after eight hours, we knew that rest was welcome. To Flush, this is one reason he was so healthy and liked the job. His job as a porter took him almost everywhere in the hospital 3 or 4 times each day. This suited him much better than being stuck in an office behind a computer like many of the other employees. The porter's job was very broad, covering a large territory but very shallow since he never stayed anywhere for more than five minutes.

He walked about 5 miles each day on the job, and about 2 of those miles, he was carrying bags weighing 5 to 50 pounds. And pushing Sigmoid or *RRR*, full of different colored trash bags. This exercise kept him healthy and avoided the weight problems faced by many senior retirees.

He often said he expected to live to 100. He still had a lot more to do and many creative contributions to make; his energy and optimism were enviable and infectious. I think he'll make 100. He wants me there to help him blow out the candles. I'm honored.

His only limitation was a need for hearing aids which he forgot to wear often. He wasn't convinced they worked, saying his problem was misunderstanding certain words. He didn't need volume; he needed clarity. His cheap ($1500 per pair) hearing aids only increased volume, doing nothing for clarity. Loud muffles were no improvement over soft muffles.

***

About my third week there, on a Sunday morning during our 9 AM break, Flush asked me if I played Frisbee. Learning that I did, Flush suggested trying a new game he'd invented called Frowling, being an inelegant combination of Frisbee and bowling. This was my introduction to the sometimes hidden but frequently practiced rascalitious side of Flush's personality.

He went out to his car, an economy import, and returned with a large plastic bag carried over his shoulder. We went to the empty, isolated physical therapy room next to Cardio Rehab. It was largely unobserved, away from patient rooms, and unoccupied on weekends.

There was no staff there to disapprove of this non-medical activity.

I began to get nervous, suspecting what we were about to do would meet the staunch disapproval of the hospital supervisors, some of whom had no sense of humor and believed fun was inappropriate. Even though there were very few administrators in the hospital on weekends, we were both a bit nervous and anxious lest we be discovered and severely chastised. This was indefensible activity, hard to defend as having much to do with our jobs and normal hospital goals of saving lives. Even the name, Frowling, branded us as insubordinate mutineers. It wasn't the dreaded F-bomb but would have been interpreted worse by certain stern administrators who didn't know anything about fun, instead, substituting a fervent propensity to disapprove. Flush reminded me several times, "It's Sunday. Nobody's here."

I was new and still on probation, so probably would have been fired. Had we been caught, I'm sure Flush would have defended me by taking most of the blame. But we proceeded without restrictive managerial interruption. This set the tone of insurgency that characterized several future mutual adventures. This was the birth of my co-conspiracy with Flush in the field of free-thinking, which would be considered outrageous renegade hazards by some if they had known. They didn't.

While explaining the simple game, he removed from the bag and set up ten hollow, plastic bowling pins, arranged haphazardly on the floor against an empty wall. There was no furniture or equipment in that area. It was completely open. Flush had scouted out the location in advance. I could tell he'd been waiting for the chance to try out his new game. He was glad I was there. We stepped back about thirty feet, and Flush handed me three Frisbees, keeping three for himself. He threw one towards the pins and missed all of them, bouncing plastic against the back wall. Ten pins still stood. Then it was my turn. I threw a beat-up old Frisbee and knocked over two pins. Flush groaned dramatically and pretended to pound on the nearest wall, exaggerating his false disapproval. Then he laughed, glad that I actually could throw a Frisbee.

Then he threw another and knocked down one pin. He didn't strut, but I detected his satisfaction. Then he said, "This is the inaugural playing of this game. I've been thinking about it for a while, but we're making history now. Your turn."

I threw again and scored one more knockdown. "You're up, 3 to 1." He threw and killed one more. "3-2," he said with puzzling satisfaction.

Now it was my turn again, the chance to put it out of reach and win the first-ever Frowling match, destined, according to Flush, to be an Olympic sport in 2050. I threw a total miss, called a "gasser" by Flush, who was creating terminology spontaneously. Then Flush threw. He hit one squarely, and his Frisbee rebounded off the wall and nudged another pin. It tottered and wobbled, but didn't fall. "I was robbed," Flush shouted. "3-3," he said, "probably the best way to end the first match. Let's go back to work."

So we did.

But he frequently challenged me to a re-match (always on weekends, absent management) which we had a few dozen times. We never kept track of our won-loss record (I think we were about even). He viewed it as insignificant; we only played for fun. We never got caught, did no harm to the hospital, and enjoyed our jobs more than if we hadn't *Frowled*.

That's how he lived. He taught me priorities.

Chapter 2: Singing & Music

On my first day of work, I was trained in the porter job by Flush. As I was pushing Sigmoid through the empty hall of WICU (Women and Infant Care Unit), where babies are born, we came across a family outside a large interior window. They were looking at a newborn baby girl and her father in the clean-up room behind the window. A nurse was tending to the baby, cleaning her and performing normal obstetric duties. Flush stopped and spoke to the happy family, two grandmothers, a grandfather, three kids and one uncle who probably didn't want to be there. The baby's mom was somewhere else, no doubt recovering from a difficult, painful birth.

I was surprised to hear Flush say, "We have a tradition here. Whenever there's a new baby, we all sing 'Happy Birthday.' What's the baby's name?"

"Her name is Linda," said a grandma proudly. All of them were very excited and happy. They had been in the waiting room overnight and exhibited signs of sleeplessness but didn't care. Linda's arrival was very welcome. I could see the relief on their faces.

We all sang "Happy Birthday" together, enthusiastically, outside the window. Flush sang harmony to a song he'd sung many times before. The baby's young father, behind the window with his new daughter, looked up, hearing us, and gave us a thumbs-up. He was ecstatic.

As we left, the family thanked us, saying we had made the birth more memorable. Later, when we saw them again, Flush suggested they name the next newborn after him. They laughed, said they'd think about it, and asked his name. As he said, "Flush," they looked astounded, and the grandfather said, "I doubt it."

"I don't blame you. Good decision," responded Flush.

Making absurd propositions, for humor, was Flush's style. He wasn't serious about his suggestion. He just wanted a friendly laugh, which followed. I came to observe that he could be outrageously comedic, saying things that most people would find objectionable and rude. But he did it in a way no one took seriously; it was always funny.

As we left, we saw the male obstetrician in scrubs. "Nice work, stork," said Flush playfully. "Thanks," he replied. "I flew a long way to get here."

I learned later that this singing "tradition" was created by Flush. No nurses ever objected, and the families always enjoyed it, so it continued whenever Flush encountered newborn families in WICU. The obstetric nurses went along with it. Even the humorless ones stifled their opinions ("Honestly, it's so unprofessional!"), so score one for human friendliness. Over the years, Flush has led singing "Happy Birthday" many times. Flush loved to sing and did so well.

About a year later, in the maternity waiting room, a family of six was comfortably ensconced, waiting for their newest member, a girl. As he often did, Flush started talking to them, convincing them to sing "Happy Birthday" to Bella, soon to arrive. They sang it together, Flush delivering his usual flawless harmony and family providing a heartfelt melody. As usual, everyone was pleased but a little surprised by the informality and intentioned frivolity of the moment.

Flush learned that the grandmother worked at a local elementary school. He mentioned his children's reading program, *Saluting New Readers*, which he had done for 15 years as a volunteer, to motivate young kids to love reading. The grandfather, Cam Bell, a retired computer expert, showed interest. Flush gave him his card and a week later received a call from Cam. Making a long story short, the two men met and started working together, making short videos of elementary kids reading their favorite books. Flush taught Cam the program, and 5 years later, they taped Cam's granddaughter's kindergarten class. Bella was thrilled, as was Cam.

These videos were shown on local public access TV and YouTube. Cam's computer experience earned him a special status with YouTube, allowing their video program to run longer than the usual limit of 15 minutes permitted to other YouTube contributors.

This was an example of Flush's unorthodox extroversion forming new friendships that contributed to his quest for a full life. To him, hospital work provided an ideal opportunity, far exceeding a college course, for learning a valuable skill. He practiced it often.

***

Another time Flush was pushing a patient in a wheelchair from the X-ray Department back to the Emergency Department. This wasn't a normal part of his job. He was doing it because the transporter in X-ray was busy. As was his practice, Flush began a conversation with the patient, a smiling older man, relieved to know nothing was broken. The man said he was a retired trombone player in an orchestra. This got Flush's attention. "Can you sing?" he asked. "I love to sing," said the patient. "Let's do a duet," invited Flush.

As they returned to the Emergency Department, the unrehearsed melody, in two parts, of "You Are My Sunshine," with Flush on harmony, brought ER docs and nurses to their surprised feet. They applauded, and the expression of great pleasure on the face of the patient was undeniable. Many times later, whenever the same patient was in cardio rehab, he encountered Flush, and they'd immediately burst into their song. It became their thing; they both enjoyed it. I'm sure it was therapeutic for the patient.

***

One morning Flush was pulling blue bags in TCU (Transitional Care Unit), a hospital wing where patients stayed while waiting to go home or to another facility that could meet their needs. Most of these patients were recovering well from an illness or accident, and almost all of them were old.

Flush heard a piano being played in the Solarium Room, where TCU patients met with visitors, worked on a picture puzzle, or watched a large screen TV. They also played Scrabble and other board games familiar to the older generation. Sudoku was becoming popular, too. This community room was at the end of the hall and opened onto a central garden.

Curious about the music, Flush entered the room and heard "Somewhere Over the Rainbow," played on a piano enthusiastically by Adele, aged 84. Flush started singing along with the piano and Adele continued playing, surprised and pleased by his voice. When the song ended, she turned to see Flush, and they both laughed, recognizing the love that each had for music together. This was the beginning of a three-year friendship that grew, adding to the joyful fullness of both their lives.

Adele's 93-year-old husband, Bryan, a WWII veteran, was upstairs for an hour doing cardio (heart) rehab with other people who gathered to exercise and be monitored in a wonderful program run by a small staff of dedicated, caring nurses and technicians. This was the same department where Flush entertained the exercising patients by pretending to trip and fall face-first onto a blue bag of towels. While her husband exercised on machines upstairs, Adele entertained a dozen patients, her piano being heard throughout that TCU wing.

Adele came twice a week, every Tuesday and Thursday, and played a variety of songs, and Flush took his morning break with her to sing for 15 minutes. They both enjoyed it, as did all the patients who heard them. Over time, Flush established one song, "The Fox," as the first they played each time. It was his favorite. He developed it by singing with different voices for different verses. He particularly excelled in one verse which went: "Old Mother Flipper-flapper jumped out of bed. A big red scarf tied 'round her head. Crying 'John! John! The gray goose is gone! The fox is on the town-o, town-o, town-o. John, John, Wake up you old fool! (This always got a laugh out of Adele), the fox is on the town-o." Flush comically imitated an old woman's falsetto voice for this verse, which always got a laugh from listeners.

Flush was good at improvising lines to songs, often bringing laughter to Adele. They became great friends, and Flush sometimes went to Adele and Bryan's house to spend an afternoon making music together. She had been playing piano since she was eight years old and played well. Though occasionally she would hit a wrong key, at which point Flush would yell, "There's a clunker!" which was always received good naturally by Adele, who was a wonderful spirit, loved by everyone. They had a lot of fun and brightened the mood in TCU.

***

This book is about NCMH, so I'm not including the many aspects of Flush's life outside the hospital. But this exception needs mentioning. One day he got several suggestions from a nurse and a CNA that a certain other CNA named Tancy was interested in him. Tancy had seen him on the floor during his daily rounds and was attracted. But she was too shy to approach him, so she did so through her two female intermediaries. Flush was alone at that time, without a woman, and Tancy was cute and friendly, so he started talking to her. They hit it off and decided to have dinner together. That developed into an exclusive relationship that lasted about a year. They dated about once or twice a week but lived separately. Every Saturday, he slept at her apartment.

Things were ok, and they enjoyed each other's company and had fun together, but eventually, Flush realized it wasn't going to be a permanent relationship that led to marriage or cohabitation. One day they had a fight over something silly and Flush said she was acting stupidly. Tancy misunderstood and thought he'd called her stupid. She couldn't see the difference between her actions, which Flush called stupid, and her being, which Flush never thought was stupid. Tancy exited the car in a huff, slamming the door behind her. Flush tried to explain and reconcile, but the remark was so hurtfully interpreted that Tancy refused to listen or talk it out. She stormed away, and that ended their romance, such as it was. Flush needed good communication with a partner, and this was not good communication.

Unfortunately, there were a couple of CNAs in TCU who were Tancy's friends and heard only her side of the fight. These women all stuck together like discarded gum under a 1st grader's school desk. Consequently, the two CNAs disliked Flush, gave him the common stink-eyed cold shoulder, and tried to punish him by silencing his singing. Both of these porky middle-aged wenches wore hanging name badges (as we all did), but they were always turned inward, facing backwards, so nobody could see their names.

I saw them often but never knew their names and didn't care to. Knowing my friendship with Flush, they always looked away whenever we passed in a hall. That was a very common passive-aggressive behavior of angry women holding a grudge at NCMH. I was furniture to them. TCU stood for "Testy Crone Unit" in my mind, and Flush concurred.

They complained they couldn't hear the patients' buzzing for help when he was singing, a totally false objection. This stupid controversy went to the supervisor in charge of TCU, who persuaded the CNAs to shut the door to the Solarium, confining the music to that one room. While this unnecessary solution was implemented, it produced very hard feelings with Adele, who was there as a volunteer, bringing entertainment to patients and TCU staff. Flush, who had seen this destructiveness elsewhere in the hospital, was not surprised and dealt with it with a tolerating annoyance, not wanting to get into trouble but unwilling to give up his singing with Adele. But both Adele and Flush were happy that his singing could continue, even if behind a closed door, and the angry CNAs frumped around as if they'd been wounded, like the sore losers they were.

Last year Bryan died, so Adele stopped coming to play the piano. Flush stayed in touch with her by phone and email. Eventually, it was obvious that Adele, suffering from the beginning stages of dementia, couldn't manage alone, so her children shut their house and moved Adele to San Jose. Flush lost touch with Adele but told me he thought of her and hoped she was well and comfortable, if possible, after losing her beloved mate of 62 years. They always seemed happy whenever they played and sang together. Adele was a very special presence, always fun and laughing; we all miss her very much.

***

Later, I learned that the piano played by Adele had been a gift donated by a patient, Paul Dettner. He had cancer and was cured by the hospital. Out of sincere gratitude, Paul, age 50, thought we (NCMH) deserved it for saving his life. Paul was a good honky-tonk pianist who would occasionally come in and livened up the Solarium Room with some upbeat tunes, which he played by ear. His style was very different from Adele's. Flush couldn't sing along with Paul, but the compelling rhythm got his fingers snapping, a rare skill Flush exhibited with the beat of Ringo.

Then one day, I saw Paul in the Emergency Room. He looked terrible. I learned that his cancer had returned and metastasized. Both Flush and I were very sad, as we had come to know Paul and admired his grit and resilience. We also loved his music and friendly personality. After Paul passed, Flush and I went to the local trophy shop and had a small copper plaque printed, which read: *"This piano was a gift from Paul Dettner (1960-2012), whose life and music touched many hearts."*

Without ceremony, we attached the plaque to the front of the upright Baldwin piano. Paul's generosity deserved recognition, and his lively charisma will certainly be missed by those who knew him. As usual, the hospital did nothing to acknowledge his gift. Without our plaque, nobody would have ever known the piano's story. The piano story has a second chapter, which is told later.

***

One of the good things about NCMH, melodies that produced a calm, friendly, informal feeling when heard, was harp music played individually by volunteers. About twice a week, a harpist, a sweet little old lady, would set up her harp in a patient hallway and serenade us with Irish melodies or Scottish strains not heard often outside the bars of Aberdeen. Flush loved it and effusively complimented Shannon, a beginner willing to slowly, tentatively pluck out simple melodies. And Flush would softly hum along, usually harmonizing without words, which he didn't know. But he knew the tunes (well, most of the time) and improvised when he didn't. This never attracted a crowd, and everyone went about their business as if unaware of any distraction.

***

In another chapter, I'll describe Flush's five years as a floor scrubber in the surgery wing, which was on two floors. He worked the evening shift when it was mostly empty, with most surgeries scheduled for the daytime. This was before I started working there, so I never knew Flush then. This was good because he never needed to train anybody else, so we probably wouldn't have developed the close friendship that served us both if I had started then. And this book probably would not have been written.

Being a floorist was another venue for his singing. Inside each Operating Room, after moving the medical "furniture" (operating table, anesthesiologists' workstation, stool, and several rolling metal shelving carriages) to one corner, Flush brought in a CD player and several CDs. His favorites were women folk singers like Kate Wolf, Iris Dement, Nanci Griffith, Laurie Lewis, Alison Krauss, Rita Hosking, and Emmy Lou Harris. He also liked some male singers, whose writing was also sometimes profound and poetic, such as Bob Dylan, John Prine, Leonard Cohen, and Phil Ochs.

As a floorist, while operating his scrubbing machine, which was noisy, he sang harmony with whomever was playing at the time, singing loud and unselfconsciously without reservation. Since it was evening when the Surgery Department was mostly empty, hardly anyone was listening outside the closed door and thick walls of the ORs, and those who were hearing him didn't object. He wasn't a great singer, but he wasn't bad, either. He just loved to sing and learning to harmonize helped him pass the time in a boring, repetitious job. He did it well.

***

Several years later, when no longer a floorist, having become a porter (a "promotion" of questionable value), Flush wrote a song and proposed it as a janitorial theme song. It was sung, whenever requested (this wasn't often), with exaggerated Flushish gusto. It was to the tune of "Never Ending Love," made popular by some singer (pretty sure it wasn't Elvis) before I was born. "Never Ending Trash" went like this:

We have never-ending trash for you
Pull one bag and soon there will be two
If you smell 'em, you'll probably go Ah-Choo!
Cause some of 'em are partly filled with poo.

We have never-ending trash for you
Most our bags are red or white or blue
If saluting is what you think to do
That is proof, you haven't got a clue

But if portering is just your life's desire
If the thought of rubbish sets your loins on fire
If you like to roll in muck and mire
When I die, you will be for hire.

***

I came to realize that Flush was much more than a porter or floorist. He was learning to expand his job beyond its description of mundane duties. As a porter, he provided some patients with the kind of friendship they needed in the hospital. He brought fun, a commodity rarely found, but usually appreciated. And his singing, which he loved to do on many occasions, improved. He was too old to make music a career but not too old to sing for fun.

When asked, Flush defended his idiosyncratic behavior. "People expect janitors to be eccentric. I'm just following an old stereotype. I don't mind being weird if it contributes to a fuller life. Most people here can't commit professional suicide, so they have to maintain a polished image, but we janitors can get away with it, so I do."

Chapter 3: Floorist

If you want plot development, please skip this chapter. If you want mild humor, read on. Before I was hired, Flush had spent about five years cleaning floors. He called himself a floorist (or phloorist?), with two o's, and at that time, was not known as "Flush."

Over the years after I was hired, and over some beers, he told me about his floorist job. Of all the things American kids aspire to become, floorist ranks towards the bottom. Not many kids develop a compelling desire to become professional floorists. He didn't. But despite his lack of preparation and passion, he made the best of operating a mop or vacuum cleaner or a machine called a scrubber often enough to actually get paid. I guess that pretty much made him a floorist. After floorizing for about 3 1/2 years, dealing successfully with a huge variety of complicated flooristic pathologies, he thought he finally qualified as a doctor of floorosophy (DF). In searching for the silver lining, he realized there aren't many floorists, and it's a career that will never be outsourced or done by a computer.

Floorist says it all when written. When spoken, unfortunately, "floorist" sounds like "florist," a homonym, so confusion sometimes results. Just don't expect him to deliver petunias.

As a floorosopher, he came to realize the profound importance of his subject. In off-duty, informal orations in evenings at his house, with a little alcohol and maybe "killer devil weed," he theorized, verbally elevating his subject way beyond any respect given by modern cultures. In his description, floors are the foundation of all civilizations, probably invented before the wheel, definitely before the taming of fire. Without floors, we're all out in the woods walking in dirt with the unhouse-broken critters, large clods of wormy peat moss clinging between our caveman-ic toes. Birds and fish are about the only living critters that don't appreciate floors. Floors are important. Unless it's raining or snowing, floors are more useful than roofs. And walls can't compete with floors unless you have nosey neighbors or live downwind from a stockyard. It behooves everyone to respect floorists and floors. Floors are here to stay. Thus, floorist. Or maybe, phloorist. Flush made up the word but couldn't decide its spelling.

As a floorist, he worked the evening shift, 3:00 PM to 11:30 PM, with a half-hour off for dinner. Several other male members of EVS also worked on floors, as floors received the most wear and needed the most attention. Continuous foot and wheel traffic removed wax and, if not maintained regularly, lowered the appearance and perceptions of a hygienic environment. Hallway and patient room floors were a major concern of EVS, easily observed by the judgmental public. Administration cared about floors and spent considerable time discussing whether a certain floor should have carpet, for quietness, or hard floor, for cleanliness. Guys cleaning floors learned different skills and equipment for each. This work was tedious, boring, and repetitious, sometimes noisy and smelly, but it kept bosses away, so we tried not to mind it.

As always, Flush's sense of humor served him, and others, well. As an opening to casual conversation, strangers asked him, "What's up?" These people, with little respect for floorism, were totally unaware of their insensitivity. Flush, feigning insult, pretended the question was a verbal slap in the face to floorists. He comically let them know that up is not a direction that interests floorists, nor have they any expertise there. Flush claimed to know floorists who, being afraid of heights, got dizzy nose-bleeds just LOOKING up. "If you want to know 'what's up?' ask an astronomer," was his usual answer.

***

During this time, no doubt out of boredom and ample time to imagine, Flush started a movement. As a floorist, he had no opportunities to converse with the public, patients and visitors he met in a later job as a porter. He was going bald and had learned a medical term, alopecia, which described the condition, a word foreign to the general public. It sounded very medical, instilling his new "therapy" with authenticity. So he started the Alopecia Support Group (ASG), which, he thought, society needed and would welcome. Not really.

Sometimes fun proves to be a mirage. He wrote in the hospital newsletter called The Grapevine. *I'm recently (about 10 years) a sufferer of this merciless scourge that decimates a fair portion of human hair but is NEVER mentioned at fundraising events. You don't see celebrities campaigning for a cure for alopecia. We haven't elected a bald president since Ike.*

Thinking that some minimal research would be appropriate, he proposed ASG to two shiny pates at the hospital, a surgeon and a surgery tech. Both, lacking humor, responded with major indifference, if not fervent opposition. Flush (floorist at that time) didn't stick around long enough for nastiness to develop, but I overheard one say, "Let's stop entertaining this nonsense. We've got lives to save." This undesirable reaction by two respected colleagues persuaded Flush to conclude that the ASG was probably ahead of its time. And some people can't see a joke.

***

In another attempt to save the world by bringing justice to a much-ignored minority, Flush decided to start IFF–International Federation of Floorists. Having dealt successfully, if not always brilliantly, with a variety of pathologies that attacked the floors of the hospital, Flush certainly deserved to be a doctor of floorosophy. He wanted "DF" printed on his name tag. Of course, this made him amply qualified to be the founder of the IFF. He sarcastically insisted that it's time that humble but dedicated floorologists, toiling thanklessly around the world for the betterment of humanity, demand recognition for their artistry. When floorists finally come together, under the proud banner of the IFF, united in their common love for "gettin' down" and "bottoming out," the world will be forced to acknowledge their subtle but universal significance.

Continuing in The Grapevine, he wrote: *Until now, you've been walking on our work, and will probably continue to do so, but if the IFF has anything to say about it, you can no longer walk on us. Ask your non-flooristical selves: 'Where would we be without floors?' The IFF has the answer: 'You'd be shuffling knee-deep in critter poop out in the woods, that's where.' Try surgery there. We dare you.'*

We IFF floorists will have a slogan: 'If your problem's above the ankles..., take it somewhere else.' And a motto: 'We floorists start at the bottom...and we stay there.'

Several months after I was hired and became friends with Flush, I was at his house and happened on an old copy of The Grapevine, which was lying in a pile of old magazines. He was out of the room tending to his dogs when I started reading about his IFF fantasy. Finding it amusing, I thought of introducing it on the internet, complete with a joking website. When Flush returned, I told him this idea. Since I had been learning floorism, he and I could write it together.

He didn't take it seriously and had few internet skills, coming from a pre-computer generation. But recognizing my education, which featured computers and the associated advantages, and thinking if I did all the work, it would be fun for a while, "Go for it" was his mild reaction, mostly to humor me. The next week I created a crude website and printed his articles (he'd submitted several) from The Grapevine. The IFF went worldwide. Flush was amused by my plagiarism, stating that imitation is the most sincere form of flattery. Soon, surprising to me (Flush didn't know what to think), we began getting a trickle of international interest. Six months later, I was swamped (well, not really, but my journalistic aspirations wanted to think so) by inquiries from around this floorized planet. The IFF was rocketing off like an elevator, floorism was achieving new heights, a rare and dizzying experience for floors.

One floorist from Norway asked if ice could be a floor and, if so, "What's the most goodest method for erasing ice skating scratches?" Since scratches in water don't last, I told him that his best remedy is summer. He wasn't happy with that remedy and said so with verbal Scandinavian dissent delivered from a safe distance.

Another floorist from Tibet asked if 2000-year-old compressed yak-dung flooring could be brought to a "sparkling shine." I reluctantly admitted we'd never encountered this challenge. I asked him, "Why bother?" which seemed to offend him. He seemed disappointed and wanted his membership dues returned, proving that some floorists were not visionaries. Since we had no membership dues, we assumed there was some confusion in the translation. Flush was concerned we might be spreading discontent unintentionally, causing problems between a yak floorist and his wife. On the website, Flush asked him if yaks had wives. The Tibetan declined to answer. We speculated that he thought we were asking if a yak was his wife. We might have lost a reader, and those speaking English were rare enough.

A floorist from Greece suggested we sponsor a floorists' Olympics, featuring events such as speed mop wringing and synchronized team buffing. Relay-wheeled bucket pushing (sprint and marathon) would produce unparalleled excitement, inspiring new levels of endurance and cooperation. Cross-country vacuuming and stairway scrodulating (I think it must be a Greek word) would certainly ride a groundswell of grassroots enthusiasm. I'm thinking of submitting this riveting idea to my local city council. Floorist Olympics would attract dull but well-behaved crowds with flattened preferences.

I needed more additions to our website. His columns from The Grapevine proved ample gold mines for this international (and growing) audience. Most took it seriously, which made me feel a little guilty about the deception, until Flush explained to me that all humor required some distortion, and we needed humor for some sources of fun, which is a real human psychological need. So I relaxed and abandoned my journalistically-inspired search for truth and added the following to our website.

We have attracted attention from The Association of Horizontal Activists (AHA), which worships everything horizontal and rejects all verticals. I'm not sure how they feel about diagonals, like stairways. They claim to sleep 23 hours per day.

The letters e, v, i, and l (evil) are all in the word vertical, which proves their theology, according to their philosophy. They say that floors are the universal symbol of horizontalism, and floorists are like priests, ripe for universal admiration. So the next time you encounter a floorist (myself or another colleague), possibly down on our humble, gnarly knees investigating a defacement, speak kind words. According to AHA, you'll be addressing a major cosmic guru. Just because floors are low, doesn't necessarily mean that we floorists are.

Also, we floorists are secure in the certainty that our work will never be outsourced. Until technology figures out how to send floors back and forth between California and India, we'll be floorizing. Until people learn to walk on walls or ceilings, we'll be floorizing. Until gravity is suspended, we'll be floorizing. Floors are forever, and universal. When you're walking here, you're walking with us. Or on us. Whatever.

I resorted to a bit of hospital boasting preachiness with the next website addition: *I'm new to work in a medical environment. I benefit from the realization that I'm part of a team making an extremely valuable contribution: saving, extending, and improving human lives. Of all the jobs outside this hospital, few directly advance such an important goal. This awareness has improved my attitude immensely, and motivates me whenever floorism becomes too mundane to maintain my interest. Even the water* boy on a *Super Bowl* championship team gets to celebrate.

This collaboration excited us both and I became aware of Flush's rare creativity. He should have been a comedian. He started to appreciate the World Wide Web and the free access it gave to small authors like ourselves to a possible large readership, way beyond The Grapevine. After a few beers, again at Flush's house, we came up with the following appendage to our web work.

In the area in California where many computer innovations originate, a team from Silicon Valley, named the "Knever Kneel Corp." ("KKC"), having developed the latest high-tech, cutting-edge, state-of-the-art, computerized mop, wrote to ask if we (IFF) would endorse their product. They claim it will "revolutionize floor maintenance as we've known it, catapulting floorism from the 14th century, well into the 21st." This turned some IFF heads. I told K.K.C. we'd put the "Puter-Mop" through its paces, test driven by our most seasoned veterans. Just send it with full insurance paid.

If their claims are to be believed, the "Puter-Mop" has a built-in GPS which can guide the operator to the nearest exit if there's a fire and the floorist is disoriented by smoke. It also has an airbag for defense against run-away gurneys, not a particularly useful safety feature in my experience. Its ability to analyze mystery spills (coffee, Coke or human effluent; lemonade or something-that-missed-the-toilet?) would be useful. The various onboard gauges (temperature, humidity, elevation, latitude, longitude, pedometer) seem like overkill to me, but they might impress the ladies and give floorists a high-tech look that everyone else at my hospital seems to have. I think "Puter-Mop" weighs 168 pounds. And we won't need the stethoscope attachment. We're awaiting its arrival.

As floorists we often did repetitious work (mop left, mop right, like a human metronome, buff left, buff right), so we had time to conceive a variety of shallow thoughts. Nothing is more shallow than a floor. Flush spoke for all floorists herein.

How many of you non-floorists can say that people regularly and intentionally walk on your work? Knowing that our work receives so little respect could be depressing. Only plumbers' work gets less respect. Even proctologists follow their names with "MD."

At least our floors are out in the open, seen by all, before being defiled.

Buddhists talk about being unattached. Flush thought that's wise advice for floorists, since our work is so obviously temporary. Unattachment is the only path to sanity, for a floorist, since floors are blemished hourly. So the challenge becomes caring about your floors while not making a commitment to them.

We floorists are also hunters. Not exactly big game, but small game can be as challenging. Nothing gets a floorist's adrenalin pumping like the pursuit of an elusive dust bunny frolicking under a bed or food cart, mocking the fastidious floorist, refusing entrapment, ridiculing, teasing, tormenting, and dancing to escape. Unsuccessful, the floorist has a choice: continue the frustrating pursuit or give up to return another day. "What if the 'bunny' ends up in a patient's dinner?" asked the conscientious floorist. The decision is made. The intrepid floorist nobly continues and eventually triumphs, possibly saving the life of a hungry patient. Nothing gives more satisfaction to a floorist like a successful hunt.

Flush actually took a small bag of captured dust bunnies to our lab to be analyzed. The lab "detectives" weren't terribly interested, so we floorists still wonder where dust bunnies come from and what they're made of.

Since Flush has a morbid fear of heights, he wondered if being a floorist was fate. No work is lower. No work better accommodates his acrophobia. Some might say it was meant to be, just his karma.

***

If floors could think and feel, would a hallway floor think an elevator floor is a great athlete? Would elevator floors think escalator floors are extremists, non-conformists, or worse, show-off Hollywood exhibitionists flaunting their flexibility?

In addition to the daily floor dirt-ectomies we perform, we floorists sometimes eat verbal dirt fed to us by protesting staff members who object to our disruptive noise or awkward electric cords or messy equipment or smelly chemicals. It's tough being popular when encumbered by so many impediments. A thick skin is sometimes practical. But revenge is another option.

***

On a cold rainy night in late December, while feeling lowly and powerless following a recent rebuke, Flush discovered, in one of the hall closets, yellow "CAUTION" tape, the kind police use to block off crime scenes. There it was, yards of official, authoritative (intimidating even) plastic tape. After some consideration, he realized he was in possession of potential domination, an instrument of revenge. With this tape, a simple floorist could block off hallways and elevators, offices, and lounges. Without noise, cords, mess, or chemicals, he could create a major pedestrian occlusion, clotting the normal flow of medical traffic. He could make a whole bunch of high-achieving professionals beg for access while waiting for wax to dry. With cautionary tape, he had rare POWER. Tread no more over this floorist! And because it was 9:00 PM, there was little visitor or medical traffic and almost no admin to notice and complain.

The week before, he had botched (nobody could tell) a hallway floor job in a patient area. It needed to be waxed over, and now was the perfect time to catapult his career as a floor tyrant. Tying one end of the tape to the hand railing, he carefully strung it across and down the hall past several offices, where he tied it off. This occluded access to three offices and two patient rooms lined on either side of 60 feet of hall length, 12 feet width. Then he applied wax with leisurely, confident sweeps of a string mop, on the hall floor, inside the influential tape "turf."

It takes at least 20 minutes for the wax to dry, so he left for 5, assuming the caution tape could command respect without his presence. When he returned, he noticed footprints in the wax and two people sitting inside an office that was clearly inside the prohibited area. One of the intruders was an upstanding member of our community, the hospital chaplain, certainly not your average scofflaw. Flush timidly charged her with violating the prohibited area defined by the yellow tape. She immediately conceded and smiled warmly. Flush left, realizing that if his" power tape" couldn't restrain a paragon of moral rectitude, it had no chance controlling unyielding doctors, determined nurses, and a wide variety of contrary technicians.

He waited until both violators had left and then, quickly, and while on guard, waxed over the offensive, highly-visible footprints. Rat dookey! he thought. Another power move foiled.

***

Diplomacy is a mostly unrecognized, but necessary, attribute required of all floorists. Flush took several demanding classes in the Floorist Academy regarding this fine, advanced skill. A valuable art is persuading a peevish nurse that her station, littered with paper scraps, is long overdue and would be improved if she could find it in her busy, busy heart to tolerate 5 minutes of vacuum cleaner noise. Or convincing another (hopefully different) nurse that briefly leaning a mop handle against a picture frame on a hallway wall is not a sign of disrespect. I bet we floorists are among the most diplomatic folks in the hospital. We have to be. We lack the authority to command anyone. Trust me; it's lonely at the bottom.

***

Before I came to NCMH, Flush worked in surgery, cleaning their mostly hard floors. Only the break room and two changing rooms had carpets, so they needed occasional vacuuming. His difficult work there was on hard floors and, because it was surgery, was considered important.

He worked the evening shift, scrubbing the floors with a big machine in all six surgery rooms. This old machine was heavy when filled with about 15 gallons of water and a separate container of super-strong floor soap. Who knows what germs lurk on an operating room floor? This scrubber had two large brushes that scrubbed in circular motions and were controlled by handles. One handle controlled the speed of the self-propelling contraption; the other turned the soap on and off. He used it every night and couldn't do his job without it.

Downstairs, on the lower level (basement) of the hospital, were three Operating Rooms and accompanying support rooms with a sterilizer, supplies, and offices needed to conduct a variety of surgeries. These three ORs were for inpatient surgeries, more serious than those performed on outpatients upstairs. There was also a large room with about six beds, for patients recovering from recent surgery before being moved upstairs to their next hospital room, where they'd stay for a few days or weeks. All these rooms were connected by several wide, crowded halls, semi-organized with different medical machines and rolling carts lining the walls.

Upstairs, on the first floor, were three more Operating Rooms, used for less serious (that was Flush's understanding) outpatient surgeries. Also upstairs were nursing administrators' offices and two large recovery rooms where patients came out of anesthesia after their operations. There was also a waiting room for relatives and friends of patients. It was carpeted, so only had to be vacuumed regularly.

It was Flush's job to scrub, wax, and buff all these hard floors regularly, working from 3 PM to 11:30 PM, five days a week. Since most surgeries were over by 5 PM, most of his work was done alone after everyone had gone home. Wearing scrubs like everyone else in surgery, Flush enjoyed the independence of this work. He did a good job and didn't slack off, which was easily possible given the lack of control and oversight by the bosses. He worked behind locked doors with very limited access and his floors looked great. The docs, nurses, and administrative staff were always complimentary about his work there.

Over time, Flush (who wasn't called that until later when he became a porter) started calling himself a floorist, with two o's. He even elevated his status to doctor of floorosophy and suggested he be honored on doctor appreciation day along with the real MDs. Of course, everyone realized it was a joke, but they went along with it. Again, Flush's sense of the absurd was evident. According to Flush, gravity was the only real boss a floorist had. And he threatened to demand that everyone walk on tiptoes when not standing still.

As floorist, Flush didn't have to wax the floors in the operating rooms. During procedures, they needed secure footing more than a cosmetic shine, and waxed floors could be slippery. But in the halls, it was different. He had to scrub and wax those every couple of weeks, and there were a lot of long, wide halls. There was rarely any foot traffic late at night, but the dr. of floorosophy hung signs on the hall doors (after scrubbing and waxing) reading:

WET WAX

1st coat— — — —9 PM

2nd coat— — — —winter

He also sang in the halls unless there was an unusual procedure happening, which wasn't often after 7 PM. And he passed the time scrubbing the operating room floors by harmonizing to the music he brought on a CD player. He loved accompanying female folk singers. He was realistic and never expected to meet them but would have been ecstatic to sing harmony with any of them if given the chance. He was old but had a good voice and the ability to find harmonies.

There was a very friendly, tight group of docs, nurses, and other staff in surgery. They had fun together and some socialized outside the hospital. Though our floorist was from another department, and did menial, unskilled labor, he became a popular fixture, sometimes a willing butt of a few jokes. It almost felt like family to Flush, and he was pleased to become on a first name basis with several surgeons and anesthesiologists and surgical nurses, whom he admired for their life-saving expertise.

One anesthesiologist (a nice guy) was a right-wing conservative who regularly debated the wisdom of the Iraq War with the floorist (Flush). Of course, the floorist, a devoted liberal (returned Peace Corps volunteer during Vietnam days), attacked President "W" as making "the dumbest mistake of any president of his lifetime. (This was before ThunderRump took that title). We didn't learn from Vietnam, and if we don't admit our mistake in attacking Iraq, some yahoo 40 years from now will do it again. Probably attack Iceland for the cold."

The anesthesiologist defended the Iraq war, usually repeating some version of "Saddam was a bad man." Or, "He poisoned his own people." Neither debater changed their opinions, but they were friends when talking about any other subjects. Both agreed that the hospital was poorly administered since Diggery Wealth took over.

One surgical technician, a youngish (about 35) man named Jebb Trouter, loved to put some sticky gunk on the underside of the handles on the floorist's scrubbing machine. Floorist, always unsuspecting, would grab the handles and attempt to drive this 300-pound machine and go, "EWWWWWW! Trouter! I know it was you." Jebb could be heard chuckling in a side store room.

One time a favorite female nurse and two male technicians, Jebb and Chas (a very funny guy), between surgeries, while waiting for the anesthesiologist and patient to show up, decided to goof on the floorist. They went into an operating room that would not be used that night, a room they knew the floorist would be scrubbing. He had his CD player there and had left to go get something. With magic markers, they wrote many graffiti on the floor. "Your fly is down." "You're being watched." "We could raise goats in here." "You're dyspeptic." "It's lonely down here." "Scrub me, buff me, ooooolala!"

Flush was not surprised, having been playfully disrespected many times in surgery in the past. Cleaning the floor was no more difficult, so he didn't really care. He sang even louder than usual when removing the insults from the OR floor.

The next day he typed a comic letter addressed to Jebb, purporting to be from the Deputy CEO. Part of the joke letter read, "You are commanded to appear in my office wearing an expensive suit and tie and a sincere expression of contrition on your fish-like face. Be on time. 2:00 on Tuesday." He gave it to Jebb, who posted it on a bulletin board, where it was read by a very young, new secretary. She didn't know it was a joke and reported it to her boss. The boss was astonished but sent it up the chain of command, and the floorist was summoned into HR. He took Jebb with him and explained it was a joke, and eventually, all was forgiven.

Flush recently received his annual performance evaluation. To paraphrase, it read, in part, "Flush successfully distinguishes up from down most of the time and can locate the floor consistently, with few errors and no hesitation." He's thinking of sending it to his high school guidance counselor, who predicted he'd never amount to anything.

When Flush was transferred to a daytime porter job after five years fervently scrubbing their floors and bringing rare humor and singing, about 30 nurses and doctors signed a letter praising his exemplary work in the Surgery Department. As always, this informal commendation was ignored by admin, totally unaware of Flush's positive influence. Most administrators had little or no sense of humor and always regarded jocularity as a waste of time. Employees' mental health, including fun, was an unnecessary and inappropriate distraction in a hospital, in their impaired judgement. Later in his career at NCMH, during a major objection fought in HR, he showed this letter to the new, hostile director of Human Resources. She glanced at it with painful dismissal, saying, "That's before my time. I don't care about it." She ignored it.

Chapter 4: Germ Testing

Several years ago, Flush injured his shoulder while pulling RRR instead of pushing it. Walking in front of it, his right arm extended backwards to the wagon and holding on to a shoulder-height handle, he damaged his rotator cuff enough to be placed on light duty. He couldn't raise his right arm above his shoulder. He had steered RRR that way to see where he was going so as not to collide with a person or equipment in the hallways he traversed throughout the hospital. It took several years before his shoulder was damaged. He was unaware of the jeopardy his shoulder was in by pulling RRR and Sigmoid from the front rather than pushing it from the back, where forward visibility was nonexistent.

The boss, Feckless Pidwell, a nice guy who solved some problems, arranged for Flush to do a different job for about three months. During those three months, Flush saw a physical therapist three times a week for an hour each time. It worked, and eventually, his shoulder was back to normal, so he went back to his normal job as a porter while avoiding surgery.

But during his recuperation and after brief training, Flush tested many surfaces for germs using an instrument called an Illuminator. There was a simple procedure involving brushing a swab across one or two square inches of the surface being tested. Each test took about five minutes. It tested for all germs, some toxic and harmful and most harmless. It just measured life, so was a reliable measure of how recently the surface had been cleaned by housekeepers.

However, it didn't distinguish between harmful and harmless germs. This was useful research for determining what items and areas needed more attention and weren't getting regular cleaning. After testing each surface, Flush cleaned each surface. He also kept careful records of what he cleaned and when and how high it scored on the germ profile.

At the beginning of Flush's training, as an experiment, one of the docs, a pathologist who read X-rays, asked Flush to measure his hand, which had just been washed. Expecting a low score, everyone was surprised when it scored very high. How could this be? Maybe the Illuminator was inaccurate. Then it was explained by Feckless that the Illuminator measured all life, so a person's hand would score high (assuming the person was alive), even though clean of germs.

As a result of some of these tests, Flush determined that most of the wheelchairs weren't getting cleaned at all. A few in the Emergency Department Waiting Room were cleaned weekly by security guards who were stationed there and often bored, doing nothing. And three wheelchairs were permanently assigned to the X-ray (formerly known as Diagnostic Imaging) Department and were regularly cleaned by the transporters. The 25 other wheelchairs, scattered in several locations around the hospital and moved, casually, to new locations, were never cleaned. This alarmed Flush, who took this information to Feckless.

Feckless hemmed and hawed and made excuses ("I'll look into it," "We don't have anyone to do it," and "Maybe we could get someone else to do it"). But the problem went on for several months, unsolved. This alarmed Flush, who was conscientious about not spreading disease. He reasoned, probably correctly, that some of the occupants of wheelchairs likely had passable germs and wheelchair occupants were more susceptible to disease than the general public. Who knew what diseases were being passed, unknowingly, through the negligence of our department? And why was Flush performing these tests if the results were ignored, nothing being done to correct problems? What kind of hospital were we?

Flush had several conversations with Feckless, to no avail. One day Flush was talking to a secretary who told him that the Lady's Auxiliary, a group of old lady volunteers, was looking for more work. Maybe they would do it. This sounded like a good solution to Flush, so he approached the president of the group. She abruptly said, "No, we don't do any cleaning." Flush mentioned this problem at various meetings and was met with skepticism by several supervisors, none of whom took responsibility to solve the problem. At one meeting, a male executive vice president asked, "How do you know they aren't getting cleaned?" Flush described his testing. Then a female nurse who oversaw other nurses spoke up, "It's true, they aren't cleaned." This lent credibility to Flush's assertion. Still, no correction was made. "Go talk to ____" was the common buck being passed. It was another example of the very common form of sweeping problems under the metaphorical convenient carpet while hoping nobody would notice.

Frustrated by the indifference of the decision-makers, Flush went to a secretary and got the list of the numbers on each wheelchair. When the list was first made, there had been 74 wheelchairs. But over the years, many had been stolen. Now there were 35 chairs, each with a number spray painted on the back of the chair. He made a spreadsheet with each number in a column on the left margin. Then there were ten columns down the paper.

On weekends the portering was slow, giving the porter about an hour of downtime. After his recuperating when he returned to portering, Flush used this hour on alternating Saturdays and Sundays to load up a cart and go around to clean the wheelies. They were scattered in groups in places around the hospital but not assigned any specific home. It took approximately three minutes each, and in the two lobbies, several were in one place, reducing travel time. With each cleaning, he wrote the date to keep a record of the cleanings. In two days, he cleaned almost all of them. But he only worked on alternating weekends. He persuaded me, a new hire learning portering, who was scheduled on the other weekends, to do it also. Together we cleaned all the wheelchairs once a week, much better than the previous once a decade.

Unfortunately, about four months later, the hat restriction (more in a later chapter) happened that alienated Flush, so he just said to hell with it and stopped cleaning them. It was never in his job description, and few people even knew he did it. Feckless didn't. No one ever thanked him or me. So I quit also, another example of the indifference instilled by a lazy, irresponsible administration. So wheelchair cleaning reverted to the previous unsanitary conditions, never knowing if we were endangering patients and the people pushing the chairs.

***

Another result of Flush's germ testing was in the waiting room of the cancer center and involved stationary chairs. It was a nice hang-out for outpatients with cancer and their families, waiting for patients to receive treatment. Cancer patients undergoing treatment have lowered immune systems and are particularly susceptible to HAIs (Hospital-Acquired Infections). Knowing this, Flush did a lot of testing in the cancer center. He tested the arms on several of the 25 chairs in this critical waiting room; they all tested high.

He reported his results to Feckless, a study with an alarming conclusion. Feckless, as usual, shrugged his shoulders and said, "It is what it is." But he had no solution other than to sell the chairs and buy new ones. We didn't have a good way to clean cloth chair arms. Flush went to the head of the cancer center and told her the results of his tests. She took it seriously and solicited solutions. Flush had been thinking about it and realized they could make removable cloth covers that fit on the arms. These covers could be washed locally, and if done frequently, would reduce the chance of HAIs.

The cancer center head, a nurse who actually solved problems, liked the idea. Before consulting Flush, in agreement with his solution, she hired a professional seamstress for $900 to make the covers. Fifty simple slip-on covers on 50 arms on 25 chairs cost $18 each. They were nice, and worked and looked ok, but Flush thought the job should have been done for half that amount. Still, he was pleased and encouraged that his testing had provoked a solution.

Feckless assigned the job of cleaning the covers, once a fortnight, in our department's washing machine and dryer. It worked for a few weeks, but gradually, as different people took that job, they weren't cleaned very often. Knowing the personnel and being suspicious of their work ethics, Flush devised a plan to see how often the covers were cleaned. Under a certain chair's cover, he wrote, in ink, a small number 1. He reasoned that when they were washed and put back on the chairs, the number would not be there afterwards. He checked it about once a week and was disappointed to see that the same cover, on the same chair, had the number 1 for about ten months. So much for that solution.

***

Another problem revealed by Flush's testing was the outside door handles. The hospital had ten entrances, but two opened automatically when anyone approached, so they didn't get touched. But eight doors were pushed or pulled open by handles which, as tested, never got cleaned.

Different housekeepers were responsible for different doors, but they only cleaned the inside handles, never the outside handles. This meant those handles, touched by hundreds of people daily, were covered with germs, some of which had to be toxic. The worst one was the entrance to the Emergency Department which could be opened automatically but was usually opened manually.

Flush told Feckless, who told the housekeepers, who cleaned them every day for a while. But like other jobs that weren't tested regularly and couldn't be monitored by the naked eye, this one probably got neglected by some of the housekeepers whose jobs rotated often and were replaced by new hires, poorly trained, rarely observed, and never tested. Irresponsibility could be ignored and swept under the rug since nobody other than docs and nurses seemed to care. That included most administrators.

Eventually, Flush's shoulder healed after he had been on light (modified) duty and completed 806 tests and done physical therapy three times a week. He went back to his old job as a porter. The results of his many tests were filed in Feckless's office and were mostly unused to correct germ contamination that had been discovered permanently.

Chapter 5: Suggestions

One of the good things the hospital administrators did was provide two suggestion boxes on the walls in different areas of the hospital. Anyone could make a suggestion and do so anonymously or with a signature. Unfortunately, the suggestions, regardless of value, were quietly evaluated by one person, unknown to all of us, who was probably grossly overworked and had little time to seriously consider the offered ideas. Consequently, almost all suggestions were rejected. If any reason was given, it was caviling about something a 6-year-old could refute. But most of the time, there was no response, either positive or negative, forcing most suggesters to think they'd dropped their ideas down a rat hole.

Flush's first suggestion was for a hospital-sponsored chorus of employees. He would be in it but wasn't qualified to conduct it. They might have to hire such a person. There were several talented chorus directors in town who might be excited about such a prospect, possibly as a volunteer. Flush reasoned that it could grow into a performing community, which would be good publicity for the hospital. Out of 850 (or so) employees, certainly 20 or 30 people would get pleasure in singing in a hospital chorus. Such things are common in this particular artistic small town, though nothing like it had ever been tried at NCMH.

Since he loved to sing, he thought there must be others, also. This idea needed more luck than was available, and that's about all that could save it. To determine interest, the hospital agreed to put a very small announcement of the inaugural meeting in the mox, a semi-functional, inter-hospital, computerized, quasi-email system available to all employees but used by less than half. Counter-productively, an intricate process of passwords and IDs was necessary for access to the mox, and everyone's password was required to be changed every three months. Most people, frustrated and discouraged, gave up on it. The administration assumed mox worked for mass communication. It didn't. Maybe I've grown cynical, but I suspect admin didn't really want good communication with employees, however, wanted to appear as though they did.

The hospital's lame attempt to start a chorus read, on mox, like this: *"The first meeting of a possible hospital chorus will take place at Rose Tomerin's house this coming Wednesday evening at 7:30. Call 265-2413 for directions."*

Flush was optimistic, hoping that 15 or 20 people would be interested. If they could get it started, it could grow and perform at various venues around town. Maybe it could wander the hospital halls singing carols at Christmas. Or could entertain at hospice functions, retirement communities, or assisted living homes. Eskaton would work, too, and with the hospital's name, the chorus would be a welcome diplomat, pushing the hospital's good community spirit and generosity. Unfortunately, none of the administrators had the vision or courage to give the chorus the support it deserved. And since it wouldn't make any money, they gave it only token recognition, nowhere near the support required to get something new off the ground.

Rose's husband, Rick, was a piano-playing choir director at the Episcopal Church and agreed to direct the hospital chorus IF it happened. It didn't. And here's how.

That Wednesday, only Flush showed up at Rick and Rose's place. Their house was a rustic cabin about 8 miles out of town on an uncommonly traveled country road. Against one wall of a cluttered living room was an old upright piano, fitting in well with the comfortable and experienced furnishings. Tidiness was not a priority with this active family. They had two teenage sons, both of whom eloquently expressed their level of interest with their absences. No other potential altos, baritones, basses, or sopranos showed. Flush and Rose sang while Rick played the piano. They pretended enthusiasm, but each realized soon enough that this goose wouldn't fly.

Nobody from the hospital put any effort into it. The indifference proved to be the prevailing reaction to any new ideas. It was clear there would be no chorus representing the hospital. The administration barely noticed or gave any support to the project. Flush recovered quickly. Wiser now, he was prepared for failure, a fortunate attitude based on a cynical reality.

***

Another of Flush's suggestions met an almost similar fate. Placed in a suggestion box, this one was ignored until he complained and got some attention. Pursuing his life-long interest in Frisbee, he invented a game in which teams of two people, standing 15 yards apart, competed against each other to see which team could achieve the most completions between themselves in one minute. He first wanted to do it in the hallway, but of course, the administration said it would be too dangerous. If so, it would be about the first injury ever occurring in Frisbee, but the hospital could never take that chance. So Flush persuaded somebody to hold a Frisbee contest at a local park during the annual hospital picnic. This was before I came.

The hospital administration, including the picnic committee, did nothing to make it happen. But they did, magnanimously, with unprecedented generosity, "allow" it.

Gee, thanks!

On the day of the picnic, Flush came with about ten Frisbees, some long twine, and a stopwatch. He strung the twine between four trees so that two parallel lines of twine, about knee height, were separated by about 15 yards (give or take a yard, or two-this distance could be estimated). He had a large sign, made by one of the friendly secretaries that said "NCMH Frisbee Tournament." This, of course, was a very wishful expectation. Even "Contest" would have been an exaggeration, considering the number of entrants, all of whom were last-minute, unplanned, improvised teams. Three teams (six people total) competed for the prize of two movie tickets. A podiatrist father and his son won. A lanky oncologist and his date (might have been his sister, hard to tell) came in 2nd. Can't remember 3rd place (last).

During the following week, Flush had flyers made announcing the second Frisbee contest, with details of time and place. Rules were too obscure to explain. The following Sunday, at a different park that was mostly empty, Flush set up the two parallel strings and a sign hung on a chain link fence, announcing the contest. Prepared for a long wait, he brought a folding chair and a book and looked for shade.

He'd been there about an hour and was thinking about packing it in when he looked across the ball field and saw two adults coming from a distance. As they got closer, he recognized one of the better administrators, Liseanne O'Donnell, head of HR, and her husband. Lisaenne was not a scowl crow; she was the opposite—a warm, friendly, empathic manager running a Human Resources with a culture of respect and welcome. We all felt comfortable going there to deal with the five people in that department, all of whom were helpful and knowledgeable.

Liseanne wasn't much of a Frisbee player but had come out of pity for poor Flush. He appreciated her sympathetic move and taught her how to throw a Frisbee. She and her husband, a good sport, played a bit and were awarded an imaginary 1st place prize. It was the last Frisbee contest Flush ever arranged at NCMH. He got the message, and Liseanne became his favorite administrator. She was what an administrator should be; her departure a year later after Diggery Wealth took over was disastrous for NCMH and Flush's career there. Her replacement had none of Liseanne's kind understanding and recognition of Flush's unusual excellence.

***

Over about two years, most of the interior hall walls were repainted, some more than once. The new colors were usually a muted brown or green, uninspiring in large areas, collectively depressing. Painters removed both wooden suggestion boxes to paint the walls but didn't replace them when the painting was done. Any organization that valued opinions and new ideas from the many employees would have put the boxes back up when the paint dried, a matter of a day. After a month, Flush asked plant operations when they would be put back up. He was told they were thrown away and would be replaced by new metal boxes approved by corporate headquarters in San Francisco. Flush asked why metal was preferable to wood and got no answer. There were no suggestion boxes for ten months until the metal replacements came. No one seemed to care about the inconvenience it caused to employees who might want to present a suggestion. We were all disappointed and frustrated by the incompetent inefficiency of managers to solve even small problems. Flush mentioned that the old wooden ones shouldn't have been discarded until the new metal boxes came. Deaf ears heard that one.

***

For years Flush had been disappointed in the many examples of poor communication, manifested on several levels in diverse forms. Highly visible, some public signs, in various places in halls, printed on computers by staff, contained misspellings. Other signs made punctuation errors, harmless but unprofessional.

For example, outside the doctors' lounge was a sign: "Doctor's Brakeroom." The apostrophe indicating singular doctor and break room was misspelled. Other hallway signs used acronyms, such as "ICCU" and "TCU" (outside the Intensive Critical Care Unit and Transitional Care Unit), unintelligible to the general public we supposedly served. The admin wasn't interested in effective communication with the public as long as they satisfied some state-wide requirement.

Very little handwriting could be read and signatures were the worst. Most of the docs weren't the only people with dysfunctional illegibility. Every manager signed their name by scratching random markings, the letters of the alphabet indistinguishable from each other, unrecognizable. Managers, who didn't want to be transparent, quickly learned to sign "left-handed without an opposing thumb." Most did it. Every pronouncement was followed by an unreadable signature, so objections could not be addressed to anyone responsible. Fear produced irresponsibility. And anonymity.

As Flush said to me, "Why do they bother to sign anything if nobody can read their names? It's a clever, officially sanctioned deception. They act as though they're so famous that everyone will immediately recognize their chicken scrawl." It was as if the intention was to be uncommunicative, to intentionally misinform, and avoid blame. It was an institutionalized, truly acceptable refusal to take responsibility for your own work. In our computer-dominated institution, cursive was a lost art, and most handwritten communication was given little attention.

This was another example of the opaque curtain covering most decisions. The total lack of transparency disguised a severe decision-making deficiency and irresponsibility unexpected in a hospital in America. Yet the administration failed to recognize and correct these destructive patterns, giving validity to a justified suspicion of intention.

Given the poor communication, it was amazing that NCMH functioned so well. But they never told us the problems, so maybe they didn't. And I never saw the thousands of computer-generated medical discussions, so I have no opinion about the communications of the medical side of the hospital. But I had a pretty good view of most of the non-medical, public side. Unprofessional communication was rampant.

When the new metal boxes were finally installed ten months later, Flush decided to test the integrity of these so-called improvements. He was prepared for failure.

Wanting to call attention to the penmanship imperfections, Flush submitted a proposal in the new, supposedly improved, suggestion box. He suggested an employee penmanship contest. This idea was rejected with an explanation that totally misunderstood his suggestion. It supposed he suggested a penmanship contest between doctors (who had notoriously poor handwriting) and everybody else.

This was not his idea at all, so he decided to dispense with the box and bypass this dysfunctional process. After this expected rejection, Flush, impatient with the bureaucracy's indifference, started to devise alternative routes to success. He was convinced the suggestion boxes, wood or metal, were disrespected by the administration and only available to appease staff and give the impression that their ideas were taken seriously. Flush went to a friendly, open-minded supervisor (Vice President of??? was on her second-floor office door) with whom he had good relations. He presented the penmanship contest to her. He didn't say that signatures were unreadable and communication in general was poor. Instead, he pitched it as a fun, community activity. Participation would be totally optional, of course. There wasn't any enthusiastic support, but she went for it.

Flush got two local dentists to each donate $25 for prizes. Flush bought two $25 gift cards, one to a local all-purpose sporting goods store and one to Staples, a local office supply retailer, which plays a minor role in this novel. There would be two divisions, one for *Most Legible* and one for *Most Artistic*. Entrants, on one piece of paper, would hand write *Northern California Memorial Hospital* on the front and their names on the back and turn it in to the HR office.

Flush persuaded a clerk in HR to design a flyer on her computer, with his help, describing the contest and the few rules and requirements. She did it, and Flush spent two days distributing the flyer to the bulletin boards in every department break room.

In the first year, nineteen people entered. After two weeks, Flush, the friendly supervisor, and the HR clerk sat down together with the entries and decided on the winners. The *Most Artistic* prize went to a man (very surprising), who was shocked that he won. So was everyone involved, since girls practiced penmanship from elementary school days and boys spent those years throwing and catching balls. The *Most Legible* prize went to a female technician in the lab. This was expected, as lab techs were trained to be precise, and accuracy was required. Both were happy about winning.

But their names were never announced anywhere, nor were the names of the two dentists who donated the prize money. It was downplayed by the hospital, with very little support. If it hadn't been for Flush's work and the cooperation of the two sympathetic women, one of whom had enough "pull" to ok such a non-medical activity and who remembered days when we still had fun in the hospital before Diggery Wealth took over, it never would have happened. But it did, inertia defeated, this time.

Flush hoped to expand participation the following year, so he produced what was known in a very small circle (the same 3 people) as *The Second Annual NCMH*

Penmanship Contest. After the two-week penmanship deadline, Flush, the supervisor, and the same helpful clerk met to award the two winners. They put all eleven entries on the floor and slowly eliminated all but five. It wasn't really fair. There was little discussion, each of the three judges deciding to remove the papers from contention without much explanation. After some discussion, they finally distilled the final five down to the victorious two.

The winner of the Artistic Contest was a super tall (about 6' 2") female physical therapist with a good sense of humor. Very sweet, shy, and always friendly, she gave ectomorphy a good name. For a year afterwards, every time Flush passed her in the hall, he'd ask her if she was continuing training to defend her title next year. "Gotta' keep those fingers limber and muscular," mimicking the advice therapists gave their patients.

The winner of the Legibility Contest was another woman who worked in the outpatient Kidney Dialysis Unit. The three judges gave the prizes to the two winners immediately, with no fanfare or public announcement.

Since only eleven people entered the 2nd penmanship contest, Flush, discouraged by the hospital's indifference, never tried another penmanship contest. This second contest had a very unfortunate by-product that caused Flush to be accused and punished undeservedly. But I'll describe that in a later chapter.

***

Like Flush, I came to realize some of this hospital's problems are caused by poor or no communication. Usually, we think that speaking and writing are the only forms of communication; of course, they are the most common and useful. But useful communication can also come in other non-language forms. Outside the hospital, traffic lights are communications that promote safety and efficient vehicular movement. Wedding and engagement rings are non-language communication media. So are the many hats and T-shirts with logos, often sports related.

Inside the hospital, the useful convex mirrors at hallway intersections around the hospital buildings told us what was around the corner. As we wheel large vehicles of varying uses, there would be collisions at corners without these mirrors. Here at this hospital, the colors of bags (blue, red, yellow, clear, green) effectively communicate to the porter the contents, so we know how to dispose of them properly. This works if everyone discards dross and dregs in the right colored bags. We got some new bags that are green. They are for recyclables, a new program, thanks to the new environmental Green Team, described in a later chapter. Occasionally a black bag shows up to confound porters. They aren't part of our accepted baggage, so we don't know their contents and don't know where to throw them. Black bags are bad communication, a foreign language to porters. And no, porters don't like to open bags to determine their contents, which can be surprising and unpleasant. All porters, early in their careers, concluded that there's a big difference between the inside and outside of colored plastic bags.

The surgery SNAs (Surgical Nursing Assistants) and Flush devised a "Language of Glove," a simple system of communication allowing them to express a certain comical insult back and forth without seeing each other. They'd place an empty blue rubber glove in a common location, usually inside a red bio-hazard barrel. Arranging the empty glove's limp fingers, they could eloquently express the universal middle finger salute. This was never taken seriously. This added fun and humor to an otherwise tedious job. When it doesn't interfere with health, fun is a good thing, even in a hospital. No, particularly in a hospital, where constant seriousness can be overwhelming and unhealthy.

***

The CEO and vice administrators on several levels controlling different departments had offices on the second floor of the main wing. They made many decisions from 9 to 5 on weekdays. All other times (nights, weekends, holidays), the administrative nursing supervisor ran the whole hospital. This was a key position in the hospital. This person, an RN, was the "coach" during the absence of all other administrators, supervisors, and managers, more than half the time when these high-paid desk jockeys enjoyed some of their many days off. Administrative nursing supervisor was an important position, occupied by eight different RNs, one at a time, on 12-hour shifts. Since these eight women rotated in this central role, it was useful for all employees to know who this was. The office was the same, but the occupier changed often. And there was no communication identifying the name of this "coach" at any given time.

Flush submitted a suggestion to install a small changeable sign outside the administrative nursing supervisor's office door. He suggested a 6-inch bracket into which name signs could be slid, easily changed by the new incoming nursing supe. This would rectify an obvious problem, he explained. Of course, this was obvious, but admin was too close to the problem and failed to see it from the point of view of the workers who were there when admin wasn't.

Two months later, he received a mox from Scowl Crow Alice saying his suggestion had been rejected. It would cost $340, too expensive. Flush was astonished that 8 small name signs and a wall bracket could cost that much. He went to a local Staples store about 1 mile away. Spending 20 minutes with a Staples manager and their supply book, they determined it could be done for $80. He got this in writing from the helpful store manager. She was much too efficient to have trained at our hospital.

Flush took this document to the manager in charge of the administrative nursing supervisor, Scowl Crow Alice. "Fine," said Alice, with a sarcastically terse, annoyed tone of voice. Her body language wasn't really warm, either.

About four months later, the bracket and name signs (one at a time), spelled correctly, appeared on the wall. And Scowl Crow Alice treated Flush as though his work was destructive. The words "nice job," "good work," or anything of the sort never crossed her lips. She must have thought his contribution made her look bad. But that wasn't his intention. She'd made herself look bad by taking the first bid (for $340) and not going to Staples, the choice of someone who cared and saw the need. She displayed the typical unspoken hostile behavior of the scowl crows, who mostly ran the show.

This important means of communication remained on the wall for about three years. Then one day, it disappeared when they painted that particular wall. There was another small sign in the same location next to the administrative nursing supervisors' door, which the painter had not removed. He just "cut" around it. No problem. But the old name bracket was gone.

Flush was caught completely off-guard. He thought that an old battle had been fought and won. Besides, all the women who occupied that office, rotating through 12-hour shifts, liked the signs. It worked for (almost) everyone. Flush went to a friendly nursing supervisor, who said she would look into it. She was sympathetic, acknowledged the need for that information, and wondered why it had been removed and not replaced. Several days later, she reported that she was told it was taken down because it didn't satisfy the visually impaired; there was no Braille. This sounded a lot like "crapadacious bullswiggle" to Flush and me since there were many signs in many halls without Braille. And neither of us could imagine a situation where a blind person would be feeling their way down hall walls reading Braille signs, one of which would tell who was the administrative nursing supervisor at that time. This was highly unlikely, a very stupid excuse for removing a useful form of communication. Our friendly source of information then told us, with obvious dissatisfaction, there was nothing she could do about it; it wasn't her department. She couldn't say so, but she knew it was more bureaucratic dysfunction.

It soon became apparent that someone in power didn't like it. The foot-dragging began. Flush went to Karina Butt, Salty Dalty's secretary, and asked what happened to the small name bracket. "We threw it away. It didn't match the color scheme of the wall." This, of course, was a well-twaddled codswallop, another explanation contributing to the growing mistrust among the staff. Flush went back to angry Scowl Crow Alice, telling her that he'd be happy to replace it on his own time if they would reimburse him for the small cost. She said, "No, you can't do it. It's not your job and is against policy. Besides, this is a small problem. We have much bigger problems than this to solve. We just don't have time for this."

"Yes, it's a small problem that could be fixed easily and cheaply. And would serve many people. We need to know who is in charge."

Scowl Crow Alice just glared at him, a lowly porter.

Flush, who never gives up easily, said, "If your shoelace were untied, would you stop to tie it, or would you dismiss it as too small a problem?"

"This is not a shoelace and I don't have time for your nonsense," she huffed away in silent turbulence.

She was incapable of understanding his analogy and thought he was just a troublemaker. Later, moody Alice passed the buck to Karena Butt, who mostly runs the small matters involving the engineers. This was one of those small matters (unlike Karena's girth). This second time Karena Butt said they wanted to use a "new style that wasn't Staples." She didn't mention anything about Braille. Or the color of the walls.

A very hostile engineer, named Rick, was in charge of handling it. Nine months later, he had still done nothing. We waited with no positive expectations. The answer to the question, "Why was the original bracket removed before a replacement was available?" never got addressed. Once again, the importance of good communication was ignored.

Flush observed that he, alone, could have fixed this problem in an hour for less than $10 since they still had the name signs. He just needed to buy another small bracket. The hospital, with all its expert personnel and resources, had taken over nine months without fixing it. "If we can't solve a simple problem like this, why should I have any confidence that we can solve the big ones?"

It was another example of the total inefficiency and dishonest management that characterized many decisions at NCMH.

Flush was again frustrated and disappointed, expressing the hope that the medical side of the hospital wasn't as bad as the non-medical side, some of which he knew.

***

Another practical problem with portering, a problem that was frequently noted but never solved, was the many contaminated IV poles placed in the soiled utility closets. These closets were small, one located in each department. They had large bins which held the many blue, clear, and green bags placed there by housekeepers and CNAs. They also had sinks, faucets, and cabinets holding a disorganized array of common cleaning supplies. We porters had to access these tiny rooms twice a shift. But also crammed into these rooms were 7 or 8 IV poles on wheels, clumsily taking up space and falling over, making trash removal difficult. We complained, as did housekeepers and CNAs, but the administrators in decision-making positions never assigned a different space for the poles. So the struggle continues, and nobody seems to care enough to consider plausible solutions. The public never saw the mess and a solution wouldn't save any money or advance any cause, so it was ignored. "Who cares! It's just those damn lowly porters making noise again when we have real problems that need our attention."

Flush told me that within the first month of his hire, 13 years ago, two of the veteran housekeepers, who had been there 28 and 24 years, said, "Don't bother trying to fix a problem. Nothing ever changes. Save your energy." Flush, by nature, was a problem solver, so complacency was not an option he accepted easily. But he was beginning to get the message. Still, he was good at detecting problems and offering solutions.

***

Another of Flush's suggestions, also ignored without explanation, was for "Wheel Day." A lot of our EVS equipment was on wheels, designed for portability around the hospital. A lot of the equipment, not in our department, was also on wheels. And many of the wheels squeaked, never having tasted lubrication. Flush suggested dedicating a day in which people brought squeaky conveyances to a central place to be oiled by an engineer. It never happened. Nobody cared. They had bigger problems, so squeaky wheels remained greaseless.

**

One of Flush's successful suggestions happened in a patient room in 1 North. The patient, a 96-year-old woman, named Bessie, was gaunt and uncommunicative, depressed for lack of community. She could talk coherently but rarely did. She'd been there in a room, alone with a bed and TV, for about 5 days when Flush first encountered her.

One day the patient's niece, a sweet woman in her 60s, visited Bessie when Flush happened to be there collecting soiled linen. It was a very rare visit for Bessie, who, we assumed, had no family nearby. The niece gave Bessie a doll, a cute baby dressed in old-fashioned frills and lace. Bessie's eyes lit up like it was Christmas morning. None of us knew she could smile, but she sure did now. "Oh my! How wonderful!" she exclaimed with joy. Bessie took the doll, cradled it like a new mother, and couldn't stop beaming. She started talking to the doll, asking for its name. The niece said, "Aetna," it was Bessie's late younger sister's name. After that, as long as Bessie was there, she was a different person when she had Aetna to hold, which was most of the time. I believe Bessie thought Aetna was alive and her responsibility. It gave Bessie a purpose, a reason to live. She felt belonging, a connection that was critical to her maternal, nurturing mental health, probably for the first time in many years.

After this success, Flush mentioned it to a charge nurse, suggesting they try it with other old women patients. The department bought three more dolls and used them later with other lonely, self-isolating patients who seemed to give up their desire to live. This worked to a lesser extent, but I'm sure it brought pleasure to lonely old women, welcoming the belonging their maternal instincts created with the dolls. Bypassing the always-rejecting suggestion box, and going directly to a charge nurse, produced a satisfying solution to one of Flush's suggestions. He was learning the best pathways in an indifferent bureaucracy.

***

All employees (except administrators) wore plastic tags identifying name, title (RN, Doctor, CNA, Attendant, etc.), and department; ours said EVS. The names were printed large enough to be read easily from 6 feet away. These tags were clipped to our shirts but could spin around facing inwards, making them impossible to see or read. One might think the chances of this were 50-50, about even, for facing in or out. But certain people fixed it so theirs were always facing the wrong way, so useless as communication media, names hidden, their anonymity preserved. Even after seeing certain people every day for five years, I never knew their names. They always had their name tags facing in. About 1/4 of the employees used this casual trick to avoid identification, and nobody corrected them.

Flush suggested, by way of the suggestion box, they print a duplicate copy to be worn by each of us so the two plastic badges, arranged back to back, would face both ways. This would mean the badge would function always, and we could learn everybody's names. Hearing nothing for two months,

Flush went to HR, which is where the badges were made on a badge-making machine. He asked what had happened to his suggestion. A secretary said they decided it would be too expensive. And they didn't have the labor to do it. This was after Liseanne retired and Diggery Wealth had assumed control of our friendly community hospital.

Flush left, frustrated, as he knew 850 plastic badges couldn't cost more than $100, a pittance for this huge corporation. And the security guards could do it in the many spare hours they logged every day. It was apparent to him that honest answers were unavailable since Liseanne retired. The truth was that certain people didn't want their names widely known, so their privacy was unofficially protected by flipping their badges. And admin supported them. Flush's solution would have inconvenienced a few high-ranking scowl crows.

***

Another of Flush's ideas involved one of his passions—Sudoku. Flush had been doing these puzzles for many years and realized their potential for teaching logical thinking to people who didn't always think logically. He created a process whereby a casually organized "team" could work together to solve a puzzle, which was projected onto a whiteboard. Later, Flush had Sudoku puzzles enlarged to 2' by 2'. Then they were laminated so could be solved with dry erase markers and reused many times. He had been volunteering with elementary students in an after-school program called Sudoku Club, enthusiastically attended by 2nd through 6th graders.

Flush knew the same process could be used in the hospital, partially to build teamwork among the staff and provide an opportunity to socialize outside the serious business of medicine, from which many welcomed an escape. Sudoku, if done regularly, trains people in the basics of logical thinking, which is not a bad skill in a hospital context. If Einstein was right when he said (or wrote, I'm not sure which), "Education is not the learning of facts. It's rather the training of the mind to think," then Sudoku was a wonderful tool, though unrecognized, to deliver that training. And as Flush foresaw, if taught wisely, Sudoku could be presented to achieve other goals, including raising self-esteem, a psychological growth. Flush realized that Sudoku, a puzzle regarded as simply a pastime by about 10% of American adults, was an organon for raising cognitive capacity in all humans.

Flush went to a friend, Phania Chriler, a young, attractive, married woman (hell of a sexy dancer at a company picnic), and proposed a Team Sudoku at the hospital for the employees. He wanted to try it once or twice to see if his process would work with employees and tweak it if it didn't. Phania, about 33, was smart and agreeable. She also had recently taken a new job, one part of which was organizing things that didn't fall into anyone else's department. Team Sudoku qualified for her help. So Flush was on a smart track to acceptance when he approached her one afternoon.

Phania didn't do Sudoku. It seems she'd tried it once or twice in the past but couldn't figure it out, so she quit without regret. "Oh, Sudoku...I hate it. I was never good with numbers and couldn't do it…. Really? Sudoku?"

Flush was getting used to this skeptical reaction. He was prepared. He produced a Sudoku puzzle from his rear pocket (an easy beginners' version), sat across from her at her desk, put the puzzle between them, and said, "Let me show you. I know you'll get it in five minutes."

He'd taught about twenty adults this way, so was getting pretty good at it. He was confident, having succeeded almost always. After explaining the three simple rules, Flush talked her through it, step by step, explaining why a certain number had to go into a certain small box, called a cell. By the third solution, Phania was exhibiting a strong capacity for rational problem-solving. By the fourth, enthusiasm was bubbling up to the surface. She drove the solution bus on the fifth cell, identifying three 7s that eliminated all but one cell, for 7, in the north-east Big Box family.

Sorry if that wasn't clear, but it doesn't need to be. Just understand that Phania was good at it, and she knew it. And Flush did nothing but cheerlead her success. She agreed he could do Team Sudoku in two half-hour lunchtime sessions, where people would bring their lunch to Conference Room 110. They'd do it twice on his day off, a Tuesday, at noon and at 12:30. Flush felt he'd need more than a half hour to get beginners started and enthused but accepted 1/2 hour as a compromise, a start. If it worked out, they'd do it again in two weeks.

Phania moxed the info to Champagne Colby, another very foxy young woman who edited the in-house weekly newsletter, OutReach. She also was the only woman from Public Relations Department who greeted everyone with a smile and friendly demeanor. Under her editorship, the newsletter had evolved into a corporate megaphone, trumpeting the hospital's events from a very self-serving, politically correct position. It no longer published short comic pieces like previous editions, known as The Grapevine, before NCMH became one of many in a chain of hospitals owned by Diggery Wealth. The excuse was that OutReach was read by the public, who might not understand the humor.

Receiving Phania's mox, Champagne bit, and agreed to print a short description of this inaugural event in next week's Outreach. But in the following week's OutReach, there was no mention of Team Sudoku and no explanation from Champagne. Small media publicity in time for the event didn't happen, much to Flush's disappointment. But Phania created a flyer, under Flush's guidance, and distributed it in several places around the campus.

On the following Tuesday, with high hopes and optimistic expectations, Flush set up his projector aimed at the whiteboard in Room 110. Attached by cable to the projector was his iPad, on which was a beginner's tutorial that Flush had spent about two years writing and designing on Keynote, Apple's presentation software. He set up eight tables and 24 chairs facing the whiteboard. He was ready and excited, expecting to introduce wisdom of biblical proportions to the appreciative adoring masses.

Noon came, but not humans.

By 12:05, he began to wonder. At 12:10, reality was sinking in, and by 12: 15 he shifted attention to the second session scheduled for 12:30. At 12:30, still zippo for attendance, except for a dejected and rejected Flush, once again with an idea unattended by his friends, or anyone else who would have become his friend had they been there. Finally, one fellow attendant (euphemism for janitor) named Charles came and, with some pathetic begging by Flush, sat through about 15 minutes of the Sudoku tutorial. He left impressed with what he had learned, saying it was too bad nobody else showed. He was sincerely sympathetic, helping poor Flush assuage his moderate disappointment.

***

The Diggery Wealth corporate headquarters decided to sponsor a suggestion contest at their 44 hospitals located in California and parts of Nevada and Arizona. Called *Innovator's Challenge*, this contest wanted practical ideas to improve the hospitals, coming with an award of $1000 for the three best ideas. The contest only ran for one month each of two years, after which we heard no more about it.

Flush's suggestion deserved serious consideration. Hospitals are very conscientious about hygiene and sterility, frequently stressing the need to wash hands and change rubber gloves often. They won't publicize it, but HAIs (Hospital-Acquired Infections) are sometimes causes of lawsuits resulting in great financial penalties. So decreasing the transfer of germs is always a primary concern. Flush reasoned that the backs of human hands are always cleaner than the fronts, including fingertips, which touch many things in the course of everyone's normal day. The backs, including knuckles, touch almost nothing all day, so must be relatively cleaner. Elevator buttons are touched by many people's fingertips every day, and so are common transporters of spreading germs. If we learn to push these buttons with our knuckles, it's likely that fewer germs will be transferred among elevator travelers.

Optimistically, Flush submitted this idea to the *Innovator's Challenge* committee. He explained its reasoning and included a poem that could be mounted inside each of the hundreds of hospital elevators. It read:

Fingers are germy
Knuckles are clean
Push buttons with knuckles
To move this machine

Several people in our hospital submitted innovations, but none were accepted. They each got a plastic water bottle engraved with the corporation's logo. Flush's suggestion, which, if accepted, could have reduced HAIs and given Diggery Wealth's 44 hospitals an admirable reputation for innovative thinking, was soon forgotten. Maybe some open-minded administrator reading this book will implement this practical suggestion.

***

Occasionally a large, expensive, non-medical item would need removal. There was really no reason for urgency, but management acted as though it cost big time to keep the item around. The first item was the piano that Adele had played while accompanying

Flush's earnest warbling. This piano had been a gift to the hospital from a former patient. He didn't give it to an unknown individual. After Adele left, following her husband's death, and after Diggery Wealth took over the management, the Solarium Room was no longer a community room where guests and transitioning patients could relax and visit. It was turned into a general storage room; the piano was against a wall behind an elaborate, medically-equipped baby bed and a gurney. It hadn't been played for about two years when Salty Dalty decided the piano had to go. They were emptying the Solarium Room to put in a new floor, a huge waste of money. It didn't need new tiles. This was two weeks before Christmas.

Salty Dalty ordered an engineer and an attendant to take everything out of the Solarium and put it temporarily in the hallway. This put the piano where it could be seen and tested. At that time, Dalty had hired an outside company of workers to help the under-staffed engineers make some improvements. There were three young men, all in their twenties, who painted the walls, moved furniture, and remodeled bathrooms. One of them happened to walk by Dalty and the piano. Old Salty Dalty asked him, "Do you want this piano?"

"How much?" asked the very surprised young man, having shown no interest in a piano before.

"It's free. Just get it out of here today," responded Salty.

"What about this plaque that says it was a gift to the hospital from a patient?"

"Don't worry about it. He's dead and nobody cares," responded Dalty with total insensitivity.

The fortunate recipient, father of a 12-year-old, musically oriented daughter with no idea what to get her for Christmas, said (not surprisingly), "Yes. I'll put it in my truck (these workmen all drove pick-ups) this afternoon." And that afternoon, he did that very happily, having been gifted a $500 bonus exclusively to him and his soon-to-be elated and appreciative family.

Flush wasn't there at that time, but later he asked what happened to the piano. There was a lot of confusion and unanswered questions, but nobody seemed to know. Officially, it had just disappeared. But it wasn't the sort of item easily stolen, which sometimes happens to computers that weren't chained down. Later we learned that Dalty had given it away to a vendor, as it was his habit to do, taking the easiest way out. After discussing several large items that had been quickly and secretly disposed of, Flush and I conceived a plan. Since most of Flush's ideas got rejected, evidence that admin opposed his creativity, we decided I would take charge of the next suggestion. They didn't hate me yet.

I composed and sent an email that read:

Hi, Betsy (our CEO) and Green Teamers (please forward this to other Green Teamers),

I have an idea that I think would bring good sense and fairness to the process of discarding valuable items, things worth more than $100 or $200. These are things too big for MedShare to take, things MedShare would have no interest in. (Medshare was the organization that took expired medical supplies and equipment and distributed them to third world countries, a fate that made sense. Why Q-tips would have expirations dates, I never knew).

Specifically, in 2014-15, NCMH gave away a $500 piano which had been a gift to the hospital from a previous patient. We also gave away a large, industrial-quality exercise treadmill, a large (6' by 11') stainless steel table from the Linen Room, and a large, nearly new, industrial-quality washing machine and dryer. All of these items were worth much more than $500 apiece.

For convenience, these items were given away, without notice, to someone who happened to be there and said "Yes" to the questions, "Do you want this? Can you haul it away?" There may have been other valuable things discarded, about which I know nothing.

I'm _not_ writing now to reverse these decisions and recover these items. These transactions are complete, as unfortunate as they were. I'm writing now to propose a much more professional process by which NCMH discards valuable equipment that is inappropriate for MedShare. I believe a **raffle,** in the future, of large, expensive items would show employees that NCMH practices impartial, considerate fairness and human kindness. It would give employees healthy opinions of NCMH's *concern for all of us, raising our morale and trust. It would be easy and cost nothing. And it would bring some excitement and gratitude to the process.*

This raffle might work something like this:

Once we decide to cast aside an item worth more than a certain amount ($100 or $200 might be appropriate), we would publicize it so all employees become aware. Then we would allow a few days for the item to be seen by anyone interested. Then, aware that the adopter would be responsible for transporting the item, prospective adopters would submit their names to a certain person. After one week, a name would be drawn from a hat, and that winner would be informed. That person would have a reasonable time (3-4-5 days) to move the item from NCMH, free of charge.

The winner would have to promise not to sell the item for 3 years. This would eliminate mercenary motives, assuring the item would be valued and used by the winner.

All details presented here are subject for discussion and adjustment. But the overall idea is valid and certainly worth consideration.

Thanks for your time. Please let me know your thoughts about this raffle idea.

Like many other communications from us to upper administrations, I heard nothing. Flush wasn't surprised. In his experience of late, admin was not communicative and unreceptive to any new ideas. They claimed to be too busy to consider anything innovative. So the unfair dispersal of valuable cast-aways continued, undermining the respect of employees for our slothful administration.

Before I wrote the suggestion, the treadmill was put in a hallway near the loading dock. Rudy (more about him later) posted a handwritten note on it saying he would take it. This item was about 10 feet long, 4 feet wide, had a heavy electric motor, and weighed at least 600 pounds. It sat there for about 10 days, with Rudy doing nothing. I was always suspicious that he wouldn't be able to get it to his pick-up, much less unload it at his house, since I doubted he had 3 strong friends needed to move it. But one day, I came to work and it was gone. New, it cost over $4000. It was used but probably could be sold for $2000 on Craigslist. The huge stainless steel table from the Linen Room, also very heavy and clumsy to move, was given to a housekeeper whose husband had a use for a big, clean table on which to display his work. The lightly used industrial washer and dryer, costing $1200 each when new a year before, were given to a friend of mine, an attendant in EVS, who gave them to his sister. These things just disappeared, unrecorded, a mystery to almost everyone.

Had they taken my suggestion, the hospital's reputation would have benefitted from their generosity. We, employees, would have gained respect for their sense of fairness, and many people would have participated in the occasional raffles. The hospital's inaction was typical of their indifference to employees' feelings, an indication of corporate's frequent decisions that excluded any consideration of employees' opinions or value.

Chapter 6: Insidious Entropy

Before 2012, NCMH was locally owned and operated and had a small town feeling, even though, with 850 employees, it was the biggest employer in the county. One year, before I became an employee, a national organization named Solucient recognized NCMH as one of the "Top 100 Hospitals in the United States." This award reflected the professional accomplishments and friendly morale everyone felt by working here. This was a big honor and every employee received a nice jersey shirt with that award clearly stated in a professional manner above the pocket on the left side in the front. Flush showed me his.

There was a corporate takeover in 2012 when Diggery Wealth, headquartered in San Francisco, assumed control of our hospital. Slowly, unnoticed, they eliminated the many small-town features of our friendly-neighborhood hospital. Our amiable and warm community environment became more formal. The hospital picnic disappeared. The annual doctor vs. staff softball game was scratched. The well-attended annual soap box derby, which included entries from the community, got a permanent flat tire. The annual women's triathlon broke its leg and ran no more. The conviviality of the meetings and the management seemed far removed now, with a more militaristic approach to all decisions, many of which were decided by economic factors.

One evening at his house, Flush complained about Diggery's changes while reminiscing about the good old pre-Diggery days. He mentioned Diggery's non-profit status, which meant it paid no taxes. He thought any non-profit organization should never pay its CEO more than $200,000 per year. And he knew Diggery's CEO made a lot more than that.

Many decisions were invariably based on profit at the expense of the common employees. It happened slowly without notice and publicity, observable only after several years. Most of the staff experienced a worsening of conditions, not so much in salaries but in many other things. The putrefaction of ethics caused common employee suffering.

Corporate and our local CEO blamed it on the bad health systems in the US that we all saw, problems brought on by health insurance companies that were siphoning off 30% of all the money spent while just shuffling papers. These huge insurance companies, major corporations supported by our venal government, just transferred money from people to providers such as doctors, clinics, and hospitals. Insurance companies didn't so much as apply a bandaid towards healing anybody. This made everyone, including the doctors, who were independent contractors, employees of the insurance megamonsters. The greedy pharmaceutical companies were also contributing to this highjacking of America's health provisions.

But the salaries of upper-level administrators remained in six figures, even a greedy seven figures for the Diggery Wealth CEO. If we complained, we could be easily replaced without notice. I often wondered what these executives did to merit that kind of salary. They wouldn't say.

Non-profit for whom?

Meanwhile, they held forums for the employees in which they complained that the hospital was losing money and might not survive. They were going to have to cut back, so get ready. At first, nobody would lose their jobs. But that changed after a while.

Personally, I've concluded that single-payer is the smart way to go, as Bernie Sanders articulated unsuccessfully. Simplify the system and spend the money towards the real healers, not the thieving paper minglers. Medicare-for-all would work for everyone but the insurance crooks. Someday, I hope.

Ironically, the hospital spent loads of money on cosmetics. I'm sure they hired a professional interior decorator, probably a color-blind bargain. Many floors were resurfaced with fake wood simulations. All walls were repainted often, usually a dull brown or a more upbeat tan or, in comparison, a false jubilant institutional dark, dull green. Most furniture was replaced with uncomfortable, good-looking chairs, couches, and desks. Nurses' stations were reconfigured, offices relocated, and overhead lights and windows were swapped, comprising so-called improvements.

We were told the hospital got $5 million, which the administration spent painting the hospital's exterior with the same color, so you could hardly tell it had been done. Two large signs appeared, saying, in large letters, "DIGGERY WEALTH," and below, in smaller letters, "Northern California Memorial Hospital." And they repaved the parking lots and painted new stripes. All unnecessary improvements, none benefitting us, but supposedly attracting more customers, not healing them any better or faster.

Many old timers noticed the slow evaporation of planned activities that were common in the pre-Diggery Wealth days, like Christmas parties and break room holiday decorating contests. These became rare and were missed but replaced by, "We just don't have the funding." As distrust grew, excuses like that were met by staff with suspicion. One day we were told that the cafeteria would have to be closed after 2:00 PM on weekdays and all day on weekends and holidays. Food would be served to patients when it was closed, but the rest of us who worked during those times had to bring our meals, be satisfied with junk food sold from machines, or rush out to a nearby fast food joint. That was tough in the 1/2 hour they gave us for meals.

They justified these closures by saying that the cafeteria was losing money otherwise. No consideration for the problems faced by the workers; well, "It is what it is," a phrase that says and solves nothing. The underlying meaning was, "Drop it, shut up, and go away."

This tautology was becoming familiar, used frequently by managers with no better explanation. Flush referred to those five words, now a common phrase, as among the dumbest in the English language, usually allowing the speaker to get in the last words, applicable on <u>every</u> occasion, without <u>any</u> thought. Nobody could argue with or dispute "It is what it is." Flush often thought of writing to the local small-town newspaper about the many internal problems at NCMH. It came out six days a week and was very professionally produced, mostly containing local news events, citizen opinions, and editorials. In a town of 12,000, it was the major source of news and opinions.

The hospital was the biggest employer in the county, with 850 employees. It also sponsored several fundraisers and had many pages on health issues and advice written by the hospital's public relations managers, docs, and nurses. Many ads for the hospital appeared on the paper's pages. The hospital had a major influence on the paper's financial bottom line, so it was very unlikely that any criticism of NCMH would ever appear. Therefore, neither Flush nor I or anyone else ever wrote to the newspaper about hospital issues. Not only would it have been rejected, but word would probably get back to admin, costing us dearly. Why risk ourselves when correction was unlikely and retaliation severe. And the newspaper would not allow anonymous submissions.

Scant comfort, "It is what it is," prevailed as everything slowly descended with no official acknowledgement or attempt at rectification.

***

For years there were two tiny restrooms, side by side, opposite the chapel, just inside the front entrance on the ground floor. They were useful and popular. One day they were locked. When we asked why, we were told the smell was upsetting people walking past. The doors were always closed, and there was a vent inside removing all odor, so this excuse of upsetting people walking past was false. A petition was circulated and received about 150 employee signatures asking for them to be reopened. It was submitted to our CEO. The next day the petition was found discarded in a trash can. The disputed doors remained locked for about 10 months. Finally, the commodes and sinks were removed, converting them into lactation rooms that were very rarely used. There were very few nursing moms, none in that part of the hospital, away from the maternity wing (WICU—Women and Infant Care Unit). These two rooms were useless, but they didn't smell bad. Another dumb decision, ignoring the pleas of the staff.

***

We had six elevators that transported everyone between three floors. These six elevators broke down frequently and could only be repaired by an outside contractor. They weren't dangerous, just inconvenient. Sometimes an elevator was inoperable for several hours, but no one bothered to put a sign by the buttons stating such. So you could stand outside, waiting for it to arrive, for five wasted minutes before concluding the need to try another elevator in another part of the building.

Once, a female technician was stuck in a broken elevator for about three hours. She spent her time wisely playing Scrabble on her cell phone with her daughter in New Zealand. Flush awarded her the informal "Best Use" award, unrecognized by anyone but him, me, and the trapped technician.

Another stuckage occurred when a housekeeper got trapped inside for about an hour. She called for help on the phone inside the elevator, expecting to talk to someone at the hospital. Instead, she was connected to the local Fire Department. She began to panic, became very upset, and after being rescued, refused to ride any elevator at NCMH ever again. She started taking the stairways and lost weight doing so.

***

Two wonderful women, admirable and friendly members of the women's auxiliary, borrowed locally produced art and put it on certain walls in the inpatient hallways. Our community was loaded with artists of different genres, and many enjoyed displaying their works on some of the hospital walls. Every two months, these two women brought in 40 new paintings and photographs and spent a day replacing the old ones with the new ones. There were always a variety of subjects and qualities, some abstract paintings, some beautiful local landscapes of distant mountain ranges, usually snow-covered, or local rivers and waterfalls which graced our beautiful foothill county. Many of the photos were also attractive, ranging from rural sunsets to long shots of Yosemite to closeups of flowers to hawks nesting with hawkettes and penguins in group waddle in Antarctica.

These photos and paintings were for sale at the price set by the artists. They were rarely priced over $300, and some percentage was given to the auxiliary, raising money for hospital equipment. Not many actually sold, so artists didn't do it expecting a great profit. The penguin photos held the record, with eight sold, until a local, professionally successful, and talented artist displayed a few of his many children's cartoons featuring dragons.

These two women were always willing to discuss things with Flush and, later, me. For years they did a great service to artists and the hospital. Together, these wall hangings helped provide a friendly environment and a welcomed distraction from our stress. And they changed every two months, creating an artistic redesign that lent a feeling of caring and innovation to a gloomy interior.

But Salty Dalty, the operations manager, didn't like them. He opposed all art on the walls and, over two years, gradually removed many from the hall walls. He'd do this, with the support of the administration, by having the walls painted (frequently and unnecessarily), a maneuver necessitating the removal of the art. Then, after finishing painting the wall, he wouldn't have the artwork put back up. When asked, the standard answer was, "They were too confusing for the patients. They were just clutter. People complained about them." This was BS, just another false explanation that built the distrust we all had for the administration. The two auxiliary women, long-term volunteers, were very hurt by the slow but inexorable removal of their contribution.

One day an administrator said they could no longer hang any art in 1 South, an area with 12 patient rooms, on the ground floor. About ten paintings were removed from that area. This upset these "pink ladies." Her reason was, "These hallways are too cluttered. Patients and visitors get confused and can't find their rooms. Those paintings were causing a problem." She echoed Salty's disingenuous justification—just another unbelievable lie. This was a ridiculous explanation. True, the halls were cluttered, but not by those wall hangings. Rolling computerized work stations, food carts, reclining chairs, gurneys, and soiled linen hampers amply cluttered every hall except when "state" or JCAHO came to inspect. Then everything mysteriously and rapidly disappeared, producing clear hallways.

All the rooms had simple numbers, and the wall art provided mostly pretty landmarks that helped visitors and patients navigate. Some artworks were very attractive and interesting, provoking observation and comment. Others, usually wild abstracts and not so great. But dumb admin would have no understanding of reality. Everything that was attractive had to come down from the walls. The plethora of unreadable and ugly official notices, warnings, and waivers in tiny unreadable print stayed up.

***

Also, at this time, the admin said all soiled linen hampers, with blue bags, must now be inside patients' closets or bathrooms. Getting them out of the halls helped declutter a little. But the decision was not disseminated well since trickle-down rumors proved to be, once again, an inefficient communication strategy.

Consequently, for about six confusing months, some hampers were in the halls, as before, and some in the patients' closets, a declutterization deemed advisable by admin. The nurses, as usual, left in the dark where disagreement lurked, were no help in making this consistent.

At first, this was seen as an inconvenience for the porters, as it took longer to empty them from the rooms. It was much faster in the halls. Both Flush and I grumbled, as did the other three men who occasionally did porter. But soon, Flush changed his mind. Going in the rooms allowed him to socialize with patients and visitors, a skill he developed on the job and became very good at. He said making a contribution to the mood of bored and lonely patients brought satisfaction to his job.

Outside the room, in the hallway, he would first knock and then say, "Housekeeping." Then he'd enter and explain to the patient and guests (if there were any) that he was just there to empty the blue bag. While taking the linen-filled bag and replacing it with an empty one, which he put in the hamper, he'd start a conversation if the patient was receptive and coherent. If the TV were on a baseball game, he'd ask the patient, "Are you a Giants fan? What's the score?" If someone were wearing a Hawaii t-shirt, he'd ask them, "Which island are you from?" It didn't matter if they'd only been to Hawaii two days, ten years before. At least he got the conversation going. From there, it was easy. And patients were eager.

There was a blackboard in every room with the patient's name, the doctor's and nurse's names, and any notes. There was a pain scale from zero (no pain) to 10 ("Help me Jesus!") and a place the patient could express a daily wish. "Go home" was universally popular. Flush would learn their names off the board and sometimes engage in conversations like a long-lost sibling. He probably spent too much time socializing for management's liking, but he knew he was serving a valuable purpose, and the patients and visitors liked him. Almost every patient was hungry for casual, non-medical chatter, and Flush realized he could play a healing role with his seriously limited medical skills.

Moving the soiled linen hampers inside the patients' rooms did very little to declutter the hallways. All other equipment remained along one wall of most patient hallways, narrowing the passageway by about 1/3. However, occasionally an announcement was heard on the PA system. "All managers report to the board room immediately." This meant that JACHO or state inspectors were coming. Quickly, everyone removed all equipment from the halls, temporarily storing it in empty patient rooms or any place that would accommodate extra wheelchairs or gurneys or a variety of other wheeled furniture that had been useful and convenient in the hallways. I'm sure that JACHO knew this was happening, but they never made an issue and allowed us to violate a state requirement.

Another restriction that inconvenienced us was the removal of all doorstops we used to prop open doors. The door to our break room was now closed and required a key for entrance. This was a minor inconvenience, just another mandated by admin. They justified this annoyance by claiming doorstops might interfere if there was a fire, at which time all doors must be closed.

***

One of the porter's jobs on Sundays was to set up two large, adjoining meeting rooms for an AA meeting. These Sunday meetings had been occurring for about ten years without any problems. There was a sliding wall between the two rooms, which I opened for the occasion. These meeting rooms were reconfigured frequently for a variety of meetings, adjusting for the number of attendees and the purpose of the meeting. These Alcoholic Anonymous meetings were widely attended by about 70-80 mostly middle-aged regulars every week. I got to know some of them. They were all nice, friendly, and well-behaved, at least between 11 and noon on Sundays.

That part of the hospital, outpatient, was closed for the weekend, but we happily opened this wing for them. It was a good way to serve this community for free, something they appreciated, and cost us nothing other than the 15 minutes it took me to set up the tables and chairs. It was my job to arrange 13 tables, ten around a large rectangle and three for coffee and donuts, which AA supplied each week. I also put enough chairs for everyone around the tables. A few men, who had arrived early to chat, were happy to help me. It was a bright spot in my mundane day.

Then one day, I was told we wouldn't supply these rooms to AA anymore. Admin said it was too dangerous and we couldn't provide security for that part of the hospital. This was ridiculous. There had never been any problems with these people. They were always on their best behavior. I wrote a letter to admin, stating their good behavior and my confidence in their continued exemplary comportment, to no avail. As usual, admin ignored the opinions of those of us dealing with the situation and having the experience, which admin totally lacked. No admin was ever there on weekends, so they never encountered this AA group. The AA moved two weeks later to Horseman's Lodge, about a mile away. It charged them for rental. They were unhappy with NCMH but never said so. It was a black eye for us, but corporate, in their collective obtuseness, never realized it.

And there was no adverse publicity or public notice, so the community at large never knew.

***

For many pre-Diggery years, Brahm's "Lullaby" was played softly over the PA system whenever a new baby was born in the hospital. It was a very sweet and charming gesture, and a personal tribute to a happy occasion, much appreciated by the new parents and waiting family. Staff also felt like we participated in good news, not a common feeling in a hospital. It only happened 3 or 4 times a week and only lasted about 45 seconds. Then, for some totally unknown reason, the music stopped. We didn't notice at first. We all took it for granted and paid little attention. After about two weeks, Flush noticed and asked, "Why?" "Oh, I heard it yesterday," the administrator lied. He got the same false answer from a different administrator. They were unwilling to admit the change. When Flush complained to Betsy Socutesome, the CEO, she said she hears it often. As usual, the admin defended Diggery by denying the change. Everyone accepted the loss and went on, as usual. Just another small cut in our environment, making us less human and less friendly. We were getting used to the militarization of our environment, accepting the loss of another warm, friendly practice.

Robert Mugwump sarcastically suggested that we play some music whenever someone died. Maybe *Taps* on an accordion. Or *Somewhere Over the Rainbow*. Needless to say, his idea was not adopted. He didn't care, as it was a joke anyway.

***

One of NCMH's money-saving practices was the encouraged or forced retirements of the old timers, some of whom had been there 25-35 years. They were mostly nurses and technicians, excellent in their skills and attitudes, having developed sincere empathy and bedside manners that only came with years of experience. But they were paid much more than rookie nurses just out of nursing school. Many veterans were offered severance pay to retire; seeing the decline of the hospital morale and the shift in duties, many accepted.

NCMH was willing to sacrifice excellence for profit. Money making was the bottom line.

I watched, over three years, most of our floor staff gradually shift from confident and friendly seniors to a group of tattooed and pierced young women, tentative and taciturn nurses who seemed unsure of themselves, only comfortable operating the computers on wheels (called WOWs—workstations on wheels) they pushed between rooms and a nursing station.

Despite the many changes, the old senior managers, vice-presidents, and CEO (all females except one token male, a mousy accountant) retained their jobs, unless they quit themselves. Often they were shuffled between offices and titles and duties, but they stayed in spite of their incompetencies and paranoid attitudes. The corporation paid these administrators handsomely to enforce its unpopular decisions. Most of these people were decent, considerate employees, but they often compromised their values and integrity to support corporate interests and were paid well for doing so. Give someone $100,000 per year, and she'll fire her sister if the corporate boss says so.

***

One of the corporate moves that provoked the most ire, particularly among the females (except administrators), was the new requirement for all to wear uniforms. These uniforms, supplied by the corporation, were of good quality, I think, as uniforms go. But that wasn't the problem. And none of the 2nd-floor administrators had to be uniformed, which contributed to our resentment.

Before uniforms, for about 50 years, we all wore a colorful variety of personally-owned scrubs. Our tops were universally lively, beautiful, and different. We all supplied and washed them ourselves; some women veterans had about 30 different tops. But despite this expense, no one complained, and many of us thought they gave our hospital some unique class. They were popular among the 95%; the nurses, CNAs, technicians, and housekeepers who did the medical work all valued this freedom of choice. So did we, porters and floorists. The colorful scrubs gave the hospital a look and feel of friendly and casual informality that seemed welcoming and fun. Around Christmas, many tops had Ho Ho Santa themes or comical reindeer patterns. During Halloween, a variety of tasteful pumpkins and funny scarecrows were displayed on many scrub shirts. And some scrubs were of sports teams or musical themes or cartoon characters.

With the new uniforms, each department had its distinguishing color, with names of colors designed to impart classiness. Our EVS uniforms were all "pewter," a name designed to give gray some panache. We weren't impressed. Neither were the security guards, whose color was black, though labeled "noir" by the corporation. The phlebotomists' uniforms were bright red, no doubt to conceal blood spillage; what else? Registered nurses wore navy blue, while CNAs (Certified Nursing Assistants) and transporters wore green scrubs. Not sure why they weren't called "verde." Diagnostic imaging (X-rays) were decked out in "teal" scrubs, blue-green being far too mundane for these specialists. "Ceil blue," aka light blue, was assigned to operating rooms and labor and delivery. Receptionists got orange (poor fools) and burgundy was sported by occupational therapists. All volunteer chaplains donned purple, as did volunteer ladies who ran the gift shop. Docs still wore white lab coats; theirs were the only clothing that didn't change.

The entire process took about ten months from when they first announced the uniforms and when we started wearing them. During that time, the uniform company came to the hospital for two days with an assortment of sizes, colors, and styles. Hundreds of uniforms were available for us to try on, all on racks in two of the meeting rooms. We got to choose the size, material, and style, not the color. And there were only two styles and materials to choose from. We entered our choices of size and styles in computers, along with our names and addresses. Four months later, we received our uniforms, at home, by UPS. This process took about two months before everyone was totally uniformed. I could sense a reduction of morale setting in as we all became more militarized and less individualized.

We asked the administration why they decided to spend a lot of money that way. Putting uniforms on most of the employees in

44 hospitals must have cost a huge amount of money they claim is scarce. Their explanation: having all the nurses (for example) in the same color helps patients identify who is a nurse, distinguishing her from an X-ray tech, who would be wearing a different color. I was not convinced by that explanation. When wearing different scrub tops, as we did pre-uniformization, all nurses wore name badges with "RN" (Registered Nurse) in big, inch-high letters prominently displayed. All other jobs also had their titles, in large letters, on their badges. This probably worked for most patients to identify the functions. And with each nurse, CNA, and tech wearing different tops, it was much easier to remember different people from a patient's point of view. Now, with uniforms, all nurses looked a lot alike. That defeated their purpose.

But, as always, corporate never asked us. And we had no choice, so we went along with it, with angst and grumbling. Once again, we lost our freedom and self-expression. Just another example of a corporate's insensitivity, actions that lowered the morale of most employees. And spending money they claimed was short, instead of hiring more much-needed medical personnel.

***

Another poor choice of the higher-ups was the closing of the Freebee Program. This program benefitted many employees by giving them free used furniture and supplies that were being discarded. These discards happened often, as offices were frequently redecorated with new furniture, cabinets, and wall hangings. However, the Freebee Program didn't make any money for the hospital, and it took up a small space (that couldn't be used for much else). So they eliminated this service and prohibited any discussion about its demise. There will be much more on this later in the book, as it played a big part in Flush's termination. He was the major proponent of the Freebee Program and singlehandedly kept it going. But he was punished for his advocacy.

***

One of the worst deficiencies was the failure to change most of the privacy curtains in the patient rooms and Emergency Department. These were not window curtains. These curtains were hung from the 8-foot ceiling on sliders that allowed them to be closed between the beds and outsiders whenever privacy was required. The curtains were about 7' tall and 12' wide, in a neutral gray geometric pattern that suggested nothing. They weren't pretty and were not designed to be. But they were necessary to preserve common decency and reduce the spread of germs.

They were opened and closed many times each day by medical professionals and patients and their guests. The curtains in rooms with seriously toxic patients with communicable diseases, like C. Diff or MRSA, were occasionally changed (or claimed to be), but other curtains were rarely changed and cleaned. Most patients occupied rooms for a few days and then left, and another patient came into that room. A curtain might stay in a room, unwashed, for many months, protecting the privacy of hundreds of patients over time. There was a good chance that germs were passed between patients and their guests and medical caretakers. You had to touch it to move it. Every curtain in every room was a potential carrier of germs, but few noticed, and nobody corrected this deficiency. Sometimes a contagious patient would be moved from one room to another room. The label outside the room, stuck on the door frame that identified the patient's contagious disease, would be taken down and moved to the new room along with the patient. But if a housekeeper came later to clean the room, she wouldn't know that it had been occupied by a contagious patient, so she wouldn't change the curtain. It was a dangerous lack of communication, but nobody cared enough.

When working as a part-time linen deliverer, I saw everything made of cloth coming in, after having been washed by a company over a hundred miles away. A big truck brought new linens every day and took away used linens that needed washing. If unclean curtains went out, I wouldn't have seen them, as they would have been in blue bags. But I would have seen clean curtains coming in; I never saw any such curtains coming in clean. They were never changed.

I decided to run a secret test. One slow afternoon when I was delivering linen in 2

North, I went into Room 205. On the small label at the bottom corner of the patient curtain, I wrote the date in pen. Nobody would ever notice it without looking specifically there. For many months I checked to see if that date was there. It was, for ten months. Then the curtain was taken down because they painted the walls of the room. I never told anyone about my secret test. They'd been told before and did nothing. I didn't want to get a reputation as a whistle-blower. I needed the job too much; let Flush play that role. I did it to satisfy my curiosity. Again, unwashed curtains probably caused HAIs, but there is no way to prove it. And since the hospital kept HAIs and lawsuits secret, we never knew. And the people who could correct it didn't care enough to do anything. I'm sure there were many other examples of inadequate hygiene outside my limited experience as a janitor.

Chapter 7: Dalton Takeman

The universally disliked manager of almost everything non-medical, Salty Dalty, was an egotistic authoritarian. He sat sternly and alone in his dreaded office, across from our break room, often hunched over a computer or blueprints of the hospital. Being the manager of plant operations gave this martinet far too much power, which he abused and misused, putting him well on his way towards the pinnacle of Scowl Crow Majesty. Among other responsibilities, he was the big boss of EVS, the boss of our boss, Feckless Pidwell. He also governed engineering.

Instead of leading employees <u>with</u> power sharing, which always works well and bonds people in cooperative progress, he made many enemies by using power <u>over</u> them, alienating his staff and everyone involved. Trained for years in the military, he failed to distinguish between 20-year-old rookie soldiers and 50-year-old professional civilians, most of whom knew their jobs better than he did. As the plant operations manager, he determined who got what office, when they got it, and what furniture and equipment they could have. He could fix, or not, your air conditioner or heater, your refrigerator, or break room TV. He could remove your break room TV or any other appliance if he disliked your department. He could order your break room repainted, have your department exiled for 4 months (for a 1-day painting job), and when you returned to baby shit brown walls and asked, "Where's the telephone that was here?" He'd say, "We're reconfiguring the room next door, so had to remove it."

"Where's the ceiling fan we had before you painted the break room?"

"We had to take it down. If you need another one, we'll get a floor fan."

Salty Dalty determined which hallway walls got painted, when, and which color. Institutional brown was a favorite, but sometimes he ventured outside the box with a dull beige. The walls seemed to get painted continuously. I asked a painter why the color of brown. His answer: "It hides the dirt better."

I had a suspicion which I couldn't prove but will mention here. The men hired to paint the interior walls were outside contractors, kept busy continuously painting, often unnecessarily. I suspected some kickbacks to Salty Dalty from the painting company. There were just too many walls painted and repainted, colors changing often everywhere in hallways, offices, and empty patient rooms. As usual, the hospital spent large sums on cosmetics, changing non-medical features to attract the public's business. That seemed to be Diggery Wealth's strategy.

Dalty also changed the floors from carpet to tile or from tile to fake wood or from fake wood to carpet. The cosmetics were in constant mutability, including pictures, usually landscapes or still-life flowers, hung on office walls. Some walls had dull black and white photos of ferns or mushrooms. Certain walls in the basement had many old pictures of a variety of past citizens and doctors who had helped establish the hospital 50 years before.

Salty always had an answer, and whether it was relevant, accurate, or logical was never considered. Dalty said it, end of discussion. He controlled most of the non-medical decisions made in NCMH and did so with a harsh dictator's scorn, if necessary, in a nasal voice that mostly resembled that of a menstruating (for the first time) teenage ingenue.

Dalton Takeman had been a military man and carried himself like an officer. Always neatly dressed in pressed slacks and long-sleeve business shirt and tie, he walked with a formal purposefulness that said he was busy and important and not to be bothered by anything as trivial as friendship. He ate alone, somewhere, never with friends in the cafeteria like everybody else. I never saw him laugh and doubt he had any friends. When he grew a short goatee, a tidy little grayish specimen in an attempt to be "cool," it was observed that he looked like a used Studebaker salesman who hustled cub scouts on overnight campouts. He often clashed with Flush on many minor incidents, usually some infraction like a hat, innocently performed by Flush. Sometimes it seemed Salty Dalty secretly wanted to get Flush fired. So Flush, even more than everyone else, avoided Salty Dalty.

One day I went to Flush's house, where we sometimes partied and watched sports on TV. In his bathroom, on the back of his toilet seat, was a prominent framed sign which read, in inch-high lettering:

Here you push
It's not your fault
Giving birth
To another Dalt

This amused but didn't surprise me, considering Flush's talent for denigrating his enemies. This opinion was shared by almost all 850 of Dalt's co-workers. All 6 engineers who worked directly under Salty Dalty detested and avoided him.

***

A sign in the hall outside Dalt's office read **Plant Operations**. One morning we came to work to find, temporarily appended to the sign, an attachment that reads, "In a hospital, anyone who operates on plants probably flunked out of med school."

It lasted until just after 9, to much hilarity of those who saw it, until Salty Dalty came to work and entered the office without noticing it. His very stout secretary, a pear-shaped endomorph named Karina Butt, asked him, "What should we do with the new sign?"

"What new sign?" asked the testy one.

K Butt pointed to the door and shook her head in that direction, an expression of disgust on her round porcine face. Salty Dalty stepped back into the hall, looked up to see the sardonic alteration, and reached up with an angry swipe, tearing the wit out of public view. He stormed back into his sheltering office, slamming the door as he exited dramatically from view. For several days, there emitted from Salty's office a low-key investigation to determine the guilty graffitist. Salty didn't want the administration to learn about it, as they might still be unaware of his unpopular reputation among the manual laborers. So Salty called several engineers and housekeepers into his office, one by terrified one, for a grilling, in violation of our union contract. He never figured it out.

I suspected Flush; he was the most likely among those with the witty humor and nerve to do such a thing after considering everyone with the ability, motive, and opportunity. I asked Flush when we were alone, and he looked at me, smiled, and walked away. That was early in our friendship and he was reluctant to trust me yet. But I eventually learned that trust was very rare at NCMH among employees. I'm pretty sure Flush was the culprit.

***

About four years after the first Hat battle (more later) between Flush and Salty Dalty, there was another Hat battle. Flush had gone to a garage sale and bought a unique ethnic hat. It was from a small native village in Guatemala, hand-made by craftswomen with many hours of fine work. It had many bright colors and was unique in North America. He called it his "Happy Hat." Everyone who saw it around the hospital liked it with common notice and praise. "What a beautiful hat!" was commonly heard in Flush's presence. It seemed to make people laugh and light-hearted, except in serious circumstances. Flush thought it was good therapy, a needed distraction from the constant worry and occasional despair commonly experienced in our dull, colorless environment. His job as a porter didn't require a formal appearance and took him everywhere to be seen by many in the course of a day. This very colorful hat contrasted widely with our mandated pewter uniforms.

One day, wearing it in Salty's outer office while using the copy machine, Flush was challenged by Salty. "What's that on your head?" demanded Salty. "You look foolish."

"It's just a hat. Many people like it and when I don't wear it, they ask for it."

"Well, I don't like it. It's not officially sanctioned. It violates our standards. Take it off."

Flush went to our boss at that time, Feckless Pidwell. After some negotiation and intercession with Salty, it was agreed he could wear it on alternating Mondays. So it became Monday's Happy Hat. At least this once, Feckless had semi-successfully represented and defended an employee in EVS. Flush felt that was a victory, very rarely experienced with Salty Dalty. The hat continued its popularity and Flush wore it in partial protest against the encroaching prohibitions denying informal individuality that were dominating management's controls since Diggery Wealth's takeover.

***

The first year I was there, the administration held a contest for the different departments. The challenge was to decorate our respective break rooms for Christmas. The winning department would receive a pizza party for their lunch.

Two of our best, friendly, popular, and most conscientious housekeepers got very busy and spent several evenings, on their own unpaid time, putting up many decorations, giving a sparse habitat a cheerful holiday appearance. The Christmas decorations in our break room, all brought and assembled with great care, became quite extensive. Holly, wreaths, mistletoe, and a small tree represented the natural world while streamers, bunting, tinsel, ornaments, reindeer, sleighs, Santa, elves, a manger with Joseph, Mary, and baby Jesus said, "We're gonna' win!"

But they made a critical error that pissed off old Scrooge Dalton, whose office was across the hall. In order to make the Christmas tree, a real cedar, stand, they'd anchored it with two wires attached to the wall with small screw hooks. These hooks made tiny holes in the newly painted wall, offenses which Salty Dalty found indefensible. With despotic rage, he demanded all decorations be removed, along with our couch. This was a heart-breaker for the two women who had put so much effort into a communal contribution. Since the decorating project took form over three days, and was almost finished and greatly admired and appreciated by the 28 EVS employees who did nothing but observe, we all felt very sorry for the two housekeepers who had invested so much time, energy, and generous holiday spirit. It was very tasteful and expressive of the joy and spirit of a merry Christmas, all ruined by Salty's narrow need for total subservience and disregard for others' independent creativity. Our shock and despondency were palpable when we came in the next day to a dreary, empty break room sans a much-used couch. Needless to say, we reacted badly, though the depression was held to mild grumbling, nobody willing to jeopardize their job. I can't describe the frustration and disappointment of the two housekeepers whose unselfish work was so blatantly abused. The rest of us considered Salty Dalty a total fascistic a**hole. If Christmas ever had a downside, like a clogged-up, charcoal-plugging chimney seriously impairing Santa's progress, Salty played that role. There was no joy around him.

***

Flush wrote a poem, wisely unsigned, which he hung on the bulletin board. We all knew he wrote it, but management couldn't prove it, so it went unpunished. And no party for us.

Holiday Poem

I'd like to write a happy poem,
that makes us all feel cheerful
But that would be a lie, you see,
'Cause really we're real fearful.
Afraid of doing something wrong,
it happens everyday,
they changed the rules; what's up was down,
no matter what we say
So silently we work and choke,
on our words unspoken,
they claim to "Humankindness,"
but for us, that's just a token.

Chapter 8: A Hat & Scowl Crows

Some people thought he was pushing the envelope to be annoying, but I knew better. Flush wasn't even trying to make a controversial point. We just needed to be more friendly and informal and less army. Of course, seriousness was important when necessary, such as medical discussions in a hospital. But after three days of talking about blood pressure, body temperature and waste elimination, and catheters, most patients (being human) crave some balance produced by, at best, humor, but even talking about last night's baseball game would help. Also, employees needed more humor, not less. Our morale was unpleasantly low. Somebody once said, "A laugh is an instant vacation." That somebody wasn't anybody in our administration.

One day Flush showed up with a hat, a modest, dark blue baseball cap with "Flush" printed in white, inch-high letters on the front. On the back was "The Peristalsis of NCMH" in smaller lettering. The hat was new, clean, and conventional, except for the words Flush had hired a seamstress to sew on. As his job took him all over the hospital several times each day, many people saw it. Many laughed with approval. The reaction from everybody (almost) was amused appreciation, and if he forgot to wear it, people asked, "Where's the hat? We want the hat." Most employees knew his nickname and job and what "peristalsis" meant and recognized the analogy. But a few others, lacking humor, and determined to instill a serious, military-like, no-nonsense atmosphere, disapproved. If it wasn't formally approved, it didn't belong. For some reason, neither Flush nor I ever determined that about 75% of these stern authoritarian women were seriously steatopygous (known in Houston as *Thunder Lizards*), a condition called derisively, on the street, as lard butt.

These were the scowl crows who disliked everything about Flush. And most of them were older female supervisors and administrators who, in positions of status, had lost their ability to see the big picture while focussing on minor details. Most of them were RNs who, earlier in their careers, realized they lacked the nurturing disposition necessary for good nurses who deal with patients. So they went to graduate school and, advancing their careers in the health industry, building on their RN degrees, became directors with master's degrees. They had private offices and titles and authority over their departments, which they exercised with little concern for the work the floor nurses were doing with warmth and devotion. This position relieved them of actually dealing with sick people and gave them more power over nurses while getting paid well in a hospital. There were some very good older female administrators and managers, but the many scowl crows, with personal problems of their own, lowered morale, an impactful force to which the CEO and board of directors seemed oblivious.

Scowl crows were no fun to be around, at least in the context of a hospital. Who knows what they were like when off duty? They created a tense atmosphere of unfriendliness, scary demeanors, and fake competency. Many of them weren't very bright. They sometimes made stupid decisions that adversely influenced our work, decisions made in small private offices without ever consulting the people whose jobs were made more difficult, less efficient, and ineffective.

They walked around the hospital when they weren't hunkered down in their cramped offices, scowling at everyone, including each other. Walking down the halls, they regularly cold-shouldered us workers, never smiling or offering verbal greetings, always snubbing us. They were very poor examples of the "Humankindness" that the corporation had displayed everywhere in large print. And they looked like they were living miserable lives that they deserved.

When the crows weren't scowling, they were scorning, snarling, and scoffing. These were passive-aggressive, self-important managers who produced only disgruntlement, surreptitious rebellion, indifference, and disrespect to a place that would have been better off in their absence. Of course, they took a dim view of Flush's open friendliness. They were experts at turning a good thing into a bad thing. And they had power.

Flush wore his new hat for about two weeks. But it was only a matter of time before the collective opposition of the scowl crows was registered. Someone, who was protected with anonymity, filed a formal complaint. The cruel wheels of restriction began rolling over the poor hat, even before Flush could remove it from his head. At the inquisition, a real kangaroo court, Flush faced two scowl crows in Salty Dalty's private office. I was there, having recently volunteered as a union representative, called a "shop steward," whose duty was to accompany employees to these "trials," seeing that they don't get steamrolled by unfair corporate practices and punishments. Having no power myself, I was useless except as a witness and advocate who was always ignored.

At first, in a phony attempt to appear reasonable, they applied logic. Or what they thought was logic. They knew Flush was popular, as was the hat, so they wanted to tread lightly, if possible, even though they held all the cards.

"Flush is a bad word. How could you put it on a hat? The public sees it. What if everyone in the hospital wore hats like that?" they demanded in rude, accusatory tones.

"What if they did?" replied Flush, who was aware of the danger and needed to keep his job. He wasn't going to lose it for the sake of a hat.

"There would be chaos and disrespect. The public would think we weren't serious. The hospital would suffer a bad reputation."

"You're probably right about that, but your supposition is false. Everyone would never wear hats like this. They just wouldn't. It's a silly 'what if,'" responded Flush calmly. He wasn't going to roll over and cave. "Your hypothesis is based on specious logic," Flush continued. "If it were valid, I could use it to prove we shouldn't be in this room."

This was met by puzzled looks from both the scowl crows. They were thrown off guard, rarely having been challenged, never having to defend themselves. "What do you mean?"

"By your logic, I could say, 'What if everyone in the hospital were in this room? That would be deadly; people would get crushed. Therefore we shouldn't be in this room.' That *what-if* reasoning can't apply to my hat unless it can also apply to us in this room."

The two scowl crows were stunned, temporarily unable to rebut his logic. They sat, embarrassed and speechless. Now what? I thought.

One of them finally broke the embarrassing silence. "Look, Flush is a rude word. You can't wear it around for the public to see."

Then I entered the altercation. "That word is a common medical term in hospitals. There are big boxes of supplies that have 'Saline Flush Solution' written on their sides. They're very common and the empty boxes are often left in the halls for the porter to collect. And it's a common practice in medicine to flush toxic liquids out of the body. It's not a bad word. Doctors and nurses use it often."

"We don't care what you say. You can't wear that hat here. There are rules against it."

I foolishly responded. "In poker, a royal flush is a winning hand, much valued. Everyone hopes for a royal flush."

"If you can't stop this nonsense, I'm going to ask you to leave," came the angry scowl crow's rebuttal addressed to me.

"Show me the rules," requested Flush, barely able to restrain his aversion and temper.

This brought the senior crow, Dalton Takeman, in white shirt and conservative tie, to his computer. Salty Dalty (as he was labeled outside his hearing by everyone I knew) was a rare male among the mostly female scowl crows. He was hated by everyone who worked under him. Obviously irritated, he spent several minutes vigorously punching the keys, searching the company's rules and regs. We sat in uncomfortable silence, staring at the various plaques displayed ostentatiously on Salty Dalty's walls. Finally, he found a rule and, with unwarranted pride, turned his computer for us to see. It read, "All employees must dress in approved attire."

Of course, this left it all open to subjectivity. Flush mentioned other employees who wore baseball caps with Giants and 49ers logos who were unrestricted.

He mentioned the nurses, CNAs (Certified Nursing Assistants), and housekeepers who were allowed to wear a large variety of very colorful, often comic, tops. This happened before Diggery required uniforms for everyone but administrators. Some of these shirts were seasonal and celebrated different holidays, including Halloween and Christmas. This was good, in Flush's opinion, producing an atmosphere of informality and friendliness to the public. The scowl crows knew that permissiveness with women's attire certainly avoided confrontation with the women. This hospital would have started a very serious rebellion of several hundred women had the administration prohibited self-expression and personal taste in female employees' tops.

"And you might be setting a bad precedent, and we can't tolerate any insubordination," spoke the other scowl crow imperiously. I later heard she was a retired one-star general in the US Army. Her name tag was worn backwards, facing away from view, which concealed her name intentionally, but everyone was afraid to call her on it.

The scowl crows weren't afraid of prohibiting Flush, who mostly stood alone. Despite the many unspoken hat supporters among employees, the scowl crows stood together in their narrow interpretation of the rule regarding Flush's hat. When it became obvious that they were unyielding, Flush stood up angrily, put the offensively profane hat on his head, and left the room, obviously disappointed (with easily perceived irritated undertones). There was no doubt left in the room as to his opinion. He went to his immediate boss, Feckless Pidwell, and took off from work the rest of the day. We never saw that hat at work again. Flush reasoned that, on this issue, he'd wisely come from his interest rather than from a position. Flush was not as good an employee thereafter, intentionally refusing to do a few extra small things he used to do that were not in his job description. And the administration wondered why general, across-the-board morale was so low.

Chapter 9: A Scowl Crow Re-evaluated

One afternoon a few months later, there was an announcement on the overhead PA system. "Porter please call 6040. Porter call 6040." I saw Flush go pale. I knew it meant trouble.

I asked him, "What's the matter?"

"That's Kate Kram's number. She's the general who outlawed my hat."

I knew from previous hall encounters and the infamous "Hat Exclusion Trial" that she was one of the most bone-chilling scowl crows to march the halls of mercy with fearsome intentions and a butt the size of a ravenous hippo's. Her military demeanor sucked all the humanity from the air around her; one felt like saluting as she passed wordlessly, staring straight ahead (all scowl crows had mastered the tunnel look), tromping like a worried mule pulling a no-nonsense plow. I later learned she had been in the army for 28 years. Figures.

With little enthusiasm, Flush removed his right rubber glove, threw it into a trash can at a nurses' station, picked up a phone, and dialed 6040.

"Nurse Kram speaking."

"Hi," attempting to be friendly. "This is Flush. You paged me."

"Yes." She refused to call him Flush. "I need your help. Someone threw away a pair of slippers that belonged to a patient. They're in one of the blue-soiled linen bags you picked up in 2 North. The daughter's upset. Says they had sentimental value. Something like a present from somebody. We need to find them. Now. Where are those bags from 2 North?"

"When were they thrown away? I've been there twice so far today."

"I'm not sure. Probably this morning, but I can't be sure. Where can I meet you?"

"I always take the bags out to the San-i-Pack dock. Do you know where that is?"

"I can find it. I'll meet you there in five minutes."

Flush hung up with a noticeable look of relief. "For once, I'm not in trouble. Still, this looks like a miserable next hour I'm facing. Call 911 if I don't come back within…2 days."

This San-i-Pack area Flush referred to as his "office" was outdoors, at the back of the hospital, surrounded by chain link fencing. This was near where truckers delivered a variety of supplies all day long, a sometimes busy place called a loading dock. Also, there was a large crushing machine that compressed cardboard boxes of all sizes into forms that could be transported distances to be used for some kind of recycling; I'm hopefully surmising.

For years this area had been the place where all the dregs were hauled and separated, each different colored plastic bag going to a separate destination from the other colors. Over the years, some of these bags, strong but not impenetrable, had broken, spilling a variety of dross on the concrete floor. Since the hat prohibition, Flush stopped cleaning that area. It showed, but almost nobody but porters ever looked, and nobody complained about the sloth and grunge. The porters were real slobs behind the scenes. We didn't care about sanitation on the San-i-Pack dock; tidiness didn't apply. I'm pretty sure there was no poop, but I wouldn't bet on it. Owing to low morale resulting from the distance between staff and management, indifference had set in; staff were satisfied with a "C" if grades were given. They weren't.

The smell from the San-i-Pack because of sterilizing toxic bio-meds by heating them to 286 degrees was usually noxious, provoking many complaints with descriptions ranging from fetid to poisonous to lethal. Employees entering the hospital from the back parking lot always picked up the pace when passing Flush's outdoor "office." Flush never complained about the vile conditions. I think he realized that the appalling offensiveness repelled administrators, which was a good thing with some of them, from Flush's viewpoint. And since his job was considered "unpleasant" by most of the female co-workers, he was secure in that position. Few wanted his job.

I later heard from Flush what happened with Nurse Kram. It was a hot summer day in the high 90s, and the San-i-Pack dock was exposed to direct sunlight. Nurse Kram removed her white coat and hung it on a fence post. Flush tore off two large plastic bags from a roll and laid them on the concrete in the center of his "office." Then they started emptying the blue bags, one by one, quickly sorting through dirty sheets, towels, gowns, bedspreads, wash clothes, blankets, and blue pads (ugh). This went on without much conversation for about five minutes. Not comfortable but no longer frightened, Flush got down to the job, happy to be working in cooperative coordination with a scowl crow. This had never happened to him before. The paths of the two, one at the head, the other at the foot of an institution, had never crossed outside a hallway. I doubt they'd ever exchanged two words in twelve years.

Flush was surprised when she broke the silence. "I was raised on a farm in Nebraska. Dairy farm. I'm used to this kind of work."

"You know how to milk a cow?" asked Flush, thankful for the break from an uncomfortable silence.

"Hell, yes! I even won a blue ribbon at the fair for doing it when I was eleven. I milked seven cows in one hour. The highlight of my life up to that time."

Flush was surprised to hear her cuss, if "hell" can be so considered. But at least she was sounding more human. Having her down on her knees, amongst the bags of dirty linen, looking for a pair of old blue slippers, was earning some "creds" in Flush's value book. Standing up and waving her hand in front of her face in obvious discomfort from the stifling heat and smell, Nurse Kram said, "I'm sweatin' like a whore in church."

CRASH! Flush's heart did an ecstatic somersault, and laughing unexpectedly, he looked at her differently ever since. He realized she wasn't always a scowl crow, and he'd witnessed a friendly, down-home side to her that he could live with. Their relationship changed for the good. From then on, they had a good conversation. She told him she had raised six foster children and had been a nurse for 38 years. She said, "I'll have a beer with Jesus and the devil at the same table." This removed all his doubts.

Nearing the end of the bags and feeling discouraged, in about the 60th bag (no one was counting), she found the slippers. Expecting silk, considering the urgency with which the daughter had demanded the search, they were surprised to find tattered K-Mart synthetic, Taiwan-made foot gear. The slippers might have been special to the daughter, but only for sentimental reasons.

"Gimme five," said Flush, holding his hand out to Kate. She slapped his hand, spun around, put her hand, palm up, behind her, and he returned the gesture. Never, before that day, would Flush have expected to be high (or low) fiving with a scowl crow. With great joy, they hugged triumphantly, and Flush admitted that he had been reading her wrong all along. As they parted, Flush said, "It's great to see another side to you. Thanks."

For several weeks thereafter, whenever they passed in the halls (about twice a week), they'd say "Hi." A couple of times, Flush said to a sad Nurse Kram face, "You need a hug," and he gave her one. But over time, their friendship wore thin; she scowled, even at Flush, and they reverted to their old formal ways. I know Flush was disappointed that the momentary warmth evaporated (he thought a variety of friends was an integral ingredient of a full life), but he still saw Nurse Kram with new eyes. Now she was only a part-time scowl crow with mitigating circumstances in his appraisal. Despite her professional, no-nonsense demeanor, he knew she was a sweetheart with a difficult job that didn't encourage her to reveal her connection with humanity. He told me he'd be happy to have a beer with Kate someday, off the clock, if she drank beer. She probably did when released from the suffocating restraints of her highly responsible profession.

Chapter 10: Some Wonderful People

I don't want to give the impression that everyone was a jerk. We had many fine doctors, nurses, and technicians at NCMH, some of whom became casual friends while on the job. Flush helped me learn who the friendly ones were, the professionals who respected us janitors and willingly engaged in non-medical conversations when they had the time. I grew to admire most of these professionals even though I had no idea about the subject or the quality of their work.

As an undergraduate at a state university, I knew several premed students who were preparing to become doctors. These people, young men and women, were among the brightest students, though not necessarily the ones with the highest IQs. But they were usually the most arduous students. On Saturday afternoons, when the rest of us were attending sporting events or bars, playing Frisbee on the campus lawns or poker in our dorms, these serious premeds were fervently memorizing the names of human bones or the function of our kidneys. On Saturday evenings, when slacking friends and I were trying to meet girls at bars and parties, and girls were doing the same with us, those same premeds were studying liver functions and memorizing Latin names of bacteria. On Sundays, when my ilk went home to visit family, those same premed students stayed behind learning how to defeat virus pandemics. They were all trying to achieve good enough grades to get into very limited openings available at med school, which was highly competitive. They took this admirable attitude into their careers, the fortunate ones who made it that far and became doctors or nurses. Their sacrifices for the rest of us should be recognized and applauded. I was honored to work helping them save and improve lives, probably the most important job any human can attempt; school teachers come in a close second.

Most of these premed students were very fortunate to have that strong "calling" in their youth. They knew they wanted to be doctors or nurses early in life and were determined and motivated in that direction without any hesitation or ambiguity. They might not have known their specialty, be it eyes, bones, hearts, brains, feet, or skin, but they could determine that later in med school. I envied them for this certainty, a direction I didn't have when I was exploring career options without any positive direction. While I was drifting around in an ocean searching for a landing spot, these students had already landed on their chosen island and were building their future, of which they were positive. I came to realize how important hospitals are to civilization. As Flush pointed out, if civilization ever crashed, as happened in some science fiction novels, hospitals would be the last institution remaining, way beyond governments, schools, banks, manufacturing, and commercial enterprises.

My admiration for the nurses who worked with patients is equally strong. Under the guidance of doctors, nurses, mostly female, did all the hands-on work necessary to rehabilitate sick patients with a variety of health problems. Nurses regularly do so with competence and grace, making friends with patients who desperately need help. Few are aware of the work nurses do, with 1/3 the recognition and salary of doctors but twice the ardently concerned unpleasant duties they perform. Nurses are the professionals that cure patients by watching and measuring vital signs and alerting docs when things change. Nurses deserve more credit than society gives them, as they unselfishly perform work that's sometimes dangerous but necessary in the service of patients, all of whom are strangers, usually sent home well, never to be seen again.

Also deserving of praise are the CNAs, certified nursing assistants, who lack the education of nurses and usually do the dirty work, like wiping soiled butts of totally immobilized patients, changing their diapers and soiled sheets, and emptying their bedpans full of sickly excrement. These people, almost always women, are predominantly obedient and satisfied with that station, performing these unglamorous chores eight hours a day, sometimes for 25 years, without complaint.

One doctor, a surgeon named Bob Heat, had a good sense of humor and always had time for Flush, who loved to joke. Heat was thin and trim, and being single and about 60, only slightly balding, was interesting to many single nurses after he broke up with a particularly pretty younger nurse. Dr. Heat often wore scrubs on his way to or from the Surgery Department, where he performed a variety of common surgeries. But he sometimes appeared in a sports coat and tie, with a colorful shirt that matched perfectly, always clean and pressed, looking dapper and professional. Could have been a model for GQ Magazine. Whenever Flush saw him so attired, he'd fake admiration, saying, "Whoa, what's this? A wedding?" Dr. Heat said, humor unrestrained when with Flush, "Don't get excited. It's a rental."

I don't know what kind of surgeon he was. But he was there a long time, so I assume he was good. He also was there early most mornings, visiting patients in their rooms or typing on a computer in a nurses' station. I think he was in the hospital more than any other doctor, even on weekends, which gave me the feeling that he loved his work. The other docs didn't have his conscientious attendance, which indicated special caring about his work and the people he cut open and repaired.

Another time Flush told Dr. Heat of his *gerd*, a disease of the esophagus caused by acid backing up from the stomach into the esophagus while sleeping. Heat spent five minutes drawing a crude diagram of a rolled-up blanket under the mattress, raising the head so less acid rose to cause problems. He gave it to Flush. Flush said, "Wow. An original Heat! Someday this will be worth a lot of money when the world recognizes your undiscovered artistic talent." They both laughed. The drawing, a scribble, was crude and worthless but evoked laughter with Flush's exaggerated evaluation.

***

Another doctor, a hospitalist, was Ali Ahmed Hagi, a younger doc (about 35) who had only been there about a month. Taking a page from Flush, who liked to welcome newcomers, I introduced myself and greeted him, suspecting he might have felt like an unwanted (dangerous?) minority. Tall, about 6'4," thin, and clean-shaven, he had no accent and dressed like us, giving no hint of his Muslim background other than his name. I learned he was Egyptian but had been educated in Saudi Arabia and England. He arrived at the time of weekly, worldwide jihadist attacks. I'm sure some employees were suspicious that he might be a plant, gaining trust while plotting an assault. But aware of the possibility, I never thought so. Maybe I'm too trusting, but there was something about him that dispelled my suspicion. He seemed like a very kind doctor, happy to be here out of harm's way. He was very friendly to everyone and became our resource regarding the problems in the Middle East. He explained the Muslim perspective to me, willing to discuss the troubles in Iraq, Syria, and Afghanistan with ISIS and Al Qaida. Had he been a secret jihadi, he wouldn't have been so open and relaxed with that subject, I concluded.

I was curious and wanted a Muslim perspective, and he was friendly and relaxed enough to give it in the right place. Several times I met him unplanned in a stairway that was isolated and usually empty since most people used elevators. This was an opportunity to develop my interview skills learned in journalism classes. As the US had attacked Iraq and captured Saddam Hussein, I asked Dr. Hagi what was the reaction among Middle Eastern people. He said most considered us bullies, using our overwhelming military might to interfere with their people and countries. He said that our drones and military provoked relatively powerless young Muslim men to commit suicide bombings, their only means of retribution. Our heavy-handedness made it easy to recruit these jihadists, whose futures were dim anyway. They all died heroes' deaths and thought they'd be rewarded in Heaven. Suicide was their only means of vengeance. This opened my eyes to a different perspective and made sense to me. He wouldn't have been so open if we'd been in a more public place, but he saw a curious American in me, and we developed a casual, honest friendship. Of course, he needed acceptance and belonging in his new job in a foreign culture. And he saw me, in my twenties, of the same age as most Islamic jihadi young men who offered their lives in revenge against the American enemy.

Over the next few years, I noticed a growing number of foreign doctors, newly hired, working at NCMH. Maybe they came cheaper than American docs. Diggery Wealth would definitely make that a primary decision, as Diggery cuts financial corners whenever possible.

**

One of the most influential and loved persons on the staff was the chaplain, Jonah Perspirman. About 45 years old when he first came, of average height and weight, and clean-shaven, he slowly, over several years, earned the love, respect, and trust of everyone at the hospital. He was the only paid employee of the Spiritual Care Department, and over five years, he attracted and trained 30 laymen and women. It was all nondenominational and they probably gave as much psychological as theological help to patients.

The volunteers trained by Jonah wore purple vests and carried a clipboard with basic information about each patient. Who welcomed a visit; what was their religion; why they were in the hospital; when they were visited, etc., was written for each patient these wonderful volunteers visited. They were all caring and excellent, largely for Jonah's training and example.

In the halls, he was the opposite of the scowl crows. He understood the importance of a warm demeanor and welcomed everyone, dispelling, if temporarily, their discomfort at being someplace unwanted. Over Christmas, he played an acoustic guitar, and with a few volunteers (including Flush, harmonizing for a song or two), would traverse the halls singing carols. They weren't particularly good and had no great musical training, but "Silent Night" and "Little Drummer Boy" always brought moments of divine cheer to a place with serious problems from which there was scant escape. Everyone loved Jonah.

About two years ago, Jonah started having trouble with his speech. Small hesitancies, at first, with trouble pronouncing a few words. We didn't pay attention initially, but over several weeks it became worse. He went to his doctor and learned the terrible news. He had

ALS, also known as Lou Gehrig's Disease. There was no cure, and he was told he had about a year of life left. There was no formal announcement, but the news spread around the hospital quickly. After a very tearful goodbye "party" attended by many employees in the Administrative Board Room, where many of us spoke movingly of our love and admiration, Jonah left, retired, having touched many lives during his five years there.

Months later, he returned for a last brief goodbye at an unannounced, informal gathering. He had grown a beard, looked very thin, and could barely talk, but was the only person in the room smiling. I hugged him (as did many people) and couldn't keep from tearing up. Nobody else could either. Probably the most remarkable aspect of this tragedy was the way Jonah reacted. He was dying, and everybody knew it. There was nothing now to do but wait, mostly at home, as his mobility became limited from the disease slowly destroying him. Fortunately, he had a fine supportive wife and no kids. He always had a smile and laughter. Depression had no hold, despair no grip, and his strength, obvious before, was now without equal. I saw the value of sincere religion, for his interpretation of impending death was so uncommon to be positively inspirational. No one could fake the courage to leave life with such grace and composure. I'm crying now, thinking about his heroism and recognizing his rare ability, which must have impacted the patients he saw, some of whom had died in the hospital. Now it was his turn. If hospitals have souls, he was ours. Flush wrote a letter to the hospital newsletter. They wouldn't print it. It read:

JONAH's GIFT

It's said that every cloud has a silver lining. Since learning of Jonah's unexpected departure and the condition that's causing it, I've had trouble finding that silver lining. But the cloud is unavoidable. I could call it sad or tragic, but Jonah doesn't seem to see it that way. Even now, he's seeing the silver lining I can't see. He's the bravest man I know. But I guess that shouldn't surprise me. Jonah's special. Many people think so.

Many times in the five years I've known Jonah, I've seen his warm friendliness, fine sense of humor (even now), and compassion for patients (and the rest of us, too), all done with genuine sincerity. He has been a profound influence on many of us, a low-key, inspiring leader, as we all witnessed at his going away "celebration" in the Board Room.

I believe he has given us a gift **by his example**. While here, Jonah was Humankindness. And if we're smart, we'll take his gift, his example, and use it well. Jonah showed us, every day, how to do it. I think if we all started treating each other more like friends, the way Jonah treated all of us, and less like strangers, this could become a better place for us all to work. If we can learn to be more cooperative, with good communication (no communication is almost always bad communication), there'd be less stress and a feeling of mutual benefit and shared problem-solving. Hospitals don't produce anything; hospitals solve problems. As Jonah did, maybe we can learn to distinguish between the message and the messenger and not penalize the latter because we don't like the former. Or not reject the message because we don't like the messenger.

Jonah can be here even when he's not. Jonah's gift has to be the silver lining.

One place to start is in the hallways. In my job as a porter (the peristalsis of NCMH), I travel the hallways almost everywhere four times a day. I pass many people and usually have a brief friendly exchange. Just a "Hi" or "good morning," or with stronger relationships, some healthy playfulness. Smiles are powerful and comforting. But some employees (I call them scowl crows), when walking towards me, look straight ahead with a sour, stern demeanor, evoking a chilly cold shoulder. (I feel like the Titanic in its infamous "squabble" with that unnamed iceberg). I'm treated like a piece of unwanted furniture, necessary but resented. Their behavior is the opposite of what Jonah did.

We'll all benefit if we use Jonah's gift and not waste it. We need to become more like Jonah and less like the whale.

After Jonah left, there was a vacuum for many months. The Spiritual Care Department bumbled on without leadership, and volunteers kept coming regularly. Every day two amateur (after several weeks of training by Jonah) chaplains would come each day to minister to the patients. They wore the purple vests and spent hours or minutes with receptive patients, offering counsel other than medical or financial. They made important contributions to our patients that were not valued much by the administration. They weren't bringing in money, so received little respect from our administrators.

***

Eventually, a new professional chaplain was hired to lead the department. A woman this time, Helen Weiss was a middle-aged Jewish rabbi, the first non-Christian in that role. The lead chaplain's religion wasn't important since patients and volunteers were from a wide variety of faiths, some with none at all. These hospital chaplains never proselytized any religion and were trained to support the faith of the patient. We were a non-profit public hospital that served a heterogeneous population, so operating from any particular point of faith wouldn't have worked.

Helen was a very sweet, caring, conscientious chaplain trying to fill the shoes of a recently departed but loved and

225

remembered "saint" (in some eyes). She was just getting her feet wet in her new job when she started encountering difficulties. Helen's boss, a scowl crow nurse whose major job was managing 2 North, covered by many nurses, CNAs, and techs, was not at all interested in also managing the Spiritual Care Department, but, somehow, this new responsibility was given to her due to the cut-backs. This scowl crow, named Marianne, took an immediate dislike for Helen for reasons never revealed. Could have been anti-Semitism or simple personal bitchiness. Marianne, who always seemed tense and humorless, was never civil to me, so neither explanation would surprise me. Flush didn't like her either.

In staff meetings, Marianne would ridicule and poke fun at Helen on simple things. One time Helen had written a note and used the word "salubrious," an appropriate term for a hospital. Marianne publicly criticized Helen's vocabulary, accusing her of showing off her education while humiliating the newcomer unnecessarily in front of peers.

Once a nurse, after a twelve-hour shift, complained to Helen about her stiff neck.

Helen asked if she wanted a neck rub, certainly a kind gesture. The nurse said, "Yes," so Helen performed the rub. Later, the nurse complained to Marianne, saying she really didn't want a neck rub but said yes to appease Helen. Marianne called Helen into her office and scolded her. Marianne said she would have done the same thing as the nurse with a sore neck. Apparently it was ok to say "Yes" when you meant "No."

These petty incidents happened repeatedly for the first three months, Helen's probation period. Helen got through that stressful time, but two weeks later, she was called into another meeting (which was never good news). Marianne said a couple of chaplain volunteers said they didn't feel supported by Helen. So Helen was terminated with no recourse. She was relieved to escape the job stress, even though she had tried hard to bring comfort and was very good at it. She would have excelled in the position if given the chance. Marianne, who had been in an important supervisory position for 20 years and led with despotic control, manifested the kind of insensitive leadership that had become much too common at NCMH, causing serious damage to staff morale.

***

Another remarkable man I met at the hospital was a very successful, locally retired artist, even famous in cartooning circles. He wasn't a hospital employee, but I met him at the hospital, so mention him here. Don Dorchester regularly worked on exercise machines in cardio rehab, where many seniors recovered from heart problems. This artist had had four heart bypass operations but was still active, highly functioning for a man in his 80s. Flush introduced him to women in the hospital's ladies auxiliary, sometimes called "Pink Ladies," volunteers who ran the gift shop and helped decorate the hallways with local paintings, which they changed bi-monthly.

They coordinated, and Don donated several of his children's cartoons, matted, framed, and glassed, which were then permanently hung in the Women and Infants Care Unit. Other cartoons were hung on walls in the cancer center and some offices. Two weeks before Christmas, for three years, Don brought many of his framed cartoons and paintings to the lobby. They were sold reasonably and were very popular. The profits were all donated to the hospital. I don't know the amount of money raised, but it was substantial and brought some holiday merriment. Don also stayed for two days each year and drew pictures for children who were waiting excitedly. He was a crowd-pleaser. Flush nick-named him GGG, which stood for Gentle Generous Genius. Everyone liked him.

This was before Diggery Wealth took over, when the mood and atmosphere changed, becoming less friendly, less small-town warmth, and more professional, serious, and generally militaristic.

Chapter 11: The Crawful Year

Prior to 2013, for several years, Mark "Feckless" Pidwell was the manager of the Environmental Services Department (EVS), where Flush and I worked. Pidwell was an employee of NCMH and had a local boss, Salty Dalty, on sight. In January of 2013, the corporate owner of NCMH, Diggery Wealth, decided to farm out the managership of EVS to an outside company called Crawful that specialized, across the country, in providing "professional quality managers" for hospitals, hotels, motels, etc.

Feckless (his nickname between Flush and me, but not used among others) was a nice guy, popular with most of the EVS staff, but consistently ineffective, rarely able to solve any of the many small problems that occur regularly in a medium-sized hospital, problems that EVS is responsible for solving. But he did stick his neck out to help with Freebee.

His was an extremely difficult job; 6 different bosses had attempted to fill it in the past 3 1/2 years since I was hired. Except for one, Brock Chill (more about him later), who transferred to a better job, they all stank badly, each in their own way. Flush had ten different bosses in the fourteen years he worked at NCMH. This was indicative of the extreme mismanagement in our department.

Feckless was single, a big man, about 6'3" and 210 pounds. He also shaved his head, not a common look for white men at that time. I doubted many women found it attractive, but I never saw him with hair, so maybe shaving served a purpose. When seated, he had a nervous habit of bouncing his left knee up and down as if he were keeping time to a rock 'n roll song that only he could hear. He was 44 years old, smiled a lot, and had previously managed in another hospital in the valley where he lived. He considered moving into Flush's spare bedroom when he first got this job up in the foothills, but fortunately for everyone, he decided against it. I think he expected a career as an EVS manager somewhere, if not at our hospital. He wasn't used to corporate bureaucracies and didn't maneuver well with the higher administration.

When Crawful came in, they offered Feckless the same job, working for them, with a decided cut in salary and no benefits. Feckless was needy and didn't want to move. So he accepted it. That worked for us EVS employees, and Pidwell seemed relieved to still have a job. For two months, nothing much changed for us. We bumbled along, but Feckless seemed insecure. There were several meetings behind closed doors between Crawful's traveling managers and poor Feckless, after which we sensed he was under pressure though still employed.

But Feckless Pidwell's days were numbered. Then, without warning, Crawful fired Feckless. He cleared out his office and left without saying "goodbye." We soon missed him. His replacement was a disaster for us.

We all concluded that Crawful never intended to keep him. They just wanted to make the switch with minimal opposition, being able to say, "We gave him a chance." Though Feckless had friends who worked under him, none of us felt the power to speak up in his defense. Fear was becoming dominant, controlling the behavior of most of us on the front lines. Almost every employee at NCMH was fearful of speaking the truth, the punishment for which was unemployment.

After Pidwell's cruel sacking, Crawful brought in Ray Lude temporarily from Texas, to oversee the switch. Supposedly, he knew how to manage and had experience in hospital EVS departments. That proved to be untrue. We employees had been misled, but NCMH management, having signed a contract with Crawful, controlled by Diggery Wealth's guidance, didn't seem to notice or care. Fifty-two-year-old Ray, away from his wife in Dallas for two months and within driving distance of Nevada's brothels and semi-nude floor shows, seemed mostly distracted with the chances for infidelity. Several of our female EVS employees complained that he stared at their chests when addressing them.

After Feckless left, Crawful also brought in a computer nerd (I forget his name) from Arkansas, who sat in the manager's office for three weeks and redesigned all our jobs. He worked strictly from the blueprints of the hospital. Using some kind of formula of square footage, he shuffled the duties of almost every job. He never wandered the hospital to see the real areas to be cleaned. He used a two-dimensional template to design three-dimensional jobs to be performed by three-dimensional humans. He never consulted with any of us workers, some of whom had been doing the jobs for 30 years.

When Arkansas finished redesigning our jobs, with complex titles (*IPSP3GRE* was typical) made to look very technical, they were posted with superficial descriptions of duties and responsibilities. We EVS employees were instructed to sign up for the jobs in order of seniority. Then he left town and went to another hospital, where he did the same disingenuous reallocation of jobs. Unfortunately, he had zero experience in any of the jobs he redesigned and rewrote them based on theory, square footage covered, and a Crawful prescription. We scrutinized his work, and it became obvious that some jobs were unrealistic and impossible to perform in eight hours. We complained. So Arkansas came back and made adjustments. They posted the new jobs again, which were still unworkable, and we all protested. Taken down again, the Arkansas nerd rewrote the jobs for a third time and reposted them on the bulletin board for us to peruse. It became obvious that Crawful did not provide the highly experienced experts who ran 400 hospitals, as they claimed. We finally accepted their third posting of jobs. Ray Lude watched with useless shrugged shoulders.

Soon, Crawful brought in their permanent manager, Bossella Wilson, to be overseen and trained on-site for one month by Ray Lude. Bossella was a 23-year-old recent college graduate, very pretty, an athlete (tennis and track) in excellent condition and the daughter of one of the supervisors in Crawful headquarters in Dallas. She told me she had hired a personal trainer to keep her in shape. She always wore expensive professional business attire that looked out of place in EVS. She was smart and meant well, but too conscientious, way over her head in this tough job, her first. Work came first to her, and developing rapport with all but two of us came not at all. She was a daddy's girl and was determined not to embarrass him.

Bossella was from Mississippi and spoke rapidly in a strong Southern accent. And she was African-American, one of three among the 857 hospital employees in this predominantly white, small-town, foothill community hospital. She told us she was dating a football player in the Canadian league who lived far away. It was often hard to understand her speech, and not wishing to be rude or disrespectful, we usually didn't ask for a repeat. So most of us misunderstood her stories, and rumors were rampant.

At first, we tried to welcome Bossella and supported her, sympathetic to her position, realizing she was in new territory and starting a new job, a racial minority with a serious age difference with her staff. Flush was the oldest, at 70, but most others were in their 40s, 50s, and 60s. Everybody but me (I was 24) saw Bossella as a kid. Her success would be a severe uphill scramble, if at all. Being inexperienced as a manager, she held very tightly to the dictates and procedures required by the Crawful powers. Apparently, after college, she had been through Crawful's two-month manager's training regimen. She ran EVS for one year like it was the army until she was transferred. Her departure was widely considered a blessing. We were the privates and she was the cruel, uncaring, tyrannical sergeant whose commands were inviolable and not to be resisted or even questioned.

Without experiencing any of our jobs, she ran EVS from written directions from Crawful's one size fits all playbook. She gave us a series of photos of the way a newly cleaned patient room should be set up, photos of the way the cleaning closet should always look, the way a cleaning cart was to be set up, and the way to mop a floor. Photos were black and white and posted around our break room. She also gave us a series of detailed written directions dictating the ten steps to clean a room, the six steps to clean a sink, the seven steps to clean a toilet, the eleven steps to clean a shower, and, somewhere, though not publicized extensively, the one step for cleaning our collective ass post defecation.

Bossella soon alienated everyone. She insisted that Charles strip the wax off floors in a process that wasted a lot of time and only worked marginally. Charles had been stripping hospital floors of wax for about 12 years, understood the equipment, and had the process down. Bossella insisted he used different stripping liquids and a different machine that was difficult to operate and did a poor job, taking twice as long. He used to be able to strip two patient rooms in a day and apply 4 coats of wax. Now one patient room took all day, but Bossella wouldn't listen to reason. Crawful said we had to do it their way, even if it was clearly inferior and inefficient. Bossella enforced the counter-productive directions made elsewhere by people who had never done the jobs and sat behind Crawful desks in Dallas wearing long-sleeved shirts, ties, and suits.

Bossella POed the porters when she insisted that clear trash bags must not touch the blue bags of soiled linen, and neither color could touch green bags. For many years, porters had put them all together in the large wagons, RRR and Sigmoid. In all the soiled utility rooms, many bags of three different colors, placed there by RNAs and nurses before porters collected them for disposal, were intermixed, touching each other with no cross-contamination or objections from anyone. By insisting they be separated in the wagons, she unnecessarily made porters' jobs more difficult and reduced our efficiency, usually requiring four trips when three were sufficient. This affected me for the two days a week I did as a porter. I disliked it as much as Flush, but he dealt with it five days a week.

This bag segregation was disputed by Flush with no success. He took Bossella to the surgery-soiled utility room. There, mixed together, were many clear, blue, and green bags. Flush said that if surgery saw no harm or risk of cross-contamination, and they didn't, why should we? Certainly, they were very conscious of preventing HAIs (Hospital-Acquired Infections) and took every opportunity to require necessary sterility and hygiene. These professional surgeons, nurses, and techs were hyper-cautious about everything, having been sued previously. Bossella responded that she didn't care what other departments did; we (EVS) were "going to do it right."

Flush and Bossella debated this for about two days. Once, in her office, Flush challenged her to show this segregation requirement in writing. "If it's really a legal requirement, it would be in writing somewhere." She spent a frustrated fifteen minutes searching her computer for some documentation that supported her position. Obviously, she had never been questioned for proof in writing. The only thing she came up with was a true or false question on a Crawful training quiz that said, "Bags of medical waste must be separated." The correct answer was "True." Flush pointed out that medical waste meant red bags, which were already separated and transported separately. But Bossella claimed that clear trash bags, containing mostly papers, blue bags of soiled linen, and green bags of recyclables, were all medical waste. This was news to all of us and the nurses and docs, but Bossella was always right, so we porters complied (when we thought she was looking). When she left a year later, we reverted to our previous integrated bag ways. Nobody objected.

In one year, Bossella tried to make many such significant changes, most of which were resisted but ultimately adopted, under coercion, by disgruntled workers. When Crawful finally came up with job descriptions that might work (and might not), they posted these jobs on a bulletin board in our break room. Then, in order of seniority, we each selected a job by printing our names next to it. Some signatures were unreadable. At that time, Fude, a 65-year-old Japanese immigrant, married to an American who also worked at NCMH as an engineer, had worked at the hospital for 31 years. She was first in seniority, had done linen for 20 years, and signed up for the new, full-time linen/East wing job. No surprise, as linen, the easiest job in our department, was always chosen by the highest seniority. Fude spoke understandable English with an accent and had four dachshund dogs, whose pictures were common, scattered around the Linen Room.

Luna, Fude's best friend and prior substitute linen person, was second in seniority, having been there 29 years. She chose a position as a housekeeper in 1 South and ICCU (Intensive Critical Care Unit). Luna cleaned the patient rooms and did other non-medical chores in those two areas. But being Fude's best friend, she hung out in the closed Linen Room often, on extra-long breaks and during lunch. This closed, locked room, with no windows and no way for anyone to monitor activities inside, was one reason linen was consistently chosen by #1 in seniority. None of us had an office except the linen person. Fude and her small clique of girlfriends gathered there to eat and gossip.

I was looking for a 32-hour-per-week job, and one came up. It was a combination of being a porter 2 days a week when Flush was off and doing linen (and East Wing) 2 days a week when Fude Dahl was off. All four days were eight hours, from 7:00 AM to 3:30 PM. This fit my needs better than any other available job, so I signed up for it. On my two linen days, Flush worked as porter. Our jobs crossed paths about four times a day, so our friendship continued. We also ate lunch together on those two days.

This was the beginning of the war between myself and the treacherous team of Fude and

Luna, supported by Bossella. I was the first male to do linen, a precedent broken despite passive-aggressive resistance from women who had controlled linen for many years. I was totally unaware of the danger that awaited me, taken by surprise by their covert opposition. Looking back now, I see the early signs clearly, but at the time, I was naive, trusting, and unprepared for the problems they caused me. I suspect these two married, middle-aged women might have treated me differently had I been a studley hunk. But being a 135-pound, 5′6″ straggly weasel didn't do it for them, so I suffered their mutual disdain. My presence doing their job made them uncomfortable in a way only women can be, seeing it as an intrusion into their exclusive club of privileged female housekeepers.

There was a two-week waiting period between signing up and starting our new jobs. The day after I signed up for the two-day linen/East wing job (and two days as porter), Luna told me, "You know, Frank, linen is much harder than you think." I didn't react but wondered why she said this. Then, the next day, she said, "There's a lot to the linen job that most people don't realize." This struck me as curious; I began to wonder why she was pretending to help me with inside advice. We weren't good friends but had never quarreled, and I never had a problem with her before. For the next two weeks, always in the break room, Luna said something several more times designed to dissuade me from continuing my earlier decision. I wanted 4 days of work per week, therefore didn't change my mind. But I now realize she wanted me to reconsider and abandon my linen job. Of course, she could have taken it herself since she was #2 in seniority, right behind Fude. But she didn't take it, probably because she didn't want to do part-time porter for two days, which was physically harder and dirtier, attracting much less respect, and universally considered a man's job. Her subtle, covert opposition to me was hard to understand, but I was beginning to become suspicious of an ulterior motive driving Luna.

My training in linen began two weeks following my signing up. Fundamentally, the job was to run the Linen Room, where a large quantity of different linens (flat and contour sheets, pillowcases, wash clothes, towels, blankets, bedspreads, several types of patient gowns, blue absorptive pads, pajamas, baby diapers and blankets, many scrubs of different sizes, etc.) were stored. The linen person delivered the correct linens to the different stations in the many departments around the hospital, stacking each station once daily.

Separate from us, clean linens were delivered in an 18-wheeler truck every day from the cleaning plant located in Stockton Valley. Every morning, the truck driver spent about an hour pushing eight large carts of linen from his truck at the loading dock into the Linen Room on the lower level near the dock. If he took too long, another truck driver would have to wait in the parking lot, as there was only room for one truck at a time to unload or load. When he finished unloading clean linen, the driver then loaded many carts of soiled linen that we porters had accumulated the day before and arranged, sometimes erratically, on the very congested and tight-fitting dock. I suspect the dock was built when less traffic clogged the narrow passageway. This usually went smoothly unless a truck had mechanical issues, a fairly common problem with this company. They often delivered in a rented truck, caused by their company truck breaking down. I'm sure this cleaning company had contracts with many hospitals throughout northern and central California, so had many trucks and drivers busy. It was a major procedure on which all hospitals were dependent.

After his delivery of clean linens, our job was to empty his carts and stack the clean stuff on the appropriate shelves in the Linen Room, which was organized in a cramped space, barely able to hold the 500 flat sheets, 300 contour sheets, 500 bath towels, 500 patient gowns, etc. The emptied carts were then pushed into the hallway and later filled with bags of soiled linens by the porter. A series of different bosses gave different instructions about where these carts should reside in the hallways, a frequent source of confusion and discussion among the porters and linen people.

Fude was friendly the first day and showed me the basics of linen delivery. The first thing she did was go to every department to research what linens each needed, which she recorded long hand on small yellow sticky Postit notes. She had her own complicated system of abbreviations, with FS meaning flat sheets, PC meaning pillow cases, BT meaning bath towels, BB meaning bath blanket (a total misnomer since this blanket was warmed and never near water, a prime ingredient of a bath), and a lot of others not too easy to learn. Fude gave each department its own sticky note. The goal was to know how many of each item was needed in each department, enough so they wouldn't run out of anything. Every day this process was repeated.

We had a large (8' long, 6' foot high, 3' wide) electric motor-driven wagon to deliver these linens. It was easy to operate, as long as you pushed the right button (there were only two buttons) that controlled whether the cart went forward or backward. But sometimes you left it in reverse and forgot, so after being stopped while unloading the linen, it quite unexpectedly went backward when you

247

started to go. If I wasn't careful, I could damage any of the many pieces of equipment, wheelchairs, IV poles, portable computers on a rolling stand (called WOWs), and strolling patients, each occupying space in crowded, narrow hospital hallways. I never hit anything or anybody (yet), mostly because I walked in front of it, able to see ahead, but 1% of the time, I had to back up, driving blind. The linen wagon was slow, with a 2 MPH top speed, and started with a quick jolt, like a racehorse out of the starting stall on a racetrack. Big and clumsy, particularly on the turns, of which there were many.

Used as a weapon, the motorized wagon could do serious damage to an enemy (certain a**hole managers) whose misfortune was to be alone, with me and my wagon weapon, in a cramped elevator, going slowly from the LL (lower level —basement) to the 2nd floor. It took about a minute to go up two floors. Caught between the back of the wagon and the closed elevator wall, a tight space of about 1′ that scowl crow would be defenseless against my "accidental" button carelessness, putting the poor victim on medical leave for

6-8 months. Scars included. I'll admit to thinking about this possibility, but I assure you I would never do something physically destructive. Some of them deserved it, and Mother Justice wouldn't bat a blindfolded eye, but thoughts are not actions.

Housekeeping of the East Wing was added (by the Arkansas Crawful nerd) to the full-time linen job, making this job impossible to perform. Somehow it escaped the understanding of the Crawful bosses that putting two jobs together to be done by one person was unworkable, totally unrealistic. East Wing was part of the hospital that held Labor and Delivery (L & D), the Nursery, and TCU (Transitional Care Unit). The 40-year-old roof of part of the East Wing had been heavily damaged in a rainstorm, so it had to be replaced. Consequently, about 1/3 of the East Wing was closed to patients. They eliminated TCU and moved L & D and nursery to the area where TCU had been. Still, from our point of view, there was far too much work for one person to do adequately when added to the linen job. Ray Lude's and Bossella's solution: "Just work faster." Neither of them had ever done either of the two jobs we were required to do. But Arkansas' new, untested job descriptions included both jobs, so they enforced this impossibility.

Neither Fude nor I could do both jobs with any conscientious excellence. But Crawful didn't care. So we both faked it. Fude claimed (lied), "No pwoblem." After an initial objection, I remained silent to the bosses and complained to everyone else, and did about half the East Wing job. The full job required cleaning 3 or 4 rooms occupied by new moms, babies, dads, and visiting families. A real mess with happy, excited humans and baby stuff. Fude, who hadn't done any housekeeping for 20 years, taught me how to clean showers, toilets, and patient rooms of new mothers and their newborn babies. Fude was tentative and clumsy with teaching this cleaning, and I was embarrassed in the presence of new moms, some of whom were breastfeeding, not expecting a strange man in their rooms. Most mothers, babies, and fathers went home after 2-3 days in the hospital. There was a lot of turnover, so we didn't get to know anyone for very long. But this was in the happiest wing of the hospital, where other departments usually housed less happy patients and visitors. Sometimes there were young fathers sleeping on a cot in the room, and often there were family and friends crowded into this 12' by 12' room, along with at least one bed and dresser and TV and tables, chairs, and clothes for at least mom, and maybe dad. The babies, stars of the day, and the reason everyone was there, usually slept or wailed, oblivious to the joy their arrival produced.

There were usually 3 or 4 occupied patient rooms every day, with young moms needing lots of attention. I was supposed to "clean" this always disorganized monstrosity and the bathrooms. It was a very uncomfortable arrangement, but Crawful designed it, and Bossella enforced it, so we were stuck. I felt blundered my way through it, two days each week.

On the first day of my training, Fude was not happy having to do two jobs in 8 hours, and she grumbled in Japanese at a muffled volume. She was mostly pretending, improvising, and guessing when teaching housekeeping in the East Wing. She barely knew the subject and had no skills to transfer her limited capacities to me, a reluctant, unenthusiastic student. I truly didn't care for cleaning bathrooms of recently birthing mothers and their squalling cherub offspring. Though it was fun, for five minutes, being among happy, celebrating (sometimes) grandmothers and aunts. Usually, the grandfathers were excited, too. The little sisters of the newborn were cute, too, and I always made them promise to be "Good sisters" to their newest family member. Following Flush's lead, I'd learned this from him. They always agreed, "Yes, I promise." I never tried this with young new brothers, most of whom were reduced to dumbfounded, well-behaved silence.

By the second day, I was getting the hang of the linen job. Fude sent me on a run alone, and I think I did ok. I made a couple of small, common mistakes, forgetting to put enough towels in 1 South and putting washed clothes in the wrong place on a shelf in surgery. But several times she said, "Faster, Frank, faster!" or "You can't do this job" or "What's the matter, Frank, you sick?" Like the previous statements by Luna, I was starting to notice a pattern, unpleasantly ulterior in nature. And not to my advantage.

On the third day of training, I approached Fude with a new idea. I hoped to win her approval and support. I was dumb and unprepared for her response. The night before, at my home on my computer, I had created a spreadsheet to record all of our linen deliveries for the whole day. I had never used that software program called "Numbers" on my iMac, so I was proud to have learned and used it so quickly. I wasn't one of those computer-savvy nerds so common in my generation, so I started thinking I was capable of delivering more than a janitor needed to do. I was proud of it. Down the left side of the page were all the different linen items that we delivered. Across the top of the spreadsheet were all the different departments we delivered to. The rows were separated by colors, making it easier to follow a row across the sheet without jumping, inadvertently, between rows.

I would carry it on a clipboard. It made it easy and organized to keep track of what I delivered to each station. I could write the number delivered of each item under each column of the department that received the item. It was the work of organizational genius, which would have cost them hundreds of dollars had they paid an outsider. It could replace Fude's system, in which she wrote the same information, using a lot of confusing abbreviations, on 15-20 separate, small yellow sticky notes.

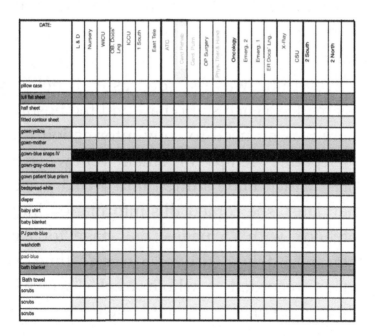

It was easy and clear to use. The morning's first task was to make rounds of every linen station in every department to determine how much of each item would be needed to accommodate the department's needs for that day. That takes about 1/2 hour. This is the same routine Fude (and Luna) used. Then, on my chart, I wrote the number of items needed in the allotted box. Then, when I made the rounds again and delivered the needed linen, I'd circle that number, indicating the correct number had been delivered to the correct department. With this system, I could record an entire day's deliveries on one piece of paper.

Everything was recorded as each delivery was made to each station around the hospital. There was no need to copy information from 20 separate scraps of small yellow sticky notes, which Fude stuffed into a coat pocket. Then later, she copied this information into a notebook with 25 pages, one page for each linen item delivered over a week's time. My system recorded a whole week's worth of information on seven pages, one page for each day of the week. Fude's system was far less efficient, requiring more time and paper, reducing the overall effectiveness of the Linen Department, run by Fude five days a week, and me, on weekends.

By anybody's neutral assessment, this spreadsheet was much better than her profusion of confusing and messy sticky notes stuffed into her coat pockets. I showed Fude my spreadsheet, expecting praise. She looked at it for, maybe, 4 seconds. "It's no good. Get rid of it!" Angry tone. I was getting more clues that I had stumbled into a viper's pit. I knew my spreadsheet was superior to her disorganized sticky notes, so I had no intention of discarding it. For the next three years, I used it to my advantage. But Fude refused to reconsider. I gave up trying to persuade her or Bossella, who favored Fude over me on every decision. I was a victim of the favoritism that several of our bosses commonly displayed. Fude was the trusted veteran; I was the bumbling rookie with the audacity to propose an improvement.

On the fourth day of training for linen and housekeeping in the East Wing, Fude complained to our temporary boss, Ray Lude, that I was too slow. True, I was learning two new jobs, but by then, I understood about 90% of the linen job and was beginning to feel comfortable and confident with linen. But that took about 7 hours each day, which left about one hour, give or take 30 minutes, to clean all of the East Wing. Previously, that had been an 8-hour job for a separate person. So I wasn't able to do the East Wing adequately. But I only did it two days a week. Fude did it 5 days a week. Or at least she was supposed to.

Ray Lude called me into his small, temporary, windowless office, where Fude sat waiting, obviously just having complained to Ray. In a nice tone, Ray asked, "Are you having problems with the new job?"

I was very surprised to be called in and challenged by this temporary boss, unknown to me. I thought I was doing well under adverse, unrealistic circumstances. "Well, yes, there's more work than anyone can do well," I stuttered, beginning to feel extreme stress.

"You'll just have to find a way. I know the job can be done. If you can't do it, we'll find somebody who can."

Woah! Sounds like I might be fired. This was getting serious. I suggested: "You need to come with me and see what we have to do. Just shadow me for an hour or two." I was hoping he was a reasonable man with some sympathy for the working staff below him doing all the real work. As his next response makes clear, I might as well have been hoping for invisibility.

"I'm not going to shadow anybody. I'm too busy and don't care." (pause) "We had an expert design this job, all of these jobs, and we do this in 400 hospitals across America. So I know it can be done."

That claim of success in 400 hospitals across America was often heard, spoken by all Crawful managers. It was a line they had been taught at some amateur management school they all attended before coming to us. Three different Crawful managers made the same claim in the same phrase. I was dumbfounded, psychologically ambushed, totally without response. I needed help and thought it might come from Fude, who had told me several times the two jobs were too much. She was honest with me on that subject. So I was expecting an ally.

Good luck.

Turning towards Fude, who had been silent so far, I asked, "Haven't you had trouble doing both jobs?"

"Well," very tentatively, "I can do it. I just go faster. You too slow. You can't do this job."

Stocky Ray Lude wore a big grin above his pale triple chins. I wasn't any slower than she was, which was compulsively speedy. But Fude was now twisting the knife she had just delivered to my unprotected back. I now started to see more clearly. Fude and Luna were trying to remove me from the linen position. And they would sink to this putrid level. But "Why?" That would have to be settled later.

Those few words by Fude sunk my raft. I left, stating (insincerely) that I'd "focus and work faster," which, translated from falsity to truth, means I'll just skip a lot of cleaning and get a D+ on my East Wing report card. So I limped along and stayed below the radar until Ray the pig left, which was about 2 weeks later.

On the fifth day of my new job, I was training Carolina in the porter job. I was training her because Flush, whose regular job was porter (I was his replacement), was on vacation. She was a small, sweet woman of average intelligence and a great laugh. I liked her but had reservations about her being able to handle the porter load, which was physically demanding, even for men. Carolina's last name was Irkley, the same as Luna's. They were sisters-in-law, having married brothers. I gathered that the two women were close friends, not good news for me in my struggles with Luna.

Carolina and I were up in 2 South, a crowded section with 14 patient rooms and a nurses' station. Carolina was learning how to operate Sigmoid, the large, blue push wagon in which we collected the many colored bags of soiled linen and trash. She was too short to see over the top and in a crowded area, started pushing it. Going about three feet, she hit an old man in a wheelchair who was directly in front of the wagon. Carolina wasn't pushing fast, and the patient wasn't really hurt, but that's always a bad move, justifiable or not. I felt responsible since I was training Carolina, so I apologized to the old man. He was nice about it and assured us he was alright. Several nurses saw it, and I was surprised Carolina didn't bother apologizing to the patient.

Later, I was going to show Carolina the blue bags of soiled linen. We were to pull in Cardio Pulmonary, a unit on the second floor, far from the Linen Room. Outside the door, we were approached, unexpectedly, by Fude. "You forgot to take enough towels to ICU yesterday," she said accusingly, an inappropriate chastisement in that context. She wasn't doing her linen job; her cart wasn't with her. She had come to berate me again, this time when I was a porter teaching a beginning porter.

"Sorry. I'll try to do better." Carolina and I walked into Cardio Pulmonary. Fude followed us. "You forgot to take enough towels to ICU yesterday." Her angry tone was amplified now.

"Ok, I got it," I replied, starting to get a little irritated by her badgering about a minor infraction for which there was no remedy, having happened yesterday.

Fude again: "No. You make mistake. Not enough towels in ICU. Yesterday." She was loud this time, embarrassing me and Carolina.

"I understand; you don't have to keep repeating yourself." I was getting defensive, wondering why she was doing this.

Fude said, "You no good. I not train you anymore!" in a hostile tone. She stormed away down the hall and around a corner and started crying in the arms of the manager of Cardio Pulmonary, Mikela Grouch. I couldn't hear the words clearly, but tears were evident.

I was stunned by her over reaction and didn't know what to do. I said to Carolina, "I'm sorry. I didn't mean to hurt her," which was true. I always tried to avoid conflicts, particularly with Fude, since we had to work together. I continued training Carolina but felt uncomfortable the rest of the day. I prepared myself for another admonishment from Ray Lude, who seemed to derive pleasure from scolding any of us. This Crawful team was becoming oppressive, disrupting a previously productive department without us having a clue.

The next day I was again summoned into Ray Lude's temporary office. This time I was told to bring a union representative as my witness and counsel. Mikela Grouch had written a complaint about me and my supposedly harsh words to Fude. I asked for a copy of Mikela's report, but Ray would only read it to me and allow me to copy it in my handwriting while he read it. For some reason, he wouldn't just print out a copy. And there was a copying machine nearby. I told my side of the story. I had been hounded by Fude and never raised my voice in anger. I was more of a victim than she was. Ray let me go with a warning. He seemed mildly sympathetic, saying he had been in a similar situation in the past. It was my first experience with him in a semi-supportive role. But once again, I was on the defensive, aware that Fude resented me and was no good at disguising her efforts to undermine me with cunning sadism.

About three days later, when I was again in Cardio Pulmonary as porter, I saw Mikela in a hallway talking to another technician. Fude walked behind her and gave her a friendly pat on the butt, the sort of very unusual gesture never seen among professionals in a hospital. I was very surprised. Both Fude and Mikela were married, so lesbian interaction was unlikely, but this indicated a stronger friendship than I expected. The two women didn't work in the same department and Fude was about 30 years Mikela's senior, so I was mystified by this unusual, casual, and covert sexual interplay. Mikela didn't react or say anything, and Fude just walked past her and out the door. Strange and inexplicable, it helped me understand Mikela's letter attacking me. I wrote about this strange "pat" to Ray without suggesting any homosexuality; he had nothing to shed any light on it. We two men were both flummoxed by the "pat," which was particularly improper in a hospital hallway.

Two months later, Fude was diagnosed with cancer. By then, I didn't trust her and our paths didn't cross often since we worked different days on linen. She retired soon after, and I always wondered if her illness, undetected at the time, could explain her earlier hostility and extreme emotional reaction in Cardio Pulmonary. After Fude's retirement, her job was posted. It was full-time, benefitted, day shift, 7:00 AM to 3:30 PM. It went to Luna, who now had the most seniority. Everyone who had ever done linen, including me, knew it was the best job in our department, so it always went to the highest seniority. Luna continued Fude's undeserved and unexplained opposition to my presence in linen. For the rest of the year, she made my working life difficult.

About once a week, she'd comment like, "Carolina does a wonderful job, why can't you?" This was a lie. Carolina hated porter work, did it poorly, and quit three months later. But the truth was irrelevant to Luna's slippery lips.

Another Luna preference, heard at least once a week. "When I come in after you've been doing linen, I always have to do extra work. I'm tired of doing your work." By now, I realized she would say anything to get me in trouble, which she did, with Bossella.

After Ray Lude left town permanently, we were burdened with the constant solo managership of Bossella Wilson. Luna excelled at schmoozing every new boss we had, and we got a new one almost every year. Opportunism was her pattern. Luna spent at least an hour every day in Bossella's office, pretending to help the new boss with scheduling, ordering, discipline, union rules, and who should be disciplined and fired. Luna was the self-appointed welcoming committee and made herself Bossella's best friend and go-to advisor.

In the second month of Bossella's calamitous regime, she held a mandatory meeting, the first meeting of our department attended by everyone in about five years. She was following a Crawful formula supposedly designed to bring our fragmented department together. Thirty-one chairs were arranged outside a big square of tables around the periphery of the room, so everyone could see everyone else.

"I heard a rumor that you were a Dallas Cowboy cheerleader?" Flush asked Bossella as we were gathering and starting to sit. Flush made that up as a compliment, hoping to get on her good side. He was the only one of us EVS employees who would ask such a question, being better educated, older, and more self-confident.

Smiling, she said, "No, but thanks for asking." She was flattered.

After briefly describing her background and college graduation, Bossella asked us to say something good about our jobs. As we went around the room, one by nervous one, everyone said some variation of, "I like my job because of all the great people I work with." Evidently, Bossella was told by Crawful that this might help raise our rapidly falling morale. "People here are nice," or "Most of my co-workers are friendly." About 25 housekeepers and janitors echoed each other with some sort of unimaginative cliche, nobody willing to deviate from the well-established path of safety. Bossella was pleased and satisfied that this maneuver was successfully raising morale and producing cohesive team-like feelings among us, as Crawful's directory of good management had predicted.

Then came Flush's turn. He said, "This job gives me good physical exercise that contributes to my health, working enough to keep my old body in good shape. And I value a job that is necessary for the health of many people who badly need our help. It makes me feel useful. And I like to work for an organization that saves and improves lives. I'm also thankful that I have survived so far. The fates of three men who worked my porter job in the past eight years Paul Darwin, Rocky Smith, and Tom Fretzell, all younger than me, all died of cancer. Most of us were friends with these three, all gone. I've escaped it."

There was a long, uncomfortable silence and an angry glare from Bossella, who was unaware of our past losses, but knew this depressing statement wouldn't help increase the morale, the purpose of our round-the-table statements. At least Flush was original, but it was interpreted as gross insubordination by Bossella. She knew now to never give the floor to Flush. When it was my turn, I said I liked the money. This got another dirty look from Bossella, the first of many over the next ten months.

Then Bossella gave a short speech awarding the *"Employee of the Month"* to Luna, along with a check from Crawful for $50. No one was surprised, as Luna had a well-established reputation for brown-nosing. Crawful was trying to raise our morale with this artificial mechanism. They didn't have a clue about inspiring us to care about excellence or stewardship, thinking beyond our individual, self-centered selves towards a larger objective. They thought giving $50 to the *"Employee of the Month"* would motivate us to work harder. This was a first for us; no other manager had ever given a monetary award or any recognition of superior monthly performance.

Crawful was trying, but their efforts were predictable and mechanical, mined from a corporate playbook. They had been brought in to replace semi-functional management and had done so at many other hospitals and hotels. Their first task was to gain the trust and respect of disgruntled employees, many of whom hated their jobs and previous bosses. Bossella said we would have a meeting every month, and someone would win $50 for

"Employee of the Month." This got our attention, as many of us had financial problems. But it didn't really affect our behavior or attitudes or make us better or more motivated to do our manual, usually thankless, jobs. We did important, unskilled jobs but rarely got recognized or shown any appreciation. And the chance to win an extra $50 was slim in a world where favoritism, blinded to genuine excellence, determined the winner based on subjective measures. Crawful realized it and stopped the $50 bonus after two months.

I was called into Bossella's office three more times during Crawful's stressful year. Luna was always sitting there, having just complained about my poor performance. I always said the same thing: The job, as designed, with both linen and East Wing, was unrealistic and impossible to do well. Luna always lied and said she managed. There's no way she did the WICU job well (and twice she grumbled to me about it), but she wanted to make me look negligent or deficient. So she made the biased contrast between her and me, as had Fude. Bossella had to defend Crawful's job designs. So I was always threatened and stressed, when doing linen/East Wing, feeling inferior and inadequate. And pissed off.

I showed my innovative spreadsheet to Bossella, an accounting system that I was using successfully. It was much better than Luna's sticky note accounting system, which she had learned from Fude over the 20 years they had worked together. Bossella reacted the same way that Fude and Luna had done. "It doesn't work. Get it out of here." Her negative appraisal, based on Fude's and Luna's bias, echoed their words completely, with no objective appraisal.

"How do you know it doesn't work?" I asked. "You never gave it a chance."

"I just know," Bossella replied with no reason at all. She just voiced Luna's subjective, untested, self-serving evaluation. "It is what it is," as though that explained something.

I was fed up with the subjective irrationality. "You're being narrow-minded. You never even considered it."

"One more word, and you're going to HR!" said Bossella, who loved to threaten us. I sat there, frozen and powerless, abused by a lousy manager. She stood up, walked to the closed door, opened it, and gestured to me to leave.

I did.

I had been commanded by three women, who outranked me, that my recording system should be rejected. There was no doubt in my mind that it worked and was far superior to the Postit note system they preferred. I didn't care if they wanted to ride a bike with a flat tire, but I shouldn't be forced to. All I asked for was an objective judge to evaluate the two systems. So far, I have been unsuccessful, owing to whatever is the word to describe the opposite of misogyny. They were just biased against men in the Linen Department. So I wrote the following email and sent it to HR, our CEO, and our district union director.

There is a disagreement about the performance of part of my job in delivering linen, a job I now do on weekends. When I first started doing linen, I developed (on my own time, at home, on my computer, without charge to SNMH, taking about 13 hours) a simple one-page spreadsheet for keeping track of all the linen we deliver to other departments. For three years, I used this system successfully without problems. This system is superior, in several ways, to the clumsy Postit note accounting system that Luna uses and Bossella insists we all employ now. Bossella has never done linen delivery herself, even for five minutes, yet she imposes this inefficient system on those of us who have to actually do the job without consideration of my viable alternative. I have tried repeatedly to present my superior system, but Bossella refuses to give it a fair hearing. This is insulting to me and destructive to the hospital. It also severely diminishes any respect I might have for her as a manager. Is this good leadership? It is not.

Can she? Yes. Should she? No.

I am writing now to request a hearing to compare the two systems by people with authority who can (and should) open Bossella's mind to opinions held by her more experienced employees. I just want, and expect, a dispassionate, even-handed, objective panel that can evaluate the two systems based on their merits, not on position or personality.

Thanks for your time.

Frank Veritas.

To my surprise and severe disappointment, I received a short email from Juyn, the new director of HR, politely denying my request. She said her hands were tied; department managers were given free reign to decide policies and nobody could interfere. I was told to comply with her policy. I was POed and continued my simple system, but only on weekends when neither Luna nor Bossella were there. I got retribution when our next boss was hired.

***

Most of us hated Crawful and Bossella and were grateful when they lost the contract after one year. We heard that Crawful had managers in six other hospitals in our corporation, Diggery Wealth, and they all were migratory after one year. We applauded their departure. Flush wrote a poem in celebration:

The Crawful Way
Salute and Obey
Have nothing to say
That, my children's
The Crawful Way

Never say "No"
Never ask "Why?"
The Crawful Way is
Do or die

So if you've a mind
To think on your own
To solve problems outside the box
Just take my advice
Keep ideas to yourself
'Cause here they've the value of rocks

Flush showed this poem to a few of us, but for self-preservation, he didn't post it anywhere publicly. When her year was over, Bossella left without any notice. One morning we came in, and her office was empty. Any impression she'd made was negative, her absence unmourned. She had packed up at night to avoid any unpleasant goodbyes. Wise choice!

Chapter 12: Finally a Good Manager

Crawful finally woke up and realized Bossella's inadequacy as an EVS manager. To our collective relief, she was transferred away. We didn't care where. There was probably a good reason for keeping her destination a secret, as it wasn't a promotion. Then we got lucky for one year.

Diggery Wealth realized Crawful's misrepresentation of their expertise, cancelled the contract and replaced them with ErrorMake, another outside manager supplier. ErrorMake claimed to supply experienced managers to hospitals and restaurants. This relieved Diggery of that responsibility, and our local administration could claim to be outside that burden, providing them with another "pass the buck to ErrorMake" maneuver.

ErrorMake assigned us an over-weight, 42-year-old, single, male manager from Kansas with real leadership capabilities and a relaxed, casual, friendly manner. He knew how to create a team feeling in EVS. After working at the hospital for three years, under three different managers, I concluded he was the first who ran the department well, had our respect and didn't piss off most of his staff. Morale increased under this new guy.

He came to work on his first day, a Monday morning, and spent most of his time in the office on the phone and computer. By 10:00 AM, he'd posted a short notice on the bulletin board in our EVS break room. It read: "INTRODUCTORY MEETING. This Wednesday at 3:30 PM, I hope to meet all of you in the Solarium room. I want to introduce myself and start getting to know you. The meeting is optional, but I hope everyone can come. Light refreshments. Brock Chill, EVS manager."

The meeting was held in the same room where Flush had sung with Adele's piano playing. This room was now cleaned up and used for meetings. There were plenty of other meeting rooms available. Flush and I never understood why this room couldn't be the Freebee Room, as its location and size would have been perfect, just what Freebee needed.

Rectangular tables were arranged in a large square, with 31 chairs on the outside. Everyone could see everyone and every chair, but one was filled. We all wanted to meet the new boss. Considering our last disastrous year, working for an incompetent, inexperienced tyrant, with hope and trepidation, we curiously attended this new chapter that would have great or grave consequences for our work lives. Some took advantage of the refreshments, store-bought fruit punch and cookies.

Brock came in about 3 minutes late when all of us were seated and chatting amongst ourselves. We had seen him briefly in his office or the hallway but hadn't really spent any reasonable time together. He'd spent most of Monday and Tuesday in meetings with administrative staff, but we knew what he looked like. Dressed in casual Midwest clothes, long chino pants, short sleeve shirt with a pattern unseen west of the Rockies, no tie, no socks and loafers. He was about 5'10" tall and 260 pounds of solid friendliness. He was beardless, with short blond hair of unnoticeable style. Nothing pretentious, and easy to like. Smiled a lot and seemed confident and happy on his fourth day in California. He spoke as a friend, not as a manager. I liked him after five minutes.

Brock started by telling us briefly his background. Three years of college, where he played varsity baseball and football for Kansas State, having been raised by his single mom (Dad died when he was 8) in Kansas City, Kansas.

"In my senior year of college, I had a stupid motorcycle accident—any of you ride a motorcycle? A good way to get killed—I broke my leg and collar bone, had a concussion and lost my athletic scholarship. My leg was in a cast for six months, with 3 surgeries and a year of physical therapy. And headaches. That was 20 years ago, and I'm mostly OK now, but my leg hurts sometimes, even now.

"At about that same time, my mom came down with cancer, lost her job as an accountant, so I quit school and supported her by driving trucks for Pepsi. That's why I never graduated college."

He went on to say he was unmarried, was also previously a high school athletic coach, and was 42 years old. He'd been in California for four days. Loves it, so far, and is willing to learn and adapt. Hoping to see Yosemite soon; heard they have some big trees and rocks there. Looking for an affordable apartment. Company was paying for his hotel, for now, but they're pressuring him to find something permanent and cheaper. Also, he asked if anyone could recommend a shop to replace a burnt-out headlight.

Driving through the mountains on Interstate 80 three days before, he'd been stopped by police and given a warning. He can't drive at night now, and didn't need to, since his local hotel was near several restaurants, but should get it fixed soon. He might want to go to a movie some evening.

Then he got serious.

"I'm new at EVS managing and hospital work, and need your help. I believe I can only control myself, and any attempt to control you will eventually backfire. I can try to persuade you and offer suggestions, but when we're not together, you will control yourself.

If I try to do more, you'll just get angry, do less work and be mad at me. It won't work, and we'll all fail. None of us will be happy that way, and I want to make us a winning team. I've been on losing sports teams, and it's no fun. To succeed, we have to work together. I'm the boss, so have to make the final decisions sometimes, but I'll always want your ideas and opinions, particularly since you know your jobs a lot better than I do. If you have any suggestions or complaints, my door is always open. I believe that with good communication and cooperative attitudes, we can do good work together and have more satisfying lives. I really need you and hope we can learn to work together. Don't think I'm a push-over. I won't like it, but I will fire you if you take advantage and cheat the job. But I'll try to work with you first."

He paused, deciding whether or not to say more. "Any questions?"

All of us were too shocked to speak, never having had this kind of boss. But Flush, never short of words, and a sports fan of amateur abilities, said, "We're happy to see you and I hope we'll do what we can to welcome you. On a different note, what was your greatest athletic moment?"

"I had two, both in my junior year. Against Nebraska, I recovered a fumble on our goal line with 39 seconds to play

—I played defense—usually tackle—and we upset a highly-ranked team and won by two points. We only won three football games that year, but that win made our season. They were ranked number 3 in the nation and were bowl bound. And in the spring, I struck out seven guys from Missouri State in four innings. I know I don't look like a pitcher, but I had a tricky curve that was never hit, and I usually got it over the plate. But my fast ball was only in the high 80s, so the pros weren't interested. That summer was my accident. Dumb!"

There was a long silence.

"Ok. Please drop by my office and introduce yourselves one at a time when it's convenient. I'm looking forward to working with you."

The meeting ended, and we all felt great relief. It was a new, happy day. There was hope. Brock was one of us, from a blue-collar background. Being an innocent- appearing Midwesterner, he dressed conservatively for California. He was a confident, competent manager, new to the ErrorMake. Everybody liked him.

The first week of his employment, I was in Brock's small, uncluttered office. On an almost empty bookshelf, conspicuous for its gapping vacuum, were two lonely books. One was "Extraordinary Leadership" by Joyce Anastasia. He said it had been a textbook from his managerial training, giving guidance and advice that he found very useful. He said if he succeeds, it would be partly due to the wisdom found in this book. He described it, saying, "It says good leadership uses power with; bad leadership uses power over. That's the main difference." I was immediately impressed and encouraged that we finally had a tolerable manager.

I saw another book, "Choice Theory" by William Glasser, M.D. I had heard of Glasser in a psychology class, and Flush was an advocate of Glasser, so I was interested. I asked Brock about it, and he offered to loan it to me, explaining it was a source of great influence on his life, another guide to his managerial style. Brock was a soft- spoken, understated Midwesterner, never resorting to hyperbole. When he said Choice Theory would change my life, I believed him. I read it. He was right. I mentioned it to Flush, who was happily impressed. On a different occasion, Flush was in Brock's nearly empty office and saw the same two books. Flush, an avid reader, had read both books and found them wonderful guides to management. He was greatly relieved that we might have a good boss. In our discussions, we agreed and were relieved by our good fortune.

Some traveling geek from ErrorMake rewrote part of my linen job, eliminating the East Wing part so it became realistically possible to perform well. Doing linen alone, as it had been done before Crawful's ill-advised adjustment, two days per week, was again enjoyable and without stress (except for Luna's disparaging, deceptive intrusions). And the new mothers in WICU got decent service, finally, since they had a full-time housekeeper instead of Luna and me cutting corners. This was a very happy development from the previous job description designed by Crawful's unrealistic traveling geek. It was welcomed by both Luna and me, allowing us to perform one job well. But we still disagreed on one major issue; Luna had seniority over me, so she tried to force me to abandon my spreadsheet entry system. She had persuaded Bossella to oppose it, and this restriction was still in effect under the new manager, Brock. But he knew nothing about it.

I showed Brock my highly efficient and effective spreadsheet for recording all the various linen deliveries on one neat sheet on a clipboard. Brock reviewed my spreadsheet and congratulated me after seeing Luna's scattered, error-prone system. He liked my system so much that he asked if he could forward it to his corporate boss. I was relieved and flattered and said, "Yes." I gifted them several hundred dollars' worth of improved work which they could apply to other hospitals' linen departments. I was proud and honored that my creativity was finally being recognized and respected after years of being ignored by ignorant managers.

However, Brock clarified that he would allow Luna to decide for herself and would not enforce my system on her. I knew Luna was too stubborn to ever admit that I, a male, had made a useful contribution to a job she'd been doing for twenty years. I knew she would continue her unprofessional, disorganized recording process. That was good enough for me. She could tattoo her linen notes on her body parts for all I cared.

At another meeting, early in his managership, Flush and I met Brock in his office to discuss another issue. Flush was the full-time porter five days a week and I was his replacement on weekends. We both objected to an unjustifiable rule enacted previously by Bossella without any hospital support. Her rule of segregating white trash bags from blue bags of soiled linen from green bags of recyclables in our large carts, RRR and Sigmoid, was inefficient and unnecessary. We had never before separated these three colors (though we always transported the red bags of medical waste separately in special red rolling barrels). An analogy would be the body's digestive system separating different foods, say vegetables and meats, so we pooped them separately, to ensure a turnip in the small intestine never touched a pork chop. A lot of unnecessary concern and drudgery. And twice the pooping.

We pointed out that in the Surgery Department's trash room, like the trash rooms in all other departments, the white, green, and blue bags were all in one large cart, touching each other. Also, these bags were industrial quality, unusually strong. They seldom ripped, so chances of their contents touching, mixing, and contaminating each other were minimal and probably harmless in the unlikely event that should happen. We asked Brock to rescind this stupid rule. He looked into it, confirmed that Surgery didn't follow that segregation, and figured that if it wasn't important to the people most conscious of contamination, it wasn't necessary to him either. So he eliminated that annoying rule and, in so doing, increased all porters' work efficiency.

Without knowing his story, you could never tell from his bariatric body dimensions that Brock was a good athlete. Flush befriended him soon and they occasionally played a game which Flush had invented. Called Frolfing—a combination of Frisbee and disc golf—it was played with a few friends in a local park that had a disc golf course. It was a welcome diversion for Brock, who knew nobody, liked all sports, and needed a few friends. He was a willing Frolfer.

Disc golf is played on a wooded course with small discs designed to be thrown at great distances with only moderate control. They were never meant to be caught, unlike Frisbees, and, with luck, hurled through many trees towards a metal basket often out of sight from the tee, where they started. The course always had 18 holes, like regular ball-with-clubs golf. But the course had no fairways and far more trees, major obstacles that interrupted the flights of the hurled plastic discs. This sport was popular among young men mostly, though a few women played, also. Often, small groups of 3 to 7 people, with beer coolers and marijuana, carried in wheeled carts or backpacks full of many discs, traversed the course peacefully, with serious pleasure and always friendly intensity.

Flush, who had played Frisbee since 1957, when it was first introduced in a few colleges in the East, thought disc golf was only half the game since it was "all throw, no catch." So he invented Frolf, which was played with teams of two, one catching and one throwing, to his teammate, the catcher. If the catcher caught the Frisbee, it was one stroke and put on the ground where it was caught. Then the thrower on the opposing team would throw to his teammate, who probably would stand near where the first catcher stood. Then the first thrower would throw again to his teammate, who had walked about 40 or 50 feet towards the basket, and they'd repeat the attempt. If missed, it was an incompletion and cost two strokes. The thrower would then throw from where it had landed, uncaught. Usually, there were two teams competing against each other, keeping scores, with the lowest score winning the hole. There was more to it, but further explanation is not necessary.

They played on the same holes and course as disc golfers, and were regarded respectfully, with curiosity, by the younger disc golfers. Flush taught Brock the game and persuaded him to join when they were both off work. Brock, having played Frisbee before, became a willing and competitive partner during the year he was with us. He was definitely the only manager who could fit into that extracurricular activity. And the only one Flush ever considered inviting. Brock maintained a professional distance, so they never partied together off-duty, but Frolfing was a chance for them to be friendly without violating any businesslike restrictions. I played with them a few times, but I wasn't very good, so wasn't as enthusiastic as Flush.

After their third time out, Flush built his courage and asked Brock if he minded if Flush smoked a little "cannabis." Brock, nonplussed, said it was none of his business what we did off duty, but he wouldn't participate. Flush and two other Frolfers then lit up and smiled more as a result. It didn't affect their playing ability or Brock's opinion. He was no beginner to party life.

Brock was also receptive to Flush's efforts to improve the Freebee Program. Being working class and cooperative, he was easily persuaded to purchase a large tarp to cover the furniture that Flush and I stored outside near the loading dock. Once, I counted 23 office chairs, a large table, and a file cabinet, far too much to fit into the cramped Freebee Room. This tarp, while not perfect, protected this furniture from the winter rains and snow. Other than a larger room, this was the best we could do. Flush was particularly thankful and expressed it to Brock.

But unfortunately, after one year with us, Brock attracted the attention of ErrorMake's upper management and was given a bigger responsibility; he was transferred south to Ventura County. He came up once, several months later, with a tan; our ex-boss had found a way to rent a house on a Southern California beach. He went from being a flat land Kansan, never having seen an ocean, to an aficionado of California living, relaxing, playing Frisbee and sand volleyball in the sun. He was happy. We weren't. We missed his democratic leadership.

Chapter 13: Termination Without Cause

After Brock transferred to the coast, ErrorMake followed their usual pattern of toilet dipping for his replacement. Look out, EVS employees. Our pleasant year, in comparison a vacation, was over. To manage EVS, ErrorMake hired a young, inexperienced woman named Dora Kinney, the unmarried mother of an illegitimate two- year-old. Occasionally she brought the child to work. We all recognized that Alice, the toddler, was adorable, a little blonde angel, so at first, we gave Dora a lot of lenient tolerance for her noticeable managerial incompetence. She was the only manager in the hospital to bring her child to work, which was surprising. But most of us in EVS were easy going, not enforcers of social mores, so we got used to it. And it didn't happen too often.

Unlike Bossella, Dora was not a "looker." She was unattractively heavy, with a humongous stern that swayed side to side on the rare occasions when she waddled down the halls. Her face was flattened, with a smushed nose that protruded from chubby cheeks, above over-sized lips. Her unmarried state was not surprising.

In her second month with us, Dora announced very quietly (almost as if she wanted to keep it unknown, unlike most perspective brides) that she was getting married. We were happy for her, knowing the difficulty of single parenthood. Her fiance never came to the hospital, so could have been a three-toed sloth, a suitable "catch" for homely Dora. Having 3 toes could have been his major selling point, as exceeding 2 (the conventional quantity possessed by sloths) by 50% would have been a significant quality, attracting a woman like Dora and giving her something worthwhile to brag about to her parents in her childhood home (a farm some place in Iowa).

At first, Flush was sympathetic to Dora's difficult position in a tough job for which she was unprepared and unqualified. By this time, many EVS employees were unhappy again in their jobs. Attendance and work ethics were low again. Most of us didn't care about the quality of our work. Many did the basics and went home, thankful for a thankless job, some with good benefits and above- average hourly salaries.

Once, in a one-on-one meeting, Flush gave Dora a relevant quote from Johann Wolfgang von Goethe, a 19th- century writer and philosopher. He mentioned that the quote was printed on a shellacked board hung on a wall in his kitchen at home. It read, "It is not doing the things we like to do, but rather liking the things we have to do that makes life blessed." Flush was trying to make this part of his personal wisdom and thought it applied well to our work in EVS. He brought the sign to work, and Dora posted it on a wall in the break room for about two weeks. Few, if any, of us applied its advice. Grumbling continued as always.

I soon learned Dora wasn't really that nice and had no experience managing anything. Judging from her missing teeth, she couldn't manage getting toothpaste on the brush. Dora was 34, had zero leadership qualities, and was a poor communicator, speaking in a soft voice that commanded no respect. She probably meant well but was disorganized and way over her head as manager of our semi-functional department. She probably could have done a housekeeping job but couldn't lead us with any authority. Rarely leaving her tiny, sloppy office didn't help revise our collective opinion. We soon concluded that she wasn't management material. And her outside life had to be full of distractions, including commuting from her home 60 miles away through freeway stop-and-go traffic with a baby and rumored husband in the future.

"Where did ErrorMake find her?" was a question we asked among ourselves. And yet, despite all her problems and deficiencies, she remained our "leader" for over a year. This was indicative of the degree of consideration and concern toward EVS displayed by the NCMH administration. They just didn't care. Dora was ErrorMake's problem, and now ours, but she was expected to control and guide us. Putting her looks aside, had our NCMH administration no common sense? True, they had contracted with an outside company, but this company provided this incompetent manager and NCMH passed the buck, accepting no responsibility. Our local administration was committed to Diggery Wealth's decisions, so we had to accept them. Besides, Environmental Services was so low on the hierarchy of concerns nobody cared about our work or satisfaction.

We porters had discussions with Dora about the quality of plastic bags. Before her vapid control, we porters were happy with the blue bags. These bags contained all the soiled linens, weighing up to 50 pounds when full. Though there was nothing sharp inside, their weight made them sometimes vulnerable to ripping, but they rarely ripped. Every bag, about 150 total throughout the three-floor hospital, was changed at least once a day. Some in the inpatient departments would be changed twice a day. These were the bags most often handled by porters. It was a big part of a porter's responsibility. Then Dora ordered new, cheaper, thinner bags with a very slight color difference. I'm sure someone in accounting applauded this magnificent business maneuver, falling just short of saving us from bankruptcy, saving about $10 per month. Only one problem; they ripped.

Waiting for us porters to change them, the mouth of each bag stretched around a metal frame under a closable square lid opened by a foot pedal. We had to pull these bags, half or full, with dirty sheets, gowns, pillowcases, and blue pee pads. After pulling them from the metal hamper, we'd hoist them on top of the hamper lid and, using APEAM, tie them closed, making rabbit ears of the two corners, which are tied together. When these bags ripped, gamy threads scattered in the hall, soon detected by noses within nearby olfactory range. Heads turned, particularly those down wind, which was in 360 degrees. We porters were embarrassed, looking foolish, stuffing fetid funk into a new bag. And who knows what sort of germs were spread? We didn't. Not the sort of view that inspired great confidence in our patients and their visitors.

Unfortunately, Dora had ordered six months' worth of these cheap rippers, so we porters suffered. Dora probably saved the department $120 total with her astute financial prowess. But, as usual, no other considerations attracted awareness. Economics always trumped.

***

In her third month as EVS manager, Dora made a big mistake. This event produced distrust throughout the EVS Department and particular stress between Flush, myself, and Dora. It secured our suspicion of Dora's ineptitude.

Dora assigned one of us, a housekeeper, to a very unusual assignment. Micky Outman was on light duty due to a shoulder injury that prevented her from doing her regular job. Micky, with no experience, was instructed to get all of us to sign two papers. These two papers had many Diggery Wealth rules we were expected to follow. This was ok and not resisted. But also on these papers was a statement, easily overlooked by people unfamiliar with legalese, that said we agreed to their right to "terminate without cause." This meant that a manager could fire good, long-term employees for personal reasons, including discrimination against minorities or, in salacious cases, refusal to perform sexual acts. "Terminate without cause" was an invitation for abuse.

Several tactics were employed to get us to sign this, which made the process suspicious, unusual, and unprecedented. Micky, who really had no authority since she was just a housekeeper on the same level as the rest of us, called us into the empty break room one by one during a work day? She told each of us that these same papers had been signed by us many times in the past, which was untrue. She seemed to rush us, saying, "Just go ahead and sign it," minimizing the papers and making it seem unimportant and automatically acceptable. This worked, and every EVS employee but Flush and myself signed them without resistance. Most EVS people (all high school grads except Flush and myself), trusting the administration, didn't bother reading them closely. Over the years, we had been trained to sign papers without close examination, assuming it was harmless. A large majority of these papers contained boring, irrelevant words, in small print, in administrative vernacular of no interest to any of us. Many papers needing signatures were addressed to nurses and technicians and didn't apply to us. Most people just wanted to be cooperative and not jeopardize their jobs, so they signed anything. Dora knew this and took advantage of people's willingness to ignore details.

These totally unusual circumstances created a justifiable suspicion for anyone who read it. Flush and I both saw this as a problem and agreed to object together to that phrase. Neither of us knew their intentions, but we recognized the potential for some serious misdeeds by an unscrupulous boss, and we'd seen several. That afternoon, after I refused to sign such a self-defeating proposal, Dora called me into her office. She asked me why I refused to sign. I told her it was because of the "terminate without cause" phrase. She said that it was there because of Diggery Wealth and not her idea. I pointed out the danger of such a policy, but she just shrugged as if it were unimportant. That scared me.

I asked her why we were asked to sign it one at a time. Always before, we had signed papers in a group meeting. Her answer surprised me. "Where I used to work, there were several employees who were illiterate. I had you sign this separately to avoid embarrassing those employees." When I assured her that we were not illiterate, she just shrugged and said, "I just wanted to protect you."

I asked her why Micky was assigned the job. She said, "Micky was on light duty (this was true), and she could do it without aggravating her shoulder." This explanation was disingenuous and increased my suspicions about Dora's motivations. Several minutes later, she summoned Flush to her office. He, too, expressed his passionate opposition to such a wicked phrase. He didn't hold back and attacked Dora for this insensitive phrase being passed off using skulduggery and subterfuge. Flush was more old-school ethical than most of us, so he was particularly incensed by this clumsy effort of totalitarian chicanery.

Several years before, during Feckless Pidwell's managership, there had been a rumor that the management would fire all 30 of us and rehire the whole EVS department with new, young, more malleable workers.

This didn't happen, but it scared all of us and was a possibility in the back of our minds. It was indicative of the distrust we had developed for NCMH. And with the relatively new introduction of an outside company, ErrorMake, and Dora, this possibility was more likely, in the minds of Flush and myself, both of whom were more willing to question management's motives.

Also, our department was the only one asked to sign this. Since these rules applied to all employees, why were we, EVS, singled out to sign something not required by other departments? Dora had no answers. The very unusual process, with Micky misrepresenting the papers and rushing us, one on one, was also questionable, promoting unhealthy suspicion. When Flush and I approached other EVS employees and explained the seriousness of the "terminate without cause" phrase, many wanted their papers back to cancel their signatures made under stressed and deceitful circumstances. Dora refused to return their signed papers and acted unsympathetic. This, too, confirmed our suspicions of her motivation.

Two weeks later, after some complaints by myself, Flush, and several other housekeepers, Dora came to a meeting attended by twelve EVS employees and three other middle managers who ranked over Dora. Dora claimed it was a beginner's mistake. She repeated her claim that the sentence giving them permission to "terminate without cause" was placed there by Diggery Wealth; it wasn't her doing. At the meeting, Flush spoke out about this uncomfortable incident. He said giving that kind of limitless power, requiring no accountability, was an invitation to illegal exploitation. A bigoted manager could, with this signed permission, fire an employee for being black or Jewish, Catholic or Muslim, Japanese or gay, or ugly or fat. A 40-year-old boss, married for 18 years and tired of his wife, could hire a pretty young woman, demand sex, and silence her if she wanted to keep her job. "Termination without cause" was extremely dangerous and threatened to violate an employee's civil rights, along with common decency, respect, and trust. It gave every manager unbridled power that could be easily exploited. He made good points, convincing the three middle managers. Flush was passionate in his colorful objection.

He didn't restrain his criticism and definitely provoked Dora's aversion. Diplomacy was never Flush's forte. He didn't raise his voice, pound the table, or deliver any dramatic gestures, but his voice was forceful and made serious, justified allegations. It was very rare that lower staff ever challenged managers so strongly at a formal meeting. With previous years of college lecturing, Flush had plenty of experience making points to a small audience. He displayed that persuasiveness to defeat this obvious authoritarianism.

Also at this meeting was Dora's new management partner, Turdex Darkhart, hired by ErrorMake to supplement Dora's inadequate leadership and replace her for a few months after she gave birth. It was his third day on the job. He spent the meeting starring at his cell phone. I doubt he understood the seriousness of the subject. Later, he became a major player in our battles with EVS management.

At the meeting, ashamed and appropriately embarrassed, Dora sort of apologized and offered to shred the signed offending papers, which she did (I guess) with our consent. She took them to a room next door and came back without them. But there were no witnesses to the shredding. I was so dubious by this time that I'm not sure she actually shredded them, or if she did, she had already made copies.

There was a lot of tension and stress over this incident, causing suspicion of Dora's slippery actions and motivation. She was embarrassed and acted innocent. Maybe she was. But it was unusual and destructive nonetheless. We'd had other examples of her general deficiencies, not surprising, but the clumsy deceptions of this threatening maneuver were a major wake-up call for some of us. Our trust was seriously challenged, as was our confidence in Dora's ability to lead with reliability. Her "Bozo Quotient" could best be calculated by astronomers. I realized later that Dora's (and Turdex's) retaliation was inevitable. Flush and I paid a huge price for our outspoken opposition to these paper signings.

***

About a month later, Flush's creativity and willingness to present new ideas got him into trouble. Dora pounced like a pit bull on a bunny skin slipper. More than a sweet mama, she was also a revengeful shrew with power and poor judgement. Flush's trouble came about unexpectedly. The story behind the "incident" is interesting and merits repeating now. It says a lot about Flush and our culture at NCMH. It began with the Second Annual Penmanship Contest. This was described in an earlier chapter called "Suggestions."

In this second contest, there was opposition. The much- hated manager of Cardio Pulmonary, a paranoid nurse named Mikela Grouch, provoked a brouhaha with Flush, who was caught off guard. This was the same manager who had taken me to HR several months earlier for making Fude cry about a linen mistake. She encountered Flush in their department's small kitchen, where Flush was hanging a penmanship contest announcement on their bulletin board. He did this for each department before the contest.

"What is this?" she demanded in a truculent tone.

Surprised, Flush answered, "It's just a way to have fun and improve our handwriting."

"No, it isn't! This is just another attempt by management to get our signatures and handwriting so they can trace us," she accused in a hissy fit. "Take it down, or I will."

"No, it isn't. They had nothing to do with it. I'm doing this contest," responded Flush defensively. He was surprised by Mikela's reaction since they didn't know each other and had never had a conversation. He never dreamed that someone would oppose the contest, and certainly not for such a specious reason. She ripped down the flyer with dramatic anger, so Flush left, confused and knocked off balance. He never expected such hostile resistance. The whole confrontation took about 30 seconds, and Flush forgot about it after a day or two. For him, it wasn't worth any mental expenditure. He just told himself to avoid her as much as possible. I could have told him that, as I'd had a run-in with her before. Flush hoped he'd caught her on a bad day, which happened often at NCMH.

Unfortunately, it wasn't over. Flush received a phone message from Dora saying he had to appear in HR in two days at 3:00 PM. He was to bring a union shop steward. This was a new experience for Flush. Going to HR almost always meant trouble, and Dora didn't divulge the nature of the infraction. Needing a shop steward confirmed his difficulty. This summons for an unknown offense stressed his life for two days. Flush contacted a friend, Marcy Jefferson, who worked in a pharmacy and was a bulldog as a shop steward, defending employees when they needed and deserved help. The two of them went to HR together. Flush nervous, Marcy comforting since she had accompanied many scofflaws, renegades, and disgruntled types before. And a few innocents, though not many. Prosecutors (HR in this case) made biased judges and juries.

The meeting was held in a small office with an HR desk, two bookshelves, and a round table with four chairs. The new HR director,

Juyn Lancaster, motioned them to sit at the table, which they did. Since the previous HR Director, Liseanne, had been warm and supportive, Flush assumed the new director would follow this friendliness. Wrong!

Flush asked tentatively, "What is this about?"

Juyn said, in a soft, professional voice, "We'll get to that when Dora comes."

She continued typing on her computer behind her desk, separate from the table where the accused and counsel sat. Juyn ignored them. They waited in uncomfortable silence until, six minutes later, Dora made her waddling entrance, bumping into the door jamb as she navigated the opening. While maneuvering to one of the chairs around the table, Dora's rump sent a potted plant wobbling in the corner. Her body gave the phrase "Fallen behind" a new meaning, no longer describing someone in second place. She sat, exhaling audibly, pleased that she had accomplished the athletic maneuver of taking a seat with some finality. But they were just getting started.

After thumbing through some papers, Dora opened the meeting. "There was a complaint from Cardio Pulmonary that you were rude, angry, and combative."

Flush was aghast and unprepared, having forgotten the incident from three weeks before. "When was this? Who complained?"

"It was on Monday, March 22. I can't divulge the name of the complainer to avoid retaliation."

"Well, what did I do?" countered Flush, gaining some small confidence, beginning to remember the incident.

"You spoke harshly to an employee and threatened her with hostile body language. She thought about calling security." Dora looked proud to have spoken two sentences sequentially without stuttering. It was a triumph for her.

There was a long pause. Flush was formulating a verbal defense for what was, for him, a forgotten and minuscule problem. Then Juyn Lancaster spoke softly and asked, "Do you remember this?"

Flush, old and hard-of-hearing, holding his hand to his ear, said politely, "I'm sorry, but I can't hear you. Could you please sit over here closer?" There was one empty chair around the circular table.

"No. I'll stay here," responded HR Lancaster, uncooperatively. Another long pause, with both Flush and Marcy surprised by her response and immobility.

"Well?"

Flush gathered his focus and said. "Yes, I remember it. But not that way. I never threatened her or even raised my voice. I was irritated that she misunderstood the flyer and contest I was posting. The penmanship contest was officially recognized, even though I was mostly responsible. Her conspiracy accusation was totally false.

She claimed the administration was tricking us into giving our signatures. That was paranoid nonsense. The contest was my idea."

Dora, again, softly from shyness, "You made her scared. You don't realize your own aggressive body language."

"Do I have aggressive body language now?" asked Flush, seated in a chair, arms on the arms rests.

"Don't talk to her like that," commanded Juyn from behind her desk. He heard her this time.

Another long, uncomfortable pause.

"She, Mikela Grouch, was misunderstanding our contest and I was trying to explain it to her, but she was determined to believe a false accusation. No way was management trying to get samples of our signatures for some nefarious purpose. No way. That's ridiculous. I said it then, and I'll say it now. I should have complained about her. She tore down the flyer. I just walked away."

Then Marcy, the union advocate, spoke up. "That Mikela complains about everybody. I've had trouble with her before. She's the one with the problem."

Both Dora and HR Juyn Lancaster looked at each other, and HR spoke authoritatively. "We'll discuss it now in private. You should wait outside in the front office."

Flush and Marcy left and sat sullenly in the front office chairs outside HR's office. "I can't believe this," proclaimed Marcy, sincere and justified. She sat tensed in a sturdy miff. Flush was pissed but muffled it like the gentleman he wasn't. Five minutes later, they were called back. Flush and Marcy took the same seats. Dora had not moved.

HR spoke. "We've decided to give you a warning. You must learn to moderate your approach when you talk to your co-workers. If you get angry, take a walk outside for 10 minutes. If you need help from the Employee Assistance Program—called EAP—we can arrange it."

Flush and Marcy exited without comment, Flush shaking his head in disbelief. He had just received a taste of Dora's revenge with the complicity of HR. He was seriously incredulous, a total virgin, never having been screwed so mistakenly, so unjustly, by corporate management practicing power-over rather than power-with leadership.

In his mind, Flush made the connection between this recent reprimand and his protestation of Dora's connivance regarding "termination without cause." She could have defended one of her minions but was too weak to do so, thus costing her Flush's confidence, friendship, and respect. There was no doubt that he was a victim of Dora's revenge. This eliminated Flush's enthusiasm for a third penmanship contest. The event never happened again, and few noticed or cared. Robust scrawl, mostly signatures, from many of management's pens, continued unabated, another problem uncorrected without attention.

Chapter 14: Freebee War -- Battle #1

There was a serious ongoing conflict between Salty Dalty and Flush. I call it the Freebie War. It lasted about five years. It was much more important than any Hat battle. One of the subjects of Flush's most passionate activism was the Freebee Program. It became the grounds of a David and Goliath war of less than Biblical dimensions, with Flush cast as David and the Diggery Wealth administration, including Salty Dalty (the corporate mouthpiece in this case) as Goliath. But this time, (holy cow!) Goliath wins. Yeah, that should surprise no one.

This is a corporation that shamelessly spreads its motto, "Hello Humankindness," wide and strong across the American South-West. They proclaim "Hello Humankindness" on buttons, orange T-shirts, notebooks, posters, TV ads, and painted elevator doors. They spend millions of dollars conspicuously presenting this slogan behind home plate at all San Francisco Giants home games. Saturating all of California and parts of

Nevada and Arizona, huge sums were spent to promote this regional hospital corporation, hoping it would go national.

It was a public relations campaign that was distrusted by most of the veteran employees at NCMH within a year of its intrusion. We saw, up close, many decisions that showed no kindness, human or otherwise, towards hospital staff. In a tepid defense, however, I should say they generously gave away the orange T-shirts and buttons and encouraged us to wear them at work, willing human advertisements with a corporate slogan well displayed in 2" high lettering. Many employees wore them for about a year.

That they created a new word, Humankindness, by combining two common old words, indicated a professional public relations firm was responsible for this widespread and expensive scheme by a non-profit to brainwash the public.

The corporation's covert war against the Freebee Program was another example of their hypocrisy on a small, local scale. The Freebee Program was very good, costing nothing while benefitting several hundred deserving low-level employees. But it made no money for Diggery Wealth.

Finally, after 5 years of indifferent irresponsibility, the local administration (mostly Salty Dalty, I suspect, though couldn't prove, since they always hid details behind an opaque wall that promulgated distrust), commanded by corporate headquarters, shut Freebee down completely. Nobody but Flush tried to save it, and they punished him for doing so.

Flush's background explains his passion and persistence in his mostly one-man battle to save Freebee. Flush was born at the end of the Great Depression and the beginning of WW2. All Americans lived under extreme rationing of most necessary goods, including food and gas. He was raised by parents whose values despised waste of all sorts, who often improvised and made use of things that later would be discarded without concern. New toys were rare. His toys were balls of collected string and anything that shined, like old hub caps. Flying a kite with his dad on weekends was a big thrill for him. His tricycle was rusty but greatly appreciated. He was raised to recycle and shamed for not eating all his food, and cleaning his plate, even if he didn't like it. This was common among most American kids raised during the early 1940s. If a kid resisted his broccoli, he was told, "Think of the poor starving children in Armenia who would love broccoli." Flush, among many, always responded, "Let's send it to them."

Here's how Freebee was born, mothered by a small group of concerned employees. Sometime in 2010, a Green Team, comprising about ten employees espousing ecological principles, was formed. As you might wisely expect from the name, its mission was to introduce and achieve environmental objectives in a hospital context, mostly by recycling most of the tremendous "waste" that even mid-sized hospitals regularly discard. Hospitals and the environment don't necessarily dance well together, but they can if Green Team is successful. And it was, for a while. Californians led the nation in awareness and concern for ecology and its goal of preserving the goodness of Earth. By 2010, recycling was nothing new to most of us. Before the Green Team, there was little recycling of the many hospital items discarded at our local landfill, with no concern for our environment. NCMH was way behind the rest of California in this, caused by the administration's indifference to recycling.

Salty Dalty hated the Green Team and all its efforts, and tried to weaken and undermine their activities. "Just get rid of it!" was his efficient but thoughtless motto, which meant taking all discards to the dump, regardless of their value or remaining usefulness. Recycling was too much trouble in his inconsiderate military mind. In addition to the Freebee Program, the Green Team initiated some much-needed practical programs. For about two years, they did some excellent work. The team successfully instituted green bags for collecting everyday common recyclables, distributed in appropriate places, including soiled utility rooms. Eventually, everyone helped by putting non-medical papers (nothing needing shredding), plastic containers, aluminum cans, empty drink bottles, and anything else recyclable into these green bags. We porters collected them daily, took them, and separated them from other trash. Then they were taken to some recycling facility to be reformed into park benches, plastic road signs, and those little bumps in the highways that separate lanes.

Since plastic lasts 1000 years, it must be tough. I think we should grind up used plastics and make our roads with that as a component. Added to asphalt, pebbles, and whatever they use in road making, it would reduce the cost (recycled plastic is free) and contribute to durability. It might also work in construction. Much wiser than being discarded into the ocean, where it pollutes large surface areas and sinks to the floor to kill life there. Also, old worn out tires might be ground up and added to road construction material.

This Green Team also contracted with an outside organization called Stryker, which came every month and picked up our used medical items that could be cleaned and sent to third-world hospitals to be reused. Stryker effectively recycled a lot of items that had previously been wasted in the local landfill. I think they also took perfectly good, unused supplies post-expiration. I saw expired rubber gloves, still in the unopened boxes, being rejected by NCMH and given life in a third-world country without our ridiculous standards. Same for unused "Q" tips, bandaids, and tongue depressors.

I believe the whole idea of expiration dates on these supplies was lobbied into state or federal laws by the companies who made the supplies. This way, the users, mostly hospitals, clinics, and nursing homes, had to buy more every two or three years after they had expired, an expenditure that helped drive up the cost of medicine and the profits of bandaid manufacturers. I never understood why bandaids and rubber gloves were useless after remaining unopened for several years.

The Green Team also brought in an outside collector named Med Share. This organization collected, from hospital discards, a variety of small equipment and expired surplus supplies. At NCMH, these items were collected and stored in heavy-duty cardboard barrels outside the Freebee Room. One time we gave them about twenty boxes of clear and red plastic bags that were too thin for us, so easily ripped. Boxes of hand sanitizers attached to hospital walls were given to other hospitals after we changed suppliers.

Med Share also replaced every smallish thing with a newer, superior version, which could perform more extensively. This planned obsolescence happened far too often for any reasonable person to implement effectively. New technology with computerized bells and whistles, most of which were unused by staff, having become too complicated to all but computer geeks, replaced older but still functioning equipment. Most hospital staff weren't best friends with computers. So when they introduced a newer computer technology, staff had to learn a new program. These new software programs are rarely easy when you're expected to enter important medical information accurately into a patient's only file. Several hundred computers were rejected and replaced by newer versions with difficult programs that had to be learned by all doctors, nurses, and technicians. This relearning took many frustrating hours over three months and was cursed by all whose jobs depended on them. Flush, I, and all janitors and housekeepers were relieved not to have to learn this new system. Hundreds of older, rejected computers lined the basement halls for weeks before disappearing, hauled away by some company we had never learned about. This was outside the limited control of the Green Team.

However, somebody made a lot of money when the shift to a newer version was made. And the people who were most affected by the change, those who had to use this new program daily for their jobs, were never asked. Their opinion was barely relevant. You can bet that money was the basis for the decision to upgrade.

A few years ago, the manager of EVS (Environmental Services) was Mark Pidwell, a nice guy but not a strong leader. For some reason unknown to us, Pidwell, who worked under Salty Dalty, was put in charge of Freebee, a program recently created by the Green Team. With his leadership, it went nowhere. Then Flush joined the Green Team, and, with the backing of a couple of others, was able to shame Feckless Pidwell into mild activity. He wrote a poem about poor Pidwell. It's worth repeating here.

Pidwell did well
Until he didn't.
Pidwell hid well
That what he shouldn't.
Pidwell skid well
Down the slope
To indifference
Indolence
and sloth.

The Freebee Program was a recycling of old hospital furniture and unusable supplies, mostly from remodeled offices. Nothing that Stryker or Med Share could use was included in the Freebee Program. Many used but useable furnishings, such as office chairs, file cabinets, desks, large framed pictures of beautiful landscapes, tables, etc., comprised the best stuff in Freebee. It also included a variety of used supplies such as styrofoam ice chests and freezable ice packs, 3-ring binders, empty files, discarded keyboards, batteries, discarded books from the library, and hundreds of other used items too many to list here. There were two large stand-up scales, the kind in doctors' offices where a patient stands on a platform and a nurse moves two sliders so that a needle on the right side balances perfectly level horizontally. Supposedly these measured weights more accurately. These scales sell for about $600 new. One digital scale with a wire cut didn't work but probably could have been fixed easily, and worth hundreds.

With Freebee, anyone who worked in the hospital, including 857 employees and many volunteers, could view these things and take them home, for free, after signing their name and date on a clip-boarded sign-out sheet, which Flush kept up to date. There was no oversight; it was a responsible gift to employees.

Initially, Feckless assigned the Freebee Room as part of a storage room, known, for some unexplained reason, as Classroom B. We assumed it had been a classroom 20 years before. Now it was full of a variety of non-Freebee items, such as floor scrubbers, floor buffers, beds, gurneys, floor mats, and other equipment used regularly. The Freebee items were mixed into this mess, with no way to differentiate between freebee and non-freebee items. It was confusing, but Feckless didn't seem to notice or care. His complacency was predictable. Behind a locked door and out of public sight, this dysfunctional and disorganized stew of muddled hodgepodge was indicative of management's indifference to Freebee's success. Nobody cared as long as things looked professional (organized) on the outside when seen by the public. If unseen, disorganized confusion was good enough for Feckless and Salty. Nor was the success of the new Freebee Program of any consideration beyond a measured "Ho hum."

Classroom B was easy to find and convenient to access, but the immense clutter of large non-Freebee equipment made it unworkable as a Freebee location. Had anyone bothered (Dalty was running the show, and he was a lot less than enthusiastic), they would have known that it was a ridiculous, unworkable location. With a tiny effort, they could have found a better site.

Flush and another porter, Charles, went to Feckless Pidwell requesting an alternative site for the Freebee program. Both liked this new recycling program for themselves and the 857 employees. Feckless, in a rare display of spinal fortitude, persuaded Salty Dalty, his boss, to give Freebee its own room, separate from stored equipment. According to Feckless, "Salty was not a big fan of the Freebee Program." He diplomatically expressed Salty's opposition as an understatement in order to avoid pissing Salty off, a habit that preserved Feckless' job and going-nowhere-career. He was as afraid of Salty as we were.

We were all thankful and astonished when management came to its senses and found a more suitable location. After two months, a slightly better site was established, in a tiny room in the basement, hidden away from all traffic, difficult to find, in a location impossible to describe without being led there by hand. It was up a flight of 12 steps, in a room with unfinished cement walls, concrete floor, and metal shelving on both sides. Of course, no window, so dark, and the light switch was hard to find. It was behind a door with a code (5) that few people knew. This room was much too small to hold the many chairs, file cabinets, etc.

I say "slightly better" because it didn't share space with a lot of non-Freebee items. Other than that, it was worse in every way. An unpaid pack of blind primates might design this new location while drunk; nobody who cared found it acceptable. But we had no vote or choice.

If you want to hide something in the hospital to guarantee minimal participation, this unnamed room in a hard-to-explain location would be your first choice. No doubt Salty Dalty was responsible for this location. As director of plant operations, he had unchallenged power to determine who and what goes where. Salty Dalty spent several years undermining Freebee in every covert chance he could find. Poor Pidwell, fearful of speaking the whole truth, worked under Salty Dalty, so he had to deal with this tyrant when everybody else avoided him.

Also, little effort was made to inform employees of its location or even of the existence of the Freebee Program. Flush had to lobby hard to get it mentioned in Grapevine. Surprising to Flush, who had high hopes for Freebee and saw its value, most of the administrators shunned it and acted ashamed of it. It was a very neglected stepchild, abandoned by the Green Team after it was formed. Whenever the Green Team met, which was infrequent, and Flush would beg for promotional support and to find a more suitable location, beseeching deaf ears. "That hole probably breeds rats; it's so squalid. We can do better. We're a hospital, not a refugee camp," he preached without success. Because of fear, the Green Team refused to stand up to Salty Dalty's opposition, designed to slowly starve the Freebee Program into a pale, neglected shadow of a noble effort. I suspect upper management, a cadre of well- dressed and well-paid women with offices on the top (2nd) floor, supported Salty's destruction of Freebee. I doubt any of them ever ventured into the "pit of discards." It struggled to survive.

If there was no Freebee Program, all these useful rejections would be hauled to the landfill, commonly known as The Dump in many circles less sophisticated. After the switch from Classroom B to "Nowhere room" was made, The Freebee Program limped along. Very few people had heard of the Freebee opportunity for the first year or knew where it was. Gradually, through word of mouth and no effort by administrators to publicize it, between 20-40% of the employees checked it out occasionally and took items home from the squalid room in the basement. Since it was behind a door with a code, inaccessible to the public, the secrecy also guaranteed limited participation of employees.

About 25% of Flush's home furnishings came from the Freebee Program. Flush was able to establish a shabby outdoor summer patio at his home with a variety of ugly chairs and tables and a rolling cabinet from Freebee. Four large (3′ by 4′) landscape paintings, framed and matted, rejects from recently redecorated NCMH offices, and in beautiful condition, decorated three of Flush's living room and kitchen walls. I was able to furnish my small efficiency apartment with two chairs, a desk, and a table from Freebee. Many other employees did the same. Nice stuff, for free. Thanks, NCMH!

The new Freebee Room shared a space, divided by shelving, with Diagnostic

Imaging's storage space. Flush made a sign which pointed left for D.I. (X-ray) and right for Freebee. This was necessary to prevent people from mistaking the two and taking stuff home from D.I. Had this happened, X-ray would have been upset, and Freebee didn't need any unjustified opposition, particularly from people with a big X in their name. We joked that Ray must be a pretty bad dude to be rated X with his clothes on. I'm pretty sure the signage worked to avoid that confusion.

Flush printed up papers upon which people would sign their names, the date, and the description of the item taken. These papers were stacked on a clipboard on a shelf, along with a pen or pencil. When the top paper was full of names, Flush took it off, saved it for future evidence, and started again with a clean sign-up sheet. He also put up a sign on the wall behind the shelf. It read, in large hand-printed lettering, "If you take something, (please do, it's free) remember to do the form on the clipboard below. Thanks."

Later, someone anonymously wrote on the sign, "Why? What's the difference?"

Flush, who was trying to make the case for Freebee's popularity, responded, in writing on the sign, "We are trying to build support for improving the Freebee Program. The more signatures we have, the stronger our case." Later, the same anonymous coward wrote, "Who cares Moron!"

Flush ignored the graffiti guy's poor punctuation and answered definitively, "Who cares? Several hundred employees benefit from Freebee Care. Please be more careful when insulting ("Moron") someone who is working for the common good." And he signed his name, one of several distinct differences between Flush and his unknown opponent. This seems to have ended the graffiti war.

As a side note, and independent of the Freebee War, there was nothing unique about this graffiti critic's anonymity. Fear of firing drove much of the culture on every level, so anonymity was common, accepted, and unchallenged.

After about two years, there was no Green Team since its founding mother (and highest-ranking member), Liseanne O'Donnell, retired to Florida. Rare for Human Resources leadership in most corporations, Liseanne was well-liked, supportive, and fair whenever possible. I suspect she saw the dismal future of NCMH and decided to retire early; she was 59. I also suspect she was seriously discouraged by the destructive, behind-the-scenes disagreements and incompetent decisions of the few 2nd- floor administrators (all women) with impressive titles, usually with an office with a window. I suspect their small offices did not suggest stingy paychecks, which were likely 3 or 4 times our paychecks. But since the corporate giant, Diggery Wealth, took over about five years ago, most big decisions were made somewhere else, remote from the scene of action.

After Diggery Wealth took over and Liseanne retired, HR became a scary place avoided by most. The new HR director wasn't nearly as friendly and willing to work with employees. They cut her staff to three people, and if we went there with a question, we were usually given a long- distance phone number and told to ask a series of robots and, eventually, if you were lucky, a human stranger who didn't care.

At any rate, when Liseanne left, the Green Team died a very quiet death, unnoticed, unmourned, unattended, and unappreciated. But the Freebee program limped on, mostly with Flush's occasional intervention. Flush spent, on average, one minute per week doing the very few things that needed to be done. I felt sorry for him, as it appeared he was giving CPR to a deceased, neglected rodent. He did this alone for three years, totally unrecognized and outside any part of his assigned job. He was passionate about it and couldn't (or wouldn't) quit.

In an effort to influence the top of the hierarchy, Flush asked for a meeting with the CEO, Betsy Socutesome. He did this via email, the easiest way to negotiate meetings. She responded, asking how long and about what? Flush wrote back, 15 minutes of walk and talk about the Freebee program. Flush, at the utter bottom of the hierarchy, didn't hesitate to approach the top. He had audacity.

Betsy accepted. She scheduled it for a Friday, tennis shoe day at the hospital. Better for walking, but no observable increase in talking capacity or inclination. Most of us liked her relaxed social skills. She was usually approachable and friendly but rarely effective in solving problems. Most of us had no clue as to what she did to make NCMH run. Nevertheless, she must have been favored by corporate headquarters because she was pulling down over $400,000 per year. She had a nice office, with carpeting and windows, and a secretary in a separate office who controlled access. And I guess she was doing something locally to appease the board of directors.

She sometimes came out of her 2nd-floor office and mingled around several nurses' stations, getting to know us on the front lines. She listened. She nodded assent. Maybe even promised to "look into it." And then...nothing. Unless you asked again, the subject would never be mentioned again. She forgot about it. But she smiled a lot and was friendly. Also, pretty enough to have been a high school prom queen 40 years earlier. Also, she was in good shape (unlike many of the female staff) and impeccably dressed in executive fashion. It travelled well with her Mercedes sedan. Flush called her "Captain" and sometimes joked with her about wandering down into the basement where us, lowlies, hung out, certainly not a fitting place for a respectable CEO to be found strolling. Of course, this was nonsense, and Flush said it tongue-in-cheek because the cafeteria was down there, and Betsy often ate with blue-collar workers in the large dining room that accompanied the cafeteria. She never sat at our tables, always sitting with another female administrator, but in the same room. Betsy understood Flush's sarcastic sense of humor, and didn't seem to object to his inappropriate brash approach, which lacked fake obeisance.

On Friday, Flush showed up at Betsy's office. It was his day off. He started by taking her down to the Freebee Room, a place she had never seen. They spent about two minutes, Flush making the case that it was too small and hard to find. The 12 steps made moving large furniture difficult. These items required two men to move in and out, up and down. Couches and file cabinets, tables and desks all stubbornly resisted coming and going. "We can do better," Flush appealed to Betsy's pride in NCMH.

"I'm sorry, but there just isn't any available space. There's no place to put it. We have a shortage of space." It was hard to determine if she was sincere in her apology or wasn't really interested in helping.

Then Flush led her outside the back delivery entrance near the San-i-Pack area. There, behind a chainlink fence, roofless, on the pavement of the parking lot, were 14 rolling, padded office chairs, two file cabinets, and a large wooden table in a recently remodeled waiting room. Only six employees, including Flush and me, knew about it. Unlike the assigned Freebee Room, this area had never been officially acknowledged and was only necessary to hold the overflow of furniture that wouldn't fit into the Freebee Room. Flush declared that the furniture was out in the weather and getting destroyed. His case for a larger room was strong and getting stronger. Betsy manifested sympathy as well as any unproductive administrator could. Later, a large tarp was purchased by Brock Chill from his EVS budget to cover all this furniture that was subject to destruction by weather.

Then Flush guided Betsy out into a distant, mostly empty, gravelly field where stood, on blocks, three large, locked containers. Flush suggested that one of them if moved closer to the main building, could be used as the new Freebee Room. It would cost nothing and work a lot better than the cramped rat hole currently hosting this recycling scheme. Betsy claimed not to know their current contents but knew they were full and unusable.

Then they walked around the buildings where Flush suggested possible locations for a new Freebee Room. He reminded Betsy that portable rooms on wheels had been used in the past for training when they brought in many computer teachers to train the staff on the new computer programs. One area was in an unused garden that was convenient for parking and visible to employees. It would have been perfect, as Flush opined. Betsy liked a couple of these suggested locales but shot down other possible sites. Either it would take two parking spaces (unacceptable), or a tree had to be cut down (no good), or it would look bad. Flush suggested they could paint, in foot-high lettering, Hello Humankindness on the side of whatever building they brought in. This always won support from Betsy.

After 15 hectic minutes, they parted, with Betsy saying she would bring it up with the Executive Activity Committee. Flush never heard another word from her. The total absence of a Green Team lasted about three years. Not that it mattered much since they never did anything to support Freebee after they birthed it. But Flush could always refer to the Green Team as the birth parent, which gave Freebee some legitimacy, making it an official program of the hospital. With no Green Team, there was not much to lean on when Freebee was challenged by the unprogressive forces led by Salty Dalty and a couple of his unquestioning, compliant engineers.

Chapter 15: Rudy -- Old Gruff and Spittle

Rudy scared everyone. Not because he was big and brawny (he wasn't), not because he was politically volatile (he didn't know a liberal from a rutabaga), not because he did meth or coke or heroin (at least I don't think he did), but because he was crazy. And angry. And pushed most people away with gruff hostile comments and antisocial behavior. And collected guns for hunting, so he said. He blindly supported ThunderRump (more noise than light). He was one of us, a porter in Environmental Services, with not enough education to have any ambitions beyond being a disgruntled trash man.

Without knowing Rudy, one might suspect his volatile temperament upon first sight. His hair was usually long and straggly. An instrument of hair maintenance, a brush or comb, had rarely entered that unconquered forest of hirsute entanglement. Same with soap and water. His "poor hygiene" was universally recognized. He usually sported a 4-12 day beard and untrimmed mustache. His uniform was dirty and torn and never the same day to day. And he smelled, belched, and farted on many inappropriate occasions (if there is an appropriate occasion). At meals, often eaten with a group in the EVS break room, he chewed noisily, bovine cud eruptions dominating all conversation, frequently punctuated by unsuppressed belching. I don't know if these uncivilized habits ever brought admonishments, but he never seemed to correct them.

While eating in the EVS break room, Rudy usually read a magazine called "Conceal and Carry." This magazine specialized in gun subjects and argued against any armament restrictions. It also repeatedly persuaded the readers that liberals wanted to eliminate the Second Amendment and take away everyone's guns, beginning with assault rifles, some of which had been used recently in several mass shootings. I never researched it, but I suspect the NRA subsidized this one-sided propaganda rag.

Rudy sometimes took extensive notes, and many of us speculated that he was learning to make a gun or his own bullets. He sometimes talked about hunting and was concerned about the Second Amendment. Politically unsophisticated, Rudy was a one-issue voter. He supported any candidate who supported the Second Amendment without reservation and regulation. He applied for a concealed and carry permit, but we don't know if he got that permission. If so, he surely had a gun in his battered pickup truck, kept handy since weapons were not allowed in the hospital.

Several of us suspected he was autistic, probably a victim of Asperger's Syndrome, considering his lack of social graces and civilized sanitation. A few people felt he was unfairly bullied and judged by everyone, including the administration. He was guilty of many minor offenses, but probably blamed more than justified. He talked to one or two co-workers, relating that he'd been badly bullied as a low-income foster child raised in Kentucky. If so, it didn't surprise me, though I wondered if it was a cause of his current personality and behavior. He wasn't stupid and had a very unnatural ability to recall street names in places like Sacramento, many miles away. He hadn't been a taxi driver, but, with his mental map skills, would have been a good one if he kept his mouth shut.

One day in 2016, I was eating lunch in the break room, as was Rudy. On the table between us was a Trump bumper sticker, placed there by Rudy. I asked him if he was a Trump supporter. This got a big response from him. "Oh yes! He's the only one who can save our country. Clinton wants to take away our guns. Can't let that happen."

I asked him what he was planning to do with the Trump bumper sticker. "I'm going to put it on the red wagon. Red is for Republicans." He was proud of making that connection. "We need to rally around Trump. He'll save us from disaster. Clinton would put me in prison. I support the Second Amendment."

By "red wagon," he meant the large, highly visible trash container we porters pushed everywhere and filled with a variety of trash. Flush called it RRR. Of course, the admin wouldn't let Rudy sticker it; we were discouraged from talking politics publicly. No way would the admin tolerate any kind of campaigning, particularly on something as visible as RRR.

"I don't think you should put it on the wagon. They won't like you getting political here. Could be trouble."

He paused, thinking, and then responded, "Well, I'm going to put it somewhere. They can't take away my freedom of speech!" He was adamant, so I dropped it. I was always willing to avoid disagreements with him. With weaponry, he'd be dangerous. I never saw the bumper sticker on anything at the hospital. I'm glad he took my advice.

Rudy was very closed about his personal life. Flush knew him for five years before I was hired but knew almost nothing about Rudy's background. However, once, Rudy revealed that he was raised in Kentucky by a series of foster homes, four by the time he was six years old. He was shuttled from one house to another about every fourteen months. Only one was even close to friendly. The foster parents only did it for the money and showed him little love or direction. He dreamed of being adopted permanently, but it never happened. He never knew why. Neither did we.

When Flush was the daytime porter, Rudy's job as PM porter (hours 3:00 pm to 11:00 pm) was to pick up trash bags, put them in RRR or Sigmoid, take them to the San-i-Pack area around back and sort and dispose of them, according to their colors. This was the same that Flush and I did. To do this, he pushed RRR or Sigmoid through the crowded hallways and around corners, filling the squeaky wagon with trash as he went. We were all coached on the absolute necessity of going slowly and avoiding collisions with walls, equipment, or people. Particularly people, some of whom might sue. I know Rudy often crashed into walls, leaving scrapes and scratches to the discontent of the outsourced painters employed by the hospital. We encouraged them to consider this as job security. He also ran into a few employees, never drawing blood but, in so doing, contributing to his well-established reputation as a monkey (maybe) on meth. I didn't see it, but a housekeeper saw him fall into the lap of an old female patient in a wheelchair while backing up the RRR.

Rudy's metabolism wasn't made for slow. He seemed in a hurry whenever he worked, which wasn't very consistent. A coworker described his pace as "faster than a tweaker at midnight." But he was very lazy and slacked whenever he could. He was frequently caught napping in various beds or chairs in outpatient departments closed for the night. ATC (Ambulatory Treatment Center) was his favorite; it had TV and was isolated at night from much traffic.

We porters generally set the work bar low, but Rudy never jumped over, instead being satisfied with successfully squirming under, like a reptile hustling towards a swamp. When I first met Rudy, unaware of his malevolence, I asked him casually, "How's it going?" a common greeting among friendly strangers. "I'm here," came his rancorous response as he slumped away like a porcupine in an inflatable life raft in a storm with 17 human passengers far from land. It was clear he expected to be beaten, having experienced rejection repeatedly in his gnarly past. And by his behavior, he almost deserved it. It's called reciprocal causality.

When I came, Rudy had been the night porter for about 6 years. Everyone wondered why he still had a job at the hospital. Our boss told me that Rudy had a file 5 inches thick in the Human Resources department. He did something weird every week.

One morning I was subbing for Flush as a day porter. I did the usual rounds, checking the conference rooms to arrange the tables and chairs for the meetings that would happen that day. I pulled the trash in the X-ray and Emergency departments. Then I went back to the San-i- Pack area to find its door broken, having only one wheel. The wheel was not the kind used for transportation. It, about 1.5 feet in diameter, allowed us to open and close, very tightly, the large (about four feet in diameter), heavy, round door to the San-i-Pack, where the bio-hazardous waste was cooked to 286 degrees. This wheel was made of aluminum and had been there for about eight years since they got the San-i-Pack system. It was very solid, having withstood the abuse of countless clumsy porters. It was, like the Titanic, indestructible. Until it encountered Rudy. The broken wheel didn't allow the opening or closing of the cooking apparatus, necessary to render bio-hazardous waste safe before transferring to the landfill. We were paralyzed without the San-i-Pack and the wheel which allowed us to open and close the heavy door, making it airtight when closed.

Rudy was quick to admit his guilt and thought his explanation exonerated him. It at least allowed him to take the offensive since he could have been hurt (even killed, maybe, by his dramatic account) from a defective, weakened-by-years-of-use wheel that broke off in his hands when he was applying pressure to open a stubborn mechanism. According to Rudy, it had been weakened when other porters used a 5' aluminum push pole to pry it open. Flush and I both thought he did it himself when using the push pole as a lever. It would take that kind of force to break such a sturdy wheel.

Jim, one of the few friendly engineers, was in charge of repairing the San-i-Pack. It took about a week, and eventually, a new wheel was delivered by the company repairman, who came up from Stockton, about a four-hour trip each way. The total cost for the replacement: $1000. To my knowledge, Rudy paid nothing, kept his job, and, at most, added another page in his folder in Human Resources.

Rudy's work timings were from 3:00 PM, while Flush, working the day shift, got off at 3:30 PM. This overlap was designed to increase communication and coordination between the two shifts. This never happened. Rudy spent the half hour going to all the exterior trash cans and pulling out the discarded empty soda cans, which he stashed in a plastic bag, the end of which he tied through his belt loop like a penurious, homeless transient. Those aluminum cans were later cashed in for Rudy's profit. He was paid by the hospital but worked for himself that 1/2 hour. If we saw him before he left to collect cans, Rudy would scamper away, avoiding all contact, fearing we might ask him an embarrassing question. Or whatever addlepated motive occupied his paranoid mind.

Rudy spent at least two hours every evening, while getting paid, writing angry letters on one of the hospital computers. He wrote threatening letters to Sen. Kamala Harris, Sen. Dianne Feinstein, Governor Gavin Newsom, President Trump, the hospital CEO, and the president of the corporation that owned NCMH. Rudy also hated Flush and the director of the ambulance, who rejected Rudy's application to be a paramedic, so both were regular subjects of his ranting invectives. He got away with it because oversight was very lax. The night shift EVS lead, a nice, gentle, grandmotherly woman named Meg, had long ago given up trying to get him to work, so she mostly left him alone. Being shift lead paid 9 cents per hour more and not much power or respect in our department. And our EVS managers (we had many over the years) never stayed past 5:00 PM, a schedule welcoming Rudy's abuse.

There was a small interdenominational chapel on the first floor near the laboratory, mostly empty and unattended. Occasionally a visitor or patient would stumble in, pray, and write something in a large book with blank pages, which rested, open and inviting, on a table. Over the years, people had entered many messages, including pleas to God to save their mothers, fathers, or children. Rudy, on several occasions, wrote pleas, beseeching God to let him win the lottery. When he didn't win, he wrote again, cursing God for failing to honor his request, which Rudy thought was completely justified. "Why, God, do you fale me when I am the one asking for somthing I realy need?" His anonymous handwriting and erratic spelling were easily identified. Eventually, Jonah, our chaplain, a wonderful man, sat down with Rudy and explained, over an hour, why he shouldn't use the chapel's prayer book for personal gain. Rudy got the message and stopped writing to God in the chapel. He just did it on a computer. "Deer God, why ca'nt my wife have a baby? That wold make my life wurth living." And, "Deer God, can you give me new tires for my truk? It needs them bad."

In a rare conversation with Rudy, he told me that he would believe in God when his prayers were answered and he won the lottery or had a baby. That's the kind of proof he needed. Until then, God was questionable.

For about two years, there was a flurry of holes in many walls, purposefully made by someone's shoe at about the height of an intentional kick. They were always in parts of the hospital not heavily trafficked, sometimes in rooms only accessible to employees. This eliminated suspecting the occasional disgruntled patient or visitor who might be angry at the hospital. It had to be an employee, and, of course, Rudy was the prime suspect. I wanted to see if he wore steel-toed shoes but never had a good chance to check. At about 2 holes each month, after 2 years there were about 40-50 holes. I figured the dastardly culprit would break a toe or two without supportive steel-toed foot gear. Then, for some unknown reason, the whole kicking stopped. There were rumors, but no one was ever caught or reprimanded. I sometimes thought that maybe Rudy was sometimes innocent of some of the incidents. But his well- established reputation of delinquency inevitably pointed an accusing finger in his likely direction.

In a moment of unexpected empathy, I started to feel sorry for Rudy. I knew I wouldn't want to be living his life. But then he brought most of it on himself. He didn't know how to make friends. And because he constantly thought of himself as a victim, with everyone out to get him, he usually pushed everyone away. I think shrinks call it paranoia.

One day I was doing Flush's porter job while he was on vacation (Flush loved to snorkel in the Caribbean, where he went for two weeks almost every year). I came to work at the usual time, 7 AM, and was surprised when I couldn't find RRR, the large red wagon we used to haul the trash. I looked everywhere, finally in places around the hospital that were unlikely. I couldn't find it and couldn't do the job without it. Sigmoid had a broken wheel and was being repaired. I was as lost as RRR. And it's hard to hide when you're bright (scuffed up) red and the size of an anorexic rhino. It was clear that Rudy, who had been porter the night before, had hidden it. Who the hell knew why? We learned to expect the unexpected from him.

His erratic behavior manifested the line from folk singer Kate Wolf: "There are no roads that do not bend." And if they were straight, Rudy would bend them.

I busied myself with other projects until 9 AM, when our boss at that time, Mark Pidwell, came in. Mark was a nice boss, easygoing and usually friendly, but often feckless when solving problems. He was justifiably mystified by Rudy's frequent infractions and destructive activities. We both looked for another half hour. Rolling Red Rectum was too big to be hidden for a long time and impossible to remove from the hospital campus. A 200-pound container, 5 feet tall and 6 feet long, on unmotorized wheels, should have been about as visible as a forklift in a greyhound race.

Finally, exasperated and POed, Pidwell looked outside, around the back of the parking lot rarely used. There it was, in a place it had never been before. To get RRR off the ramp, Rudy had to put it on a hydraulic lift and drop it 6 feet to the parking lot. Feckless Pidwell and I looked at each other wordlessly, shaking our heads, acknowledging that only Rudy would pull such a stunt. I went back to work, now about 3 hours behind in my duties collecting trash. Feckless promised to speak with Rudy.

The next morning the same thing happened, but I knew where to look and found RRR there. I asked Feckless; he mumbled something, but I never found out if he had talked to Rudy about it after the first hiding. After the second incident, I asked Feckless again. He said Rudy said RRR had gotten in the way. This was a totally disingenuous explanation, as there was plenty of space where we usually stored it overnight and nobody had ever removed it from circulation for any reason.

The real reason was that Rudy was crazy, and erratic behavior was normal for him. And for some reason, known only to him, Rudy was pissed at me, so he wanted to sabotage my portership; probably because Flush and I were friends. Many of us wondered how he kept his job for so long, given the many examples of unreliable, fierce behavior. Two theories predominated our thinking. Maybe the administration was afraid to fire him because he frequently threatened to sue the hospital, claiming he had a lawyer. The second equally plausible theory was that he was so potentially turbulent and temperamental that firing might provoke a "going postal" response, which made everyone nervous. Him wandering the quiet, empty halls at night with rifles was a possibility, we all thought, particularly if something upset him a lot? Getting fired could easily be that something.

Equally upsetting would be the departure of Rudy's mail-order Filipino wife, Jenny, who had to be a saint for staying with him for eight years. He was very excited when they first corresponded on the internet. At her family's request, he went to Manila to meet them and secure their approval. Somehow, he passed their inspection and brought her here after their wedding. She came to our Christmas parties in our break room. She was pretty, well-behaved, and quiet among us strangers. Jenny was about 25 years younger than Rudy, who was about 50. She spoke very broken English, which she was learning. Each year her English got better, probably from watching TV. I doubt she learned much from Rudy. She wanted a baby and Rudy was eager to comply and supply, but it didn't happen. We all feared their separation, as she was about the only friend he had, his only "success."

I hardly knew her, but after several years she expressed to others a strong desire to return to her home in the Philippines, a possible event Rudy expressly feared and opposed. Should this ever happen, it would likely be another something producing an extremely menacing response. In the eyes of management, ironically, Rudy was too dangerous to fire. At least that theory explained his continuing employment.

Chapter 16: The Lockdown

Shortly after Dora Kinney was hired, Rudy caused a major complication. As bad as he habitually was on a regular basis, this deserved and got the attention of everyone in the upper ranks who had previously acted as though he wasn't worth dealing with. Before this incident, the administration was like the three monkeys; see no evil, hear no evil, speak no evil. Sweeping all problems under the metaphorical rug was common practice frequently, but this time they couldn't do it. They reacted. Badly.

It was a Sunday evening, about 7 PM. The phone rang, and Luna Irkley, a co-worker who disliked me, started with an apology. "Sorry to be calling you at home." This was the first time she'd ever called me; our relationship was seriously strained through disagreements at work. I was very surprised by her call. "I just got a call from Dora, and this is important. Rudy did something and he's no longer welcome at the hospital. He'll probably get fired. All the doors are locked except the emergency entrance, so tomorrow when you come, you have to come in through that door."

Not too surprised by anything involving Rudy, I asked, "What did he do?"

"She wouldn't tell me. She said she didn't know and we'd find out more tomorrow at work."

"Ok. Thanks for the update." We both hung up.

Monday morning, when I came to work, I found all hospital doors locked. Each had a hastily written notice saying go to the ER entrance on the south side of Building 1. Ample gossip was full of speculation, with the usually opaque administration keeping us guessing about Rudy's offense. Rumors in this atmosphere were abundant, with administrators claiming the necessity of privacy to protect Rudy's HIPAA rights. At this time, there had been many cases around the country of lone wolf shootings. In an elementary school in Connecticut, a young man killed many kids and teachers. Other shootings were happening in Oregon, Florida, Planned Parenthood clinics, churches, and elsewhere. This heightened our fear that Rudy had threatened something similar.

Since Rudy didn't work the night before, I figured he might have done something at home, like batter his poor wife. I heard a rumor that he'd been in another hospital, officially declared a 5150, a police code for insane and generally running amuck. Another rumor said he'd threatened someone up in ATC (Ambulatory Treatment Center), where a very nice group of middle-aged nurses gave treatments to walk-ins. I think they did kidney dialysis.

Somebody in the administration (probably the Safety Officer, a very nervous and high-strung supervisor who took herself much too seriously) had distributed an old picture of Rudy to all the departments, many of whom posted it in their break rooms and above office computers. The picture was 3 years old and inaccurate, showing a pudgy, shaven-faced Rudy; now he was thinner, shaggy, and bewhiskered during the lockdown. They wanted everyone to be on the lookout for him and to call security at 444 if they saw him at work. He wasn't scheduled to come until 3:00

PM, but they were worried he might show up unexpectedly with harmful intentions. At least, that was the conclusion we all believed, considering their severe reaction to whatever it was he did. We were told he didn't know he was prohibited from coming to the hospital. Apparently, he wasn't answering his phone. More mystery.

We waited for some clarification, which never came. It was an uncomfortable atmosphere, not made easy by the administration's clumsy handling and Rudy's already well- established reputation for antisocial, unpredictable behavior, probably gun related.

One of the lockdown doors was at the rear of the hospital, near Flush's "office," used by vendors delivering various things on a daily basis. It was heavy-duty metal, designed for professional security. Many others used this door, too, including all porters, when we entered from the chain-linked "office," pushing RRR or Sigmoid from being unloaded, an event which occurred about once an hour. But every porter had a key, so it wasn't totally paralyzing for us. With the door locked, many outside vendors couldn't do their jobs. The daily linen delivery driver had to pound on the door and wait for somebody to open it. Never happened before. He was delivering clean linens in large wheeled carts. He had to go in and out about 15 times to do this. After the first entrance, he put a rolled-up towel on the ground in the doorway at the entrance, a solution that kept the door from closing and locking him out. A manager from the Receiving Department objected, saying it was his duty to keep the door locked. A small verbal kerfuffle broke out between the two men. I had a job to do, so I left before seeing their compromise. I think someone had to stand by the door full-time to let everybody but Rudy pass. Nobody had been assigned that job, and it hardly merited a full-time employee. Pretty sure the manager didn't want it.

At about 9 AM, Flush and I had had enough. We were both tired of looking over our shoulders in justified states of fear. The suspicion and distrust were stressful and unhealthy, particularly ironic in a hospital, which is supposed to create the opposite reaction. Flush suggested talking to Juyn Lancaster, even though he had an uncomfortable meeting with her recently. Juyn, obviously stressed, tentatively agreed to see us.

"What's going on? Why are the doors locked?" asked Flush.

"I can't tell you. It's a personal matter."

"Well, it's feeding a lot of rumor and speculation. What did Rudy do?"

"I'm sorry, but I have to protect his privacy. I'd do the same for you."

"I doubt I'd do anything that would cause a lockdown."

"We're doing the best we can."

"But locking the backdoor to the loading dock is causing a lot of problems for vendors. The guy delivering laundry can't do his job. He's locked out. He can't get in. And another guy is trying to deliver some equipment for Surgery. He's annoyed."

"We're trying to keep everyone safe."

"But locking the doors isn't doing any good. Rudy has the keys to the doors. Who are we locking out? Everybody but Rudy. It's like we have a castle with a moat with no water and no crocodiles. Who ordered this lockdown?"

"I'm sorry, but I can't tell you," she replied. "Why not?" Flush persisted, as was his penchant.

"Company policy," her lame explanation was common whenever any administrator wanted to pass the buck. Poor Juyn was getting defensive. "We're doing the best we can," she repeated, an explanation we often heard from ill- equipped administrators without effective solutions.

Obviously, she and a small team of unprepared administrators were facing a situation that scared them into a quick, inadequately considered decision. I suspect that Sue City Sue, the safety director known for her conservative cautiousness and overreaction to all crises, was instrumental in calling for the lockdown. Juyn was coming to the uncomfortable realization that the lockdown wasn't their best move.

Flush asked, "Are we making sense?" Embarrassed, Juyn looked down and said, "Yes."

We left, and about five hours later, our new boss (4th in two years) called us all together. The eight members of the Environmental Services day shift gathered nervously in the department break room. Flush and I attended with interest and apprehension. This latest boss, Dora, an inexperienced 35-year-old, a very soft-spoken, nervous, and scared young woman with little leadership capacity, tried to mumble something about the lockdown being "over." When asked any questions, it soon became apparent that she knew no more than we did except that it was being called off. Even though she was Rudy's boss, they had kept her in the dark, too, as to Rudy's offense. And whether or not he was fired.

Many of us would have rejoiced were it so, as it was obvious to almost everyone except HR and Rudy that he wasn't much of a fit in a hospital. Even though he couldn't ride a horse, he would have fit in much better as a cowpoke out on some lonesome range somewhere the buffaloes roam.

Then, as an afterthought, she said (kind'a mumbling), "Oh, and it wasn't a lockdown."

Flush, mildly perturbed by the untrustworthiness and opacity displayed from the beginning, asked, "Well, what was it if not a lockdown."

Dora, totally unqualified in her position managing 8 disgruntled housekeepers and attendants (euphemism for janitors), said, "It is what it is. Ask someone else." Then she walked away to her cramped and disorganized office. I'm pretty sure the third month of her new job wasn't what she was expecting. Later, Flush and I discussed the denial of what was clearly a lockdown for about fifteen hours. Flush surmised that avoidance of the word "lockdown" was to minimize the damaging embarrassment should the local or regional media get the story. It probably wouldn't look so good if it became known that a long-term employee had gone "postal," causing danger that provoked a hyper- vigilant response. To hospital public relations, perception was more important than actuality. And they managed to bury a story that about 150 staff personally witnessed and discussed among ourselves for days. Rumors dominated every conversation, largely because the administration refused to divulge any details regarding Rudy's offense.

Rudy never came that day. I assume the admin told him he was unwelcome. We never learned what it was in the administration's version, with the word "lockdown" met consistently with icy scowls from administrators and supervisors. They discussed it as little as possible, usually hiding behind a shield of HIPAA and "That's personnel information. I can't say more." The media didn't cover the story, and we saw no drop in patient numbers or professional attractiveness. We were told that Rudy had been put on administrative leave, called LOA (Leave of Absence), on our department's daily schedule. And he was on LOA for six months, getting paid, we were told, to stay away, supposedly getting therapy and taking medication that would hopefully settle him down.

Eventually, his big scary day merged into the background, becoming less of a subject of conversation, replaced by "Is he coming back?" and then becoming "When's he coming back?" Joking, we all suspected that

Rudy was really the smart one; he was getting paid for sitting at home. We all envied him for that subsidized leisure. Later, HR director Juyn assured us that he wasn't dangerous in a mandatory group meeting. Then she told us he was due back tomorrow, and we were to be friendly and supportive. Most of us were wary but had no choice. It helped to trust the decision of the administration, but trust had been strained in the recent past, so most of us were on our guard.

And then Rudy returned, having been gone for six months. For years, he had been on the evening shift from 3:00 PM to 11:30 PM, but for some reason, our management had him come back on the day shift with no specific job assignment. He was to shadow Flush for a few days and then work with others on the day shift. Rudy spent five months on day shift, supposedly readjusting to janitorial work. He repeatedly said he needed to go back to his old job on the night shift because it paid $1.40 per hour more, which he claimed to need to survive. Then, after pressure from our manager and the HR director, Rudy changed his mind and decided to take a day shift position for $1.40 less per hour.

Flush was cautious about Rudy and saw him as a real possible candidate for going postal. Despite six months of therapy, Rudy was still a friendless loner, an angry man who acted as though the world were out to get him, and he liked, studied, and collected guns. Rudy's common reading continued to be a gun magazine which he read openly in our break room, totally unaware of his reputation, oblivious to the damage he did to his effort to fit in. But then, he did little or nothing to fit in. He didn't seem to care. His actions were as antisocial as they'd ever been. Personally, I was impressed that he would read anything.

Flush was well-read in psychology books. He regarded the human brain as the most important tangible entity in the universe, at least until extra-terrestrials were proven to exist and exceed human capacities. Consequently, psychology was his principal subject of study and consideration. One of Flush's influences was psychiatrist Dr. William Glasser, whose choice theory propounded that belonging was the most consequential psychological need for all humans. Glasser had written many books, some about education, and Flush had read many of them. Choice theory proposed that after our survival needs are met, everything humans do is to meet four psychological needs. They are belonging, power, freedom, and fun. Further, Glasser wrote that all his thousands of patients over 50 years had one thing in common—they all had trouble belonging. So Flush decided to try to help Rudy learn belonging.

Flush understood that for Rudy to succeed, he needed to learn how to be friendly and have a friend. Even one would be a constructive start. In spite of his heedful vigilance, Flush spoke to Rudy about this and tried, for several weeks, to befriend Rudy. But Rudy rejected all of Flush's overtures and avoided Flush, as he had always done. For some reason, fueled by paranoia, Rudy thought Flush was his enemy. This wasn't true, and in fact, Flush represented Rudy's best chance to develop socially. Flush tried to befriend Rudy, and occasionally, in the break room, Rudy reacted to Flush's antics. One time Flush wore a white wig, both forward and backwards, which made Rudy laugh, a rare event. But Rudy repeatedly shot himself in the foot, and Flush, over time, gave up his rescue efforts.

When Rudy and Flush passed in the hallways, which happened several times every day, Flush would say "Good morning" or "Good afternoon," to which Rudy, while looking down at the floor, would grunt something unintelligible in a barely audible volume. Poor guy, but he brought it all on himself, deserving the reputation as rejected weirdo held by anyone who had been there for more than a few months. His six months off while being paid did nothing for the sanity of the unhealed Rudy post- lockdown. To see Rudy was to draw a negative appraisal, as much for his unfriendly behavior as for his gnarly looks. He redefined scowl crow, achieving Olympic status in the sociopathic events. In his past pre-lockdown job, he was the night porter, doing the second shift. In that job, he moved all over the hospital pushing a big wagon, so was very highly visible, occasionally banging into walls on tight corners. I wasn't there, but I'm sure Rudy turned a few heads over several years. Not sure, but he seemed to manifest some of the characteristics of Asperger's. If so, it explained a lot.

About that time, Flush read an article in Esquire entitled, "Everything We Think We Know About Mass Shooters Is Wrong," by Tom Junod. A fascinating article, it described many of the recent domesticated lone wolf mass shootings that have terrorized the US, murders not motivated by Islamic extremism. A special unit of the FBI, called Critical Incident Response Group, had been formed to deal with these dangerous outcasts. A subgroup, Behavioral Analysis Unit 2, assesses threats by suspects before they do anything. It encouraged worried citizens to report anyone thought to be possible candidates for committing mass shootings. Flush copied this article and gave copies to Dora and Juyn. I read it with interest.

Juyn read it and took it to her boss. Together they decided not to contact the FBI's organization. When Flush asked why not,

Juyn said they didn't think Rudy was dangerous. Then why had they called a lockdown? She had no answer. I felt sorry for Juyn, as it was clear she was expressing an official opinion she was very unsure about. Her boss wasn't there. As usual, Dora did nothing but fret when she wasn't stewing. She was as useless as a turkey neck at a vegetarian banquet.

One lunch, in the break room with Rudy and me present, Flush put an enlarged (2 feet by 2 feet) Sudoku puzzle on the table. It was laminated, so if solved, using a dry-erase marker, it could be erased and used repeatedly. It was one he used to teach kids in the local elementary and middle schools. That day he was scheduled to teach kids in an after school program, so wanted to familiarize himself with that particular puzzle. Flush started solving the puzzle while Rudy, sitting across the table, surreptitiously observed. As Flush got about a third of the way through, Rudy, interested now in this solo activity, asked, "What's that?"

"It's Sudoku. It's a mental challenge."

"I don't like math. My brain doesn't work that way." But Rudy was making conversation, rare for him.

"There's no math. No addition, subtraction, division, none of that. It's all logic."

There was a long pause in the conversation while Flush solved and Rudy watched, having put down his magazine.

"Why did you put 6 there?" inquired Rudy. This was very encouraging; there was actually a subject that Rudy might like. Flush explained how he determined the 6 in that location and continued solving. Soon Rudy said, "Show me how to do it."

Flush explained the three simple rules that dictated every move. He emphasized the total accuracy required for every answer. "One mistake and you lose. The puzzle wins. It's a contest between you and a puzzle. Except the puzzle has already made all its moves. Success or failure depends only on you, the solver."

Flush realized later it was finally a way to engage Rudy. It turned out to be an activity that fascinated Rudy. After that, he and Flush spent almost every lunch doing enlarged Sudoku puzzles together, Flush teaching, Rudy excited he could do it. It was the only time I ever saw Rudy communicate with anyone for more than a sentence, at most. And he was a good learner, picking up beginner's tactics quickly. Soon he was doing more advanced Sudokus. He even bought a book of Sudoku puzzles. Sudoku became his best friend, one he could carry with him, puzzles done in his book. I saw Rudy working puzzles down by the San-i-Pack. Instead of reading "Conceal and Carry" magazine, he did Sudoku puzzles. I doubt he gave up his passion for guns, but now he had something else that was more acceptable socially.

Watching them work together was fascinating. I'm sure it was one of the rare occasions when Rudy collaborated with anyone. Slowly Flush earned Rudy's trust, which was necessary to develop a friendship. Flush became like a father to Rudy, as he was a grandfather to me. Our ages worked out that way. This was the breakthrough we'd all hoped for and had given up finding. Even Flush thought it was hopeless, pre-Sudoku.

Now he was optimistic. Flush managed to get reciprocal acceptance from Rudy, which had been absent for nine years as they worked in the same department doing the same job, Flush on the day shift and Rudy on the night shift, but with opposing attitudes and styles. One day Rudy opened up to Flush with the rest of us during lunch listening. Rudy ignored us. Out of nowhere, Rudy exposed his guarded personal life. "Jenny talked me into becoming a mackerel snapper."

"What's that?" asked Flush.

"It's Roman Catholic. You know, fish on Fridays. We got married in the church and it was important to her. So I took classes and converted. It made her happy. It's all the same to me." Rudy's new openness was encouraging.

For months during lunch, always over a big Sudoku puzzle, Rudy gradually gained trust and opened up. He even bragged about his hunting successes, always going for deer alone. Over six months, we all saw a new Rudy forming, at least when doing Sudoku with Flush. Finally, he learned some social habits; he came out from behind the wall of distrust that had held him hostage his whole life. He even started caring more about his appearance, combing his hair, trimming his beard, washing his clothes, and changing his socks. I imagine Jenny was thrilled.

Flush said he learned a lot about teaching kids, which he did off hours in local schools, by teaching Rudy. He realized that correctly solving Sudokus gave Rudy a rare experience of success, giving him healthy feelings of independence, confidence, and, ultimately, self-esteem. It also gave him temporary control over chaos, a rare experience in his powerless life. It provided an escape from his well-established feelings of confused inferiority. Finally, he could excel in something most other adults could not do. Psychologically, he walked taller, with growing pride in his competence, totally new to Rudy. He felt good.

One day Flush brought his iPad to work to show Rudy a valuable website. Called Enjoy Sudoku, this website delivered, for free, 14 new Sudoku puzzles every day of a wide variety of difficulties, ranging from total beginner's to frustratingly semi-impossible. It also had many convenient learning tools that helped solvers recognize new and often obscure patterns necessary for solving difficult puzzles. When he turned on the gadget for the first time, it showed a photo of Flush's beloved dogs. Immediately Rudy's eyes opened wider. "What's that?"

"Those are my two most reliable friends. I've had them for nine years. They're my only family now."

"What's their names?"

"Fox and Panda."

"They're really cute. I wish I had a dog, but Jenny doesn't like them and won't let me have one. She says they're dirty."

They continued their Sudoku lesson on the iPad, with Flush recommending Rudy get one to learn more Sudoku tactics. But they mostly did Sudoku together on the large laminated puzzles that Flush brought to work every day. Rudy's attitude towards Flush had changed, as did Flush's opinion of Rudy. Other than Sudoku, they had nothing much in common personally and never socialized during off hours, but that daily half-hour spent learning Sudoku bonded them, to Rudy's benefit. Flush, a natural teacher, didn't mind either, glad he could contribute to Rudy's belated maturity and satisfaction with life. It helped relax tension in EVS, too, though management didn't notice. Neither Dora nor Juyn or any higher-level administrator ever acknowledged Flush's successful therapy with Rudy. All EVS employees, housekeepers and attendants during the day shift, witnessed its progress, mostly during lunch break, and were congratulatory in our assessment, happily relieved by Rudy's gradual change. But that was typical of an administration that withheld praise but was quick with reprimands.

Chapter 17: Freebee War -- Battle #2

Then, as often happened with most changes, there was a new rumor; the Green Team was being reformed after dying when Liseanne retired. Further rumors stated that the new chairperson of the reconstituted Green Team was a very hefty female manager of the Pathology Laboratory named Rubby Tusk, who was about 65 years used. The most noticeable aspect of Rubby's physical appearance was a hair-do that could only have been designed by a sadistic poodle groomer. White hair, tightly curled, covered her broad head, but none hung lower than the tops of both ears. And below both ears hung tiny connected rings of silvery metal, looking like a rare form of inedible stringed dry pasta. A solid wrinkled neck held the mammoth ensemble above massive shoulders, usually hunched over a keyboard.

She had not been on the original Green Team, had no connections with environmental causes, knew nothing about recycling, and didn't care. She was also overworked and overseeing an underfunded staff of scientists who spent considerable time with eyes pressed against microscopes, viewing slides of patient blood, urine, poop, and tissue samples. They were the detectives of the medical system, trained to distinguish between different bacteria and viruses, cells and toxic intruders, or whatever else was useful for diagnosing a medical problem. It was a good place to be if you're into hematology. And tiny destructors. And introversion.

Flush was happy about the new Green Team, hoping to finally get some support for his seriously listing ship, and wanted to be a part of it. From there, he hoped, to speak persuasively, advocating his personal pet. Freebee might be cured!

I happened to be in the hall nearby when Flush went to Rubby's office and softly knocked on old pork chop's open door. She looked up from her desk and said, "Yes. What can I do for you?" She didn't know Flush, as his route didn't take him into the lab or her office. But subsequent events indicated she had been warned that he was involved with the Freebee Program.

"Have you got a minute or two?"

Reluctantly and mildly piqued, she said, "I guess so. What's this about?"

"I want to be on the Green Team. I was on it before."

This time, with more volume, more irritation, "No. There isn't room."

This surprised Flush. He wasn't aware, until that moment, that he was regarded negatively for his Freebee advocacy. But this rejection had obviously been predetermined and was a precursor of future opposition to both Freebee and its champion, Flush. "We already have someone from your department. Dora Kinney is on it now. Can't have two from the same department."

This was not the case with the first and sincerely "green-oriented" Green Team. It was open to anyone interested in recycling whenever appropriate. Both Flush and myself, from the EVS department, were on the previous Green Team. There was no explanation for Rubby's restriction. Nobody got paid, so the admin didn't care.

"But I'm actively involved with an important Green Team program. Nobody else is."

"You're too late. The Green Team is already decided. We don't need more members. Now I have work to do." Rubby turned back to her computer. Flush left, puzzled, surprised, and discouraged.

Flush had heard vague rumors of the Freebee Program's demise, but there was nothing substantiating these rumors other than the indifference and inactivity of Betsy Socutesome. And now, Rubby's rejection. Since Freebee had been straggling along for five years and was serving a purpose that benefitted the employees, Flush was reluctant to recognize the impending disaster. He was still laboring under the false idea that the administration would value something that served employees.

He left Rubby's office disappointed and confused. His exclusion puzzled him, but he wasn't a quitter when fighting for a good cause: Freebee, in his mind, deserved a defense, even if done alone. I would have backed him up had it come to that. But my heart wasn't really in this fight, for I saw it as a losing battle, so I hoped he'd recognize defeat. I still needed my job and had to be careful about rocking certain boats.

One day Flush came to work and saw a large amount of discarded furniture, their usefulness considered unworthy or, more likely, inconvenient. Easy to discard when not coming from the decision-maker's pocket. Some of it was unusable and dump-worthy, but a nice reclining patient chair, two fluorescent light fixtures, two office chairs, a wheelchair, and two mats should have been Freebee materials had there been room.

Flush took pictures on his iPad and emailed them to members of the Green Team and CEO Betsy Socutesome. They ignored this evidence, so about $300 worth of used office furniture was gone two days later, no doubt hauled to the landfill by a complicit engineer, Salty Dalty's minion.

Everyone's refusal to even respond to his email, which graphically recorded undeniable evidence of wastefulness, was totally unexpected by Flush. He (almost) thought they were supportive on the Freebee issue, though evidence to the contrary was mounting.

Flush was tenacious and continued his ill-advised campaign to save the Freebee. He had friends on the Green Team, so he invited them to walk and talk on the subject. He repeated the tour he had given to Betsy several months earlier, showing them the cramped Freebee

Room and the area outside the San-i-Pack. These four women followed and listened to his ideas and appeals for help but remained uncomfortably silent and unsympathetic. Their silence was surprising, considering their membership on the re-established Green Team, which was supposedly supportive of recycling. Among these four women were Dora Kinney, his current boss; Juyn Lancaster, new HR director; Louise Humffers, Employee Health nurse; and Phania Chriler, sweet but ineffectual.

He pleaded for support of a program two of them had created five years before as the members of the original Green Team. He suggested alternative locations and reminded them that the previous year they'd brought in five large rooms on wheels, stationed in our parking spaces that were used to teach the new computerized system requiring several weeks of clumsy adjustments. Those five office trailers are gone now. Why not bring one back and make it the Freebee Room?

Flush demonstrated the popularity of the Freebee Program by showing them the names of previous participants who had taken stuff home, a total equaling 1200 signatures and 50 sheets of paper. It wasn't really that many different people since many people had used the program many times. But over one hundred employees had benefitted from Freebee over five years. It documented Freebee's usefulness, and Flush was glad he'd saved those sign-out sheets.

The four women seemed impatient and not very receptive. Enthusiasm for Freebee was low. It might as well have been the program's funeral rehearsal. It was becoming obvious that the Green Team had already decided its fate but didn't want to tell and disappoint Flush. So they went through the motions to appease him.

Later Flush realized that the members of the reconstituted Green Team had been threatened by upper management to abandon their support of the Freebee Program. Morale was low, as was cohesion among employees, and fear of unemployment was high, so none of these previous advocates was willing to speak out in support of an obviously beneficial program. They had listened in silence, embarrassed by their collective reversal, but unable to be honest to Flush about it. Their common sense observed recycling being strangled, but with their integrity sacrificed in need to keep their jobs, the situation necessitated total silence and complicity in a corporation's murder.

Flush's enthusiasm and naive trust, along with his undeniable belief in recycling useful furniture and helping fellow employees, made him reluctant to recognize the impending death of his efforts.

***

About this time, Dora quietly spread the word that she was engaged and about to get married. She wouldn't tell anyone her fiance's name or the wedding date, at first, or the location. It turned out to be in her home town about 60 miles away. None of us were invited. There was no party, congratulatory celebration, bridal shower, or even a shindig that might suggest any good tidings. At the hospital, there was zero recognition of Dora's happy day. Some of us didn't even know it was going to happen or had happened. After the honeymoon, a trip to her parent's farm in Kansas, she returned to work. Except for a ring on her left hand, we could see no difference that one might mistake for elation or even cheerfulness or satisfaction. Nothing, the product of her bereft personality.

Soon, thereafter, Dora's front started to bulge, approaching, eventually, the proportions and heft of her rearness, and she admitted to being "preggers." That was farm girl for "expecting." Flush suggested, out of Dora's hearing, that the cosmic forces were just putting her growing bow into balance with her prodigious stern to help her get up out of a chair that had been supporting her heft for several long, strained hours. He described her work chair and her being in it as "being moored in port." He liked maritime analogies. She provided inspiration.

About a month before Dora was to go out on maternity leave, ErrorMark brought in Dora's replacement, a 50-year-old drill sergeant named Turdex Darkhart. His parents, named Turster and Dexlie, had combined their names and came up with a unique and never copied moniker that labeled our newest boss. Not from the very beginning, but within a week of his arrival, we had "The Turd" pegged as an authoritarian a**h***. His previous experience as a manager had been at a Trader Joe's down in the valley, a job he'd held for seven months. Trader Joe's was a large retail store commonly spread around California's larger cities. Turdex had never managed in a hospital and barely knew what EVS stood for.

Turdex was a big man, about 6'2". He dressed impeccably in dark pleated slacks, a unicolored shirt (never white), and a tie. He wore lots of jewelry, including earrings, finger rings, a gold necklace, and a finely buckled cowboy belt. The most noticed characteristic was a 2-foot-long blonde ponytail, held together at the top, against his head, by a rubber band. He was given the nickname "Fabio" by some women as a facetiously sarcastic tag that fit this visually flamboyant poser. I doubt they said it in front of him. He wouldn't have reacted tolerantly.

On Turdex's fifth day, Flush and I went to the office and introduced ourselves. Flush felt it was important to welcome all new hires, helping to establish a pleasant working relationship with someone with few friends.

He suggested I join him, so I did. The first thing I noticed was a red MAGA hat on a cluttered shelf. I knew it wasn't Dora's. During the five-minute conversation, Turdex stated he'd been in the army for three years. He never saw action and was stationed in the US the whole time. But "it had a big impression on me." He also explained his unusual name, a combination of his parents' names.

Flush mentioned that during the Vietnam War he was in the Peace Corps for two years in Somalia, having dodged the draft with no shame. "Like Iraq, Vietnam was a very bad war" was Flush's readily expressed opinion. Being politically correct was never his vice. Turdex stiffened perceptibly in opposition, indicating a visceral reaction he kept to himself, being professionally correct and aware of the need to avoid expressing personal opinions. But I realized later it was an undercurrent of malaise between them that fed their developing mutual hostilities.

Following our meeting, Flush and I had a short discussion regarding Turdex's red MAGA hat. This was during the 2016 presidential election when both of us, liberals, regarded Trump as a dangerous threat to our country. Flush was more experienced and saw sTRUMPet as a liar and conman with an alarming background in his destruction and disregard for justice, decency, and democracy. Neither of us ever thought he'd be elected. We both were astounded that so many American voters could be so blinded by his mendacity. And we were disappointed by the cowardice of most Republican'ts for refusing to recognize and denounce The Donald's repeated lies. We were worried that it reflected a dangerous warning about Turdex's leadership. He was either sadistic or stupid. Turns out he was both.

***

For years, we porters had been taking used batteries (mostly AA, AAA, and D cells) from the several soiled utility rooms placed there by nurses after minimal use. We took them to the Freebee Room and put them in a cardboard box, all mixed together in a jumble of transportable electrical potential. Most of them had some life left. Some were almost new, as some departments discarded them after only one use. They were popular and frequently taken.

Early in his job, Turdex told Charles, another attendant in our department who worked on floors, to remove the batteries from the Freebee Room. "They're a fire hazard, all mixed in together. They could combust."

A mild protest from Charles followed. He was too afraid to antagonize the new boss and thought he was being helpful. "We've been doing it that way for about five years and never had a fire."

"Don't ever question my judgement. Just do it."

"Where should I take them?" asked Charles.

"I don't know. Just get 'em out of there. It's dangerous."

Charles took the box of batteries to a metal container shed behind the San-i-Pack and dumped them in a large plastic barrel that contained about 400 pounds of other used batteries. Turdex never considered the possibility of a fire there, fueled by a very large quantity and variety of used batteries, many much larger than D cells. They were now in an outside trailer, equally fire hazardous.

Turdex's blindness to simple logic was later manifested often in his troubled regime. When Charles related this to us, we all thought, "Oh no, we got another loser." Our assessment proved accurate.

About once every three months, someone from a refuse company came and hauled the batteries away. Because the full barrel was so heavy, he needed a special wagon to transport them away. Turdex paid no attention.

***

Still unsure of Freebee's future, Flush went to Louise's office. She was the friendly, receptive Employee Health nurse who had always been kind and friendly to everyone. Flush liked her, and she liked him. He wanted some honest feedback from a member of the current Green Team, so he asked Louise, "What's happening with Freebee? I'm getting a bad feeling."

"It looks like they're trying to end it, though I don't think the decision is final. Yet.

There just isn't any money for it or a better place to put it."

"But it wouldn't take any money. It costs us nothing. Lots of people like it."

"The people upstairs don't see it that way. They think it's too much trouble, and we might get sued."

"How could we get sued?"

"Someone might fall off a broken chair, or any accident could happen with our discarded junk."

"One man's crap is another man's treasure."

"They just see it as trouble. They don't have a budget to hire a manager."

"That's ridiculous. I've been managing it for five years with about one minute per week, on average."

"I know, but they're really worried about being sued. And they think it needs a manager."

"Have they not heard of indemnity? There are at least five thrift stores in town. They all sell used furniture and they're not worried about getting sued. And they're selling for a profit. We're giving it away. We just need to post a sign waiving our responsibility."

Louise, in a sincere, comforting nurse's voice, "I'm sorry, but I can't do anything about it."

"Well, is it killed yet?"

"Not yet. But this is one patient I can't save. The official reason is they say they need the space for something else. Not sure what. As usual, they're vague."

"Yes. Transparency is not their penchant. They worship at the Font of Obscurantism. Keep us in the dark."

Flush, discouraged, but getting used to rejection, stood up and walked out.

One of the problems that irritated Flush the most was the decision made without his presence to make a defense. They totally denied him any say, any opportunity to present Freebee's need, popularity, and fulfillment of an ecological direction so popular in California. It was another example of the admin's hypocrisy, cowardice, and narrow-mindedness. Flush was rightfully irritated and expressed it to me over several days.

One week later, Flush received another phone message on his home answering machine from Dora. "There's a meeting with you in HR this Friday at 3:00. You will need a union representative." Then she hung up.

Again, stress enveloped Flush like a python crushing a lamb. Some people would handle it without any worry or sweat. Unfortunately, Flush wasn't some people. He cared too much about life and had an old-fashioned pattern of honest integrity. He couldn't imagine any infraction that would have earned him another taxing and tense trip to HR.

He called Dora and asked what it was all about. "You'll find out Friday," replied Dora, obviously pleased that she had been less (a lot less) than helpful. Her use of power-over leadership was becoming habit-forming for her. A bitch boss was hardening in the mold of bureaucratic revenge. I wondered what it was doing to the baby forming inside. Flush's (and mine) opinion of Dora was moving from pity to a disrespectful level of animosity that rivaled a fish's for a rusty hook.

Flush called his union rep friend, Marcy, and she agreed to accompany him to his "trial." He referred to it that way. They went together on Friday to HR.

This time Dora was already there, seated firmly, hands on a stack of papers on the round table of inquisition. The table had been moved away from the corner to accommodate her expanding girth.

The meeting was contentious as Dora and HR director Juyn verbally attacked Flush. "You're taking up everyone's time talking about Freebee. Leave it alone. It's dying and nothing can be done about it. Give it up. You're forbidden to talk to anyone about it during work hours. We can't get our work done."

Flush had never been subjected to censorship and restriction of free speech. He was shocked into incomprehension. "I just want some answers. Is Freebee dead?"

Either Dora or Juyn said, "We can't talk about it anymore. And that goes for you, too." While recounting this to me later, Flush couldn't recall which bitch had said what. He was badly shaken. He had never experienced the restriction of speech common in China and North Korea. His respect for NCMH fell through the floor. As did his heart.

"Why are you killing it? You both are on the Green Team. Don't you believe in recycling now?"

Juyn was uncharacteristically open for a brief moment. "We had to close it down because someone took supplies from the X-ray store room by mistake. They complained. We can't have that."

The X-ray department's storeroom was adjoining the Freebee Room, separated by shelving, floor to ceiling, in both store rooms. This made little sense because there was a large sign on the end of the shelves with an arrow pointing left, saying "X-ray Department," and another arrow pointing right, saying "Freebee Room."

Then she followed with, "We're not going to answer any more of your questions. Stop asking them."

But Flush wouldn't—couldn't—stop. "Whose decision was this?"

Both Dora and Juyn sat in silence. Long pause. Flush fumbled with his pen. Marcy sat in disbelief. Then Juyn said impatiently, "This meeting is over. Leave Freebee alone. You can't do anything about it. Just walk away from it. It's done." She was stern, the way a matron talks to a dependent ward.

Dora slid a piece of paper across the table. "Sign this," she commanded.

Flush read it during another long silence. Nobody moved. The animosity and obstructionism were like liquid cement filling the small room, stifling life, drowning them all in an atmosphere of unavoidable defeat and failure. Marcy reached over and touched Flush's arm. "Come on, let's go." Both Flush and Marcy stood and walked out, leaving the paper unsigned.

Flush was emotionally drained beyond the use of his formidable intelligence. He was in shock. His face was pale, his steps small and tentative. Marcy thought he might fall. He didn't. At least his body didn't. I saw him afterwards and almost didn't recognize him. Part of him, pale and slumped, had died.

Defeat, particularly in this way, was impossible for him to digest.

Two days after that fateful meeting, Turdex called Flush into his (and Dora's) cramped office. Dora wasn't there, her absence by design. In a suspiciously friendly way, he said, "I need you to sign this." He slid the paper over towards Flush. It was the same paper he had not signed two days earlier in HR. The paper said he was prohibited from talking about the Freebee Program during work hours.

Flush looked it over, signed it in an unintelligible scrawl (unlike his usually neat signature), and added, in writing, "I refuse to participate in the assassination of the Freebee Program."

Two days later, on his day off, Flush went to Louise, the Employee Health nurse, in her office. Nira, the new head of the Green Team (Rubby Tusk had quit after three weeks), was there too. She was a young active nurse assigned to 2 North, where cancer patients were treated. Flush knocked on the open door to Louise's office. "I just want to apologize for talking about Freebee the other day. I didn't mean any harm."

"You're not supposed to talk to us about that," demanded Nira.

"But it's on my day off," responded Flush. "It's only during work that I can't talk about it. And I'm just apologizing. Is it really dead?"

"Yes, it's dead."

"Why? Who killed it?"

"We can't talk about it. And you can't ask us." There was anger in Nira's voice.

"Ok. I'm gone. I just wanted to apologize. Please don't get me into trouble."

Flush trusted these two women. Both had been on the original Green Team when he was allowed on it. Both had been enthusiastic supporters five years earlier. Both had been friendly to him when they occasionally met, usually in the halls. Three days later, Flush was again summoned to HR, this time by a phone message. "This is Turdex, your new boss in EVS. You are to come to HR this coming Monday at 2 PM. Bring a shop steward." Shop steward was another term for union rep.

Flush, by now, had a pretty good idea what it was about. He called Marcy and got her to agree to appear and represent him. She seemed less willing this time. He explained what had happened, and she was less supportive, though she shared his enthusiasm for Freebee. But she had been through many other cases in HR and knew the futility of opposing this heartless bureaucracy. She knew the union couldn't help much, but she wanted to support Flush, knowing his mission was already beyond saving.

The following Monday, a day off for Flush, Marcy and Flush entered HR. This time Turdex, not Dora, was there with Juyn, head of HR. In an effort to bolster his case and maybe rescue Freebee, Flush brought all the sign-out papers from Freebee. There were about 50, from five years of activity. Each paper had 22 names on it, documenting a lot of employee participation and people who supported that giveaway scheme. Proof that Freebee was popular with the rank-and-file employees.

After everyone was seated at the round table, Juyn, from behind her desk, said, "You were told not to speak about Freebee again, and you did."

Flush felt confident in his defense. "I was not to speak about it during my work hours. I was off that day."

"It doesn't matter. Louise and Nira were working."

"I just went there to apologize for the previous time."

"But you asked about Freebee. We told you not to do that. You did anyway."

"You mean I can't even ask about it on my day off?"

"That's right. What have you got there?" She pointed to the papers documenting the five years of people taking Freebee items.

"This is proof the Freebee is popular with a lot of people here. There are hundreds of signatures here. I've been saving them for years."

Then Turdex spoke up. "Give them to me."

"They're mine. I've been collecting them for five years."

"They belong to the hospital. You were just the hospital's agent. They are official hospital documents. Turn them over."

Flush, defeated again, slid the papers across the table. "What are you going to do with them?"

"Turn them over to my superior," as he nodded towards Juyn across the room. Juyn smiled.

Addressing Juyn, Flush asked, "Can I have copies?"

"No. They're mine now. I'll handle them." Flush had the impression she would destroy the evidence of Freebee's popularity.

Then Marcy opened up. "Freebee is very popular. Lots of people use it and get valuable things there. We need it. Flush has done a good job keeping it going."

Flush added, "So I can't talk about it when I'm working and can't when I'm not working. When can I talk about it?"

Juyn answered, "Only during your lunch break."

"Am I the only person prohibited from asking about the Freebee Program?"

"You're the only person who is taking up our valuable time discussing an issue that has already been decided."

"Who killed it? And why?" pleaded Flush.

"This issue is resolved and finished. Stop asking questions that are not relevant."

"After Kennedy was assassinated, did they stop asking questions? Did anyone say, 'It's done, no point in any questions'?"

"This is not Kennedy's assassination. We told you. No more questions! You are being put on notice, and you're close to being terminated. You now have two strikes against you. This meeting is over." She turned away and began typing on her computer.

Flush and Marcy stood and walked out. In the hall, Flush said, "They're really hiding something. They are ashamed of killing it and want it to die unnoticed. They don't want any discussion because they know they look hypocritical. They are embarrassed, so no one will be held responsible for the decision to kill recycling. I can't trust this place anymore."

***

The summer was hot, but the hospital's air conditioning worked well and saved all of us from a nearly disabling discomfort. I'm sure Dora was thankful, if not much else, but she never expressed it to anyone. She just hunkered down in her cramped office more than usual. She stayed on the job, doing nothing, until shortly before the birth of her second child. Most of us felt sorry for her. I also felt sorry for her new husband.

Dora remained working until two days before the due date. She had her baby, another girl, on Halloween. Turdex was now alone and in charge. He was the worst I'd yet seen. He made no effort to hide his meanness.

Goodbye, Humankindness.

Chapter 18: Flush's Last Year

This is easily the most difficult chapter for me to write. I'd been working in EVS at NCMH for five years, during which I'd become a good friend of Flush despite our age difference. He "adopted" me as a grandfather, I being the grown grandson he didn't have. We spent many evenings watching sports and talking at his house. He was one of the few friends I'd made through my work. After he left NCMH, my life became empty and my job a chore that lost most of its psychological reward. I still got paid and did my job, but without any joy, ambition, or learning and with much anger that I had to repress. I suspect many other workers miss him, too, as he was unique and made many friends among the frontline employees and docs, nurses, and a few administrators with their integrity intact.

Have you ever had a cruel neighbor beating their dog or child, unable to interfere to stop it? That's how I felt regarding the severe mistreatment meted out to Flush during the last year of his employment. They made his life miserable, gave him very little work, and caused him stress and misery that was hard to witness. For the first time in his life, he started taking medication to combat his depression. I sympathized while unable to intercede, partially for lack of power but also from fear of losing my job.

Flush's last year was filled with "trials" in HR and many emails he sent in his defense to HR and management. As his union representative, I sat with him through many stressful meetings in HR. He often cc'ed me in his emails to management. I'm including here only a small portion of this battle, emails, and incidents that summarize this last miserable year.

Over the years, I watched Flush slowly becoming less involved with NCMH. When training me five years ago, he had an infectious, supportive, and zealous attitude, bringing humor and fun. But in the ensuing years, I saw his cooling interest and evaporating enthusiasm, resulting from his advancing age (he was 74) and the disintegration of the hospital's "Humankindness" towards employees. Our last boss, Turdex, was a determinant, causing Flush's forced and unwelcome retirement. Flush's body could handle five days a week easily, but his mind saw differently. Several times, he mentioned his need for more time to do things outside his job, activities that fed his soul, and making contributions that needed his talents and vision. It became clear to him that full-time hospital work was not the best use of his time. Part-time work was a better tempo for that time in his life.

But this story is not about the outside of the hospital. I'm trying to limit it to events inside NCMH, so nothing much here about Flush's other life passions.

***

To accurately relate the pressure cruelly put on Flush, I'll describe Turdex's authoritarian leadership style toward EVS employees, mainly Flush.

Turdex was in the back seat as long as Dora was there. His was a much stronger personality than Dora's, but she was the manager and he was the assistant, so he played the game and stayed quiet at first. But four months after he came, when she left on maternity leave, he became a T. Rex, running EVS as his personal regiment of quivering flunkies, totally at his cruel disposal.

He began by alienating all the overworked and unappreciated housekeepers, all women. Each department had a locked closet used by the housekeepers to store their carts and rags and soap and mops and buckets. These closets also stored regularly replaced supplies like paper towels and toilet paper. Only a few of us had keys, and the public never saw inside unless they happened to be walking by when the door was open. Each closet was about the size of an average home bathroom and contained several shelves and a sink with a drain. We used the faucet, with different twist-on soap containers, for different jobs on a variety of surfaces. Housekeepers also kept their personal items there, including clothing, snacks, purses, coats, and hats. Tidiness and cleanliness weren't high priorities in these closets, as no medical procedures took place there and housekeepers didn't have time to clean areas without such need and little public viewing. Time spent cleaning inside these closets was time not spent cleaning patient rooms, bathrooms, nurses' stations, break rooms, hallways, or sanitary equipment rooms.

But not after Turdex took charge. He commanded all shelves be removed from these closets and all floors, walls, and sinks be scrubbed by the housekeepers while ignoring their more important jobs, cleaning areas requiring sanitary conditions. And he wasn't reasonable, insisting on removing 45-year-old stains since cleaning these closets had never happened since the hospital opened 45 years before. Then he instructed no personal items should be present, not even a drink. And no rags, mops, buckets, or brooms could be stored there either, nor could toilet paper, soap, and paper towels, items which were commonly replaced daily. Housekeepers had to walk outside their departments to a common store room next to our break room to get these regular, frequent tools and supplies, wasting limited time.

The only things allowed in the closets were the cleaning carts. A cart was commanded to be set up in the approved manner, with the right equipment in the right place, and then a photograph was taken and distributed to all housekeepers. They were instructed to maintain their carts exactly like the photo at all times. This prohibited any individual preferences and no innovative improvements, all from a man who had zero experience in housekeeping and cleaning in a hospital. He was strictly enforcing unrealistic rules set by previous management (Bossella's) that had grown lax under Dora's slack leadership. Everyone in EVS resented this.

One housekeeper bought a Christmas present for her colleague and put it in her cleaning closet. Turdex found it on one of his recurring inspections that were becoming routine and took it to his office without saying anything to anyone about it.

The missing present was a mystery for two days until someone saw it in Turdex's office. After a stern lecture in front of everyone, Turdex returned it to its owner, who was almost in tears. Her new offense was insensitively handled in a way that angered the EVS staff. We all continued to dislike and fear The Tyrannical Turd. We weren't used to a boss so cruel and militaristic, even worse than Bossella. It didn't work with us civilians.

***

Turdex's despotism extended outside our department. A nurse in Surgery told me of an encounter with Turdex that had them outraged. Each department had its own break room, where employees could relax on breaks, enjoy friendly conversations, store their lunches in refrigerators, heat them in microwaves, and eat. The Surgery break room had a TV and opened into two locker rooms, men's and women's. Outside staff could enter if they had business with surgical staff. It was generally a friendly, casual, and stress-free retreat from the frequent emergencies that comprised most days in this very active department. We all thought highly of these surgical professionals and showed them well-deserved respect.

One afternoon, a nurse's 13-year-old son was doing his homework quietly in the Surgery break room, waiting for his mom's quitting time. Kids weren't often there, but occasionally, they would harmlessly wait for their parents, and nobody ever objected. The other two people there, a nurse and a technician, were reading quietly.

Then Turdex entered. He was outside his territory and had no authority outside EVS, but that didn't stop him. He was the self-appointed roving "sheriff," not used to limits placed by hospital protocol. He approached the kid. "What are you doing here?"

The poor kid was stunned into overwhelmed stuttering. He'd been there many times before, never challenged. "I'm waiting for my mom," he managed to explain.

The nurse, very surprised by this unusual intrusion, finally spoke up. "He's ok. He's May's son. We're with him."

"Well, he can't be here. This is no place for kids. He's got to leave. Now!" He turned immediately and exited, but not before having made three enemies, with more later when hearing this egregious breach of authority.

The nurse said to the kid, "Stay right there. That guy doesn't know what he's talking about. Just go back to your homework and try to forget it." I doubt the kid successfully removed the experience from his memory. Encounters with Turdex were universally unkind and unforgotten, as his reputation slowly spread like acne on a prom queen's face.

**

Then, there were the issues with keys. All of us in EVS had numerous keys to the many locked doors. When hired, I was handed a large ring with about 20 keys. They had been held by a predecessor who died from cancer before I came. I never counted them and only used seven. Taking the unneeded off the ring would have been too much trouble, so I didn't. Everyone took their keys home and was responsible for bringing them to work. This had been the functioning process for many years without incident.

We never thought much about it, as it was never a problem. I guess there may have been petty theft, but nothing significant. Nobody would risk their job for a roll of "hot" toilet paper. And there were cameras in every hallway, suppressing nefarious options.

But all those extra keys bothered Turdex and he took action. At a meeting, he made us all turn in our keys. Then he made us write down the number of each key we needed. Yes, keys were numbered, and only a couple of engineers could copy them. The next day, we came to Turdex's office, one by one, and were given the exact keys we each needed for our specialized jobs. It wasn't all. Turdex had installed a metal box on the break room wall that held everyone's keys overnight. We were no longer allowed to take our keys home at night, and if we forgot, there were embarrassing reprimands. This box was locked; its key was in another smaller box with a combination that only we knew. This caution was unnecessary but made us more professional. And stressed. And occasionally, the key used to unlock the big key box disappeared, taken by some disgruntled EVS employee. This number was rapidly increasing with Turdex's obstructive despotism.

Another incident involving keys highlighted Turdex's dishonesty and incompetence. One day, we ran out of folding paper towels used in bathrooms to dry one's hands. This was a big problem, as paper towels were needed in every restroom in the hospital, which were (I'm guessing now) about 120. In addition to restrooms, they were required in every patient room and hallways in every department. These towels were the only way to dry our hands; there were no air-blowing machines.

It was Turdex's job to order supplies, a task for which he was untrained and ill-fitted. Turdex claimed he had ordered 26 cases of these multi-fold paper towels, each case containing 10 boxes, each box containing 4000 towels. This would last us about one month. He then claimed they had been stolen from our supply room, which was near his office and our break room. Since all EVS employees had keys to that room and, because of his new restrictions, often entered during our regular work activities to pick up a variety of supplies (far more than just paper towels), we were suspected of the theft. At least by Turdex's reckoning.

For a stressful few days, we were all interrogated in HR, one at a time, to determine who had stolen the towels. We knew this was silly and a waste of time and morale, but Turdex insisted and controlled the questioning, which determined nothing.

Nobody confessed. Big surprise. Someone contacted the man in charge of ordering all supplies for the whole hospital; he was nicknamed "Moose." That wasn't his real name, but how everyone knew him. He worked down on the loading dock and received supplies from vendors, and then he and his crew delivered them to departments around the hospital.

These paper towels always came to our supply room about every month. Moose looked at his records and discovered that those towels had not been ordered the month before and so had not been delivered. Turdex was covering up his own mistake by blaming us.

When confronted with this information, Turdex swore he had ordered them and someone must have tampered with his computer. This was extremely unlikely. And it was equally unreasonable to believe one of us had snuck in and loaded 26 cases of paper towels into a truck to sell them while risking his job. Besides, there was a camera mounted in the ceiling outside the supply room that would have recorded the theft. This camera recorded nothing larcenous. However, some administrators had become paranoid and saw thievery everywhere, so this fit into their paradigm; they supported Turdex's theory.

Turdex maintained his innocence and blamed us. So he demanded we all turn in our keys to that room, a counterproductive requirement that angered us and slowed us down from our hectic pace of cleaning and delivering common basic supplies. After that, Turdex put one key (to the supply room) in our break room, where we had to sign it in and out whenever we needed supplies.

If you've ever stepped in a pile of recently planted dog poop on your determined way to a formal occasion, you can recognize our collective reaction to this unreasonable and unnecessary remedy. Turdex was cementing his opposition from most of the workers he depended upon to run EVS with a degree of happy efficiency.

***

Flush was the oldest of 857 employees and valued time more than money. He told his friends he expected to live to 100 or more, and he had a lot to do before graduating upstairs.

It wouldn't get done if he worked full-time. At least, that's what he told himself.

He had used up all his PTO, having taken off one day out of five assigned to his full-time job of 40 hours per week. He worked a four-day week for about eight months before having to change something. During that day off, he usually did volunteer work teaching Sudoku to kids in local elementary schools, work he valued, work original to him, work that made important differences in the psychological growth of kids between 6 and 12 years old.

Since working four days a week was no longer possible, his choices were: going back to a schedule of five days of work a week (giving up his volunteer work with kids) or going to per diem (less days per week), a major reduction after 13 years of full-time work. Our contract gave full-timers many benefits, including health insurance and matching retirement funds. Also, seniority in job selection. Per diems had none of these. Still, burned out with destructive and tyrannical leadership, and a cruel suppression of communication, Flush chose to go per diem. He didn't realize the danger of this decision. It proved to be decisive.

Over the years, he had seen other per diems, almost always the newest hires, be treated well by caring managers. Previous managers worked with per diems, arranging their schedules and jobs to fit the workers' requirements. Flush expected the same considerations for himself. He never saw the chainsaw of mismanagement coming. Turdex and Dora were the new sheriffs in town, and they didn't give a plumber's butt crack for any consideration given to per diems. And they had a particular hatred of Flush. It was sad to watch.

Flush agreed, in HR, to go per diem in October, about three weeks before Dora left on maternity leave. Per diems were always used to fill in when full-timers were off, either as scheduled or on vacation or illness. Though he didn't realize it at the time, voluntarily giving up full-time and going to per diem proved to be a very fateful decision, making his future employment far less enjoyable than before.

At first, everything went ok with Flush. He preferred working on weekends, which was good for management because most full-timers wanted off on weekends. This gave him weekdays off, which was when his school volunteering was done. So Flush was given work two days a week, Saturdays and Sundays, which was good for both sides.

Another reason Flush wanted weekends is that there are few managers in the hospital on weekends. He had learned to avoid a few people, scowl crows, most of whom were managers or superintendents. Dora was gone for four months while having her second baby, which left Turdex in charge. He and Flush clashed, and Turdex was off weekends. Tranquility by avoidance.

They needed someone on weekends to do the linen job when Luna was off. This had been a comfortable and efficient process for many years. Our housekeepers were used to this. Luna and I trained Flush to do weekend linen; after three days, he was ready to fly solo. Since I did it one way and Luna did it another way, he was taught two processes. I don't think it confused him too much.

There were at least two ways to deliver linen. These two processes became a source of disagreement that adversely affected Flush's job. There was my way, learned, with significant adjustments, from Fude three years before. And Luna's way, which was less efficient and more work. Luna and I did our different methods without strain. We disagreed but avoided the issue since we worked different days. As long as the job got done, nobody complained. That went on for about three years. It didn't become a problem until Flush started doing the weekend linen job, and Turdex decided to make his life difficult.

My way to record delivered linens used the spreadsheet I had created. It was rejected by Luna, who preferred writing on 20 little yellow scraps of paper called Post-its. She resisted any progress unless she thought of it. Later, Turdex prohibited her from using the yellow scraps of paper and insisted she record deliveries on 26 pages in a three-ring notebook that was clumsy to use and took extra time finding the right page to record on. Luna might have reconsidered her opposition to my simple, easy, one-page spreadsheet, but she was too deeply opposed to me doing linen, so she followed Turdex's flawed 26-page accounting system.

She and Turdex usually worked collaboratively. It was Luna's pattern to brown nose every new manager. No surprise; she became a well-earned recipient of Turdex's favoritism.

Another aspect of my method is that it cuts about an hour off the job done by Luna's method. Like Fude (Luna's predecessor), the first thing in the morning, I went around the whole hospital recording (on my spreadsheet) exactly what each department needed to fill their stations. At the same time, on this first trip, I delivered bath blankets (the most popular and bulky linen item).

Luna didn't do this basic research before delivering; she never knew exactly what each department would need. Instead, she loaded our motorized wagon with a variety of the most used linen items, hoping she had everything she would need to fill each station. She was about 80% correct this way but usually had to return with items a department needed that had not been delivered. My method was exact. Luna's way was built on probability, but it was not accurate regarding quantities, so she had to correct her estimates. She made more trips than I did to do the same work.

When Luna and I taught Flush how to do linen, we each taught him our process. Flush recognized the superiority of my method and decided to deliver my way. With my spreadsheet.

He made the analogy with two other departments, pharmacy and dietary. Both departments know ahead of delivery exactly what needs to be delivered. Pharmacy didn't load up a wagon with a wide variety of pills and then go to each department to distribute them. Dietary didn't fully load a wagon with generic dinners and then take them around to be distributed. Both departments knew what was needed and delivered that much.

Luna's system did the opposite. Flush knew the difference.

Everything went well with Flush doing linen on weekends. He made a couple of small mistakes, but nothing worth mentioning or complaining about. It was scheduled regularly, and the battle between Turdex and Flush went cold on a shelf collecting dust. For four months, Flush was happy he'd made the decision to go per diem.

***

He lost his benefits, including a very inclusive health insurance coverage that came with full-time hospital employment. But he was old enough for Medicare, whose coverage wasn't nearly as good and cost more. Also, his mostly good health wasn't too demanding, so he rarely used it.

To get Medicare, he had to jump through a bunch of legal hoops caused by other indifferent, out-of-sight, incompetent bureaucrats. Medicare thought Flush still had Anthem Blue Cross health insurance, as nobody from the hospital told Medicare he was no longer covered by them. And Medicare thought Flush still had a disability, which he had four years earlier with a rotator cuff problem. So, both issues prevented him from getting Medicare; the hospital, Medicare, and his primary care doctor's billing department all thought it was his responsibility to fix it. Flush made many calls to all three bureaucracies, all of whom passed the buck with practiced efficiency, taking 10 months before it was fixed. On these calls, he addressed robots 4/5 of the time and solved nothing. One-fifth of the time, he spoke with a human and made progress straightening out the confusion not caused by him. This was another example of the major destructive dysfunction common in our healthcare system.

***

Four months after going per diem and starting his weekend linen delivery job, Flush got a stress-producing call at home on a Friday afternoon. It was unexpected and brusque. "This is your boss, Turdex. Be in HR Monday morning at 8."

"What's this about?"

"I'll tell you Monday. Be there."

"Do I need a union rep?"

BZZZZZZZ (busy tone). Turdex had hung up.

Being summoned into HR was never good news and gave Flush a weekend of worry. He couldn't think of anything he'd done, but that never stopped this management from concocting some calumny. Flush performed his job that weekend, delivering linen and befriending visitors and patients when he had the chance. And he made that chance, making friendly small talk with worried people in the halls, usually waiting outside a relative's room while a doc or nurse did a medical procedure or a CNA changed the patient's clothing or bedding.

Monday morning came. Flush and I, as his union rep this time, entered HR with some uncertainty and trepidation. Turdex was there, as was HR director, Juyn Lancaster and our union leader, Carrie Martina. We sat down at the round table. "Why am I here?" Flush asked, perplexed.

"I've been watching you and have some concerns," pronounced Turdex authoritatively.

"Were there any complaints?" asked Flush.

"No, but I called someone in Emergency and you hadn't delivered there. She paged you and then you went."

"I was on my way there when she paged me. I didn't miss Emergency. I did it."

"You would have missed it if I had not called and had you reminded."

"How can you say that? You weren't even here."

"I was at home, but my call prevented a problem."

"That's nonsense. I don't need your call to tell me the job. I was heading towards Emergency when I heard the overhead."

"Well, without me, you would have blown it. I don't want to have to keep watching you or anyone else."

Then I spoke up. "Well, don't. He doesn't need your help. He knows what he's doing. And when you're home on weekends, how can you watch him?"

"I'll be watching you, too. I've heard things I don't like." Having attracted Turdex's animosity, I, too, became worried about my job. Not sure being a union rep was smart for my "career" at NCMH. So far, he hadn't persecuted me like he did Flush, but I realized that could change quickly. I'd grown to value the job, largely due to Flush's influence.

Carrie Martina, who ran our union from her office in Sacramento, sat and said nothing. We soon learned this was her pattern. She never helped us, never defended us, and seemed to be in the pocket of HR. She seemed nice but useless. Now I realize there was an unwritten agreement between our union and the hospital, which weakened any defense a responsible union rep would have given us.

The meeting was over in ten minutes. Both Flush and I were pissed. This guy was really becoming tough to take. Though I was scheduled to work that Monday, Flush wasn't. He had to come into HR on his day off. We weren't there long enough for him to clock in and out, so he didn't get paid.

The bigger problem was the anxiety the call and meeting gave Flush. After years there, he wasn't used to the cruel treatment he was receiving. But there seemed no recourse. Turdex's superiors seemed to think he was what EVS needed. They thought previous managers had been too easy with us, and some housekeepers and attendants took advantage. This was true in a few cases, but not with Flush (or me). EVS had always performed well when managers led with us having a voice. Taking away our voice and independence backfired completely with the civilian staff of old housekeeping women and attendants, all men experienced in their jobs and resistant to cruel leadership.

***

About a month later, on a Friday, Flush got another message from Turdex on his home phone. "Be in HR next Monday at 3 PM. You'll need a union representative. And I'm canceling your work this Saturday and Sunday. Have a good day."

Flush was in shock. He spent two days wondering what he'd done wrong again, stressing out, falling into a pit of rusty angst. He called me and asked me to be his union rep. I could hear the pressure in his voice. Of course, I said "Yes."

That Monday, we went together to HR. Juyn Lancaster was there and asked us to sit around the round table. We did, and Flush asked, "What's this about? Turdex didn't say in his message."

"He'll tell you when he gets here. He had a meeting until 3, so might be a little late." We waited in silence for ten minutes while Juyn typed on her computer. Then Turdex arrived in a hurry, out of breath. He sat quickly.

Juyn said, "This is a problem for Mr. Darkhart to explain." She turned to Turdex.

Turdex rustled through some papers. He looked up. "There have been complaints about your work. I have to address them."

Flush was surprised, as was I. "Who complained?" asked Flush defensively, very suspicious.

"I can't say to avoid a retaliatory response by you."

"How many complainers were there?" asked Flush.

"Well, only one, but it was repeated several times."

"What was the complaint?"

"Your linen delivery system just doesn't work."

"What doesn't work about it?"

"She didn't say. But you can't use it anymore."

Both Flush and I knew immediately that it was Luna who complained. We also knew the system I devised and taught Flush worked well. I had been using it successfully, without complaints, for three years. Flush had been doing it for five months without complaints. The whole objection was Luna's subjective complaints to men working in the linen room. She now had a manager's ear on this, a manager who hated Flush and wanted any excuse to punish him.

Then I spoke up. "There's nothing wrong with that system. In fact, it's much better than the one Luna uses. You need to compare the two methods, objectively, and you will see."

Then Turdex replied. "Don't tell me how to do my job. I'm the manager and you aren't. I suggest you shut up and stay out of this. It's between Flush and myself."

Flush said, "He's my union representative and can speak in my defense if he wants." He looked at Juyn Lancaster for confirmation. She said, "I'm staying out of this. It's between you two." She looked back and forth between Turdex and Flush.

436

Then Turdex continued. "I have a par-based system that everyone has to use. Everyone has to do it the same way."

Thinking he had a new system, Flush said, "Then you'll have to teach it to me."

"Ok. Next Monday morning in the linen room. So you can't work linen until you learn the new system. I don't have time to teach it until next Monday, a week from today."

Then Flush replied, with anger, "So I miss two more days of work? I can't work next weekend?"

"That's right. I don't want you doing your system anymore. There were complaints and everyone must do it the same way."

"Well, let me do porter. I've been doing that for five years."

"No. I have another per diem scheduled for porter this weekend."

"Who?" Flush asked.

"None of your business!" came the terse answer.

"Well, I should have seniority over all other per diems. They've been here two or three months. I've been here 13 years."

"There's no seniority with per diems. You lost your seniority."

There was a long pause. All eyes were on Flush. Juyn Lancaster said nothing, not correcting Turdex about per diems having no seniority. I hated seeing Flush so bullied but could do nothing, and Juyn Lancaster was as useless as socks on a shadow. She sat. She could do that as well as anyone. Behind her desk.

Flush asked, "This par system. Have you done it with linen?" Flush knew that Turdex had never done linen himself, so probably didn't understand the details of linen delivery. Turdex probably knew, in general, something called a "par system" but had never applied it to this specific purpose. A new manager, he'd probably seen it in some beginners' manual of management.

Turdex fired back, "I don't have to explain anything to you. I know the par system works. Be in the linen room next Monday at 7:30. And you'd better be ready to learn. No questions asked. You understand?" His tone was demeaning and condescending. After slamming his notebook on the table, he stood up quickly and left the room.

Juyn seemed embarrassed but said nothing while he was there. After he left, she said, "I can't do anything. He's the manager and can do whatever he wants. We can't second guess our managers. I'll try to be at your training also, just to maintain order. I see there's tension between you three."

Flush was shaken up and demoralized, as was I. But he lost another weekend of work. We couldn't help thinking this was Turdex's tactic to punish Flush. It worked.

Flush was beginning to regret going to per diem. He wanted less work than full-time but didn't realize it was a license to be mistreated the way Turdex was drawing emotional blood. Previous managers, most practicing *power with* rather than *power over*, worked with the per diems and usually managed to solve problems cooperatively.

I knew if I had the chance to compare my delivery and accounting system with Luna's to an impartial panel, they would see the superiority of my system. But I never got the chance. Luna, who always buttered up all new managers, including Turdex and Dora, was a favorite, so she always got her way. At least Flush saw that my system worked better, so he used it.

I doubt Turdex realized he was punishing far more than Flush when canceling his work that weekend. Many housekeepers became more aggrieved by Turdex's tyranny. When Flush didn't deliver linen on weekends, and nobody replaced him, it put extra work on each of the departmental housekeepers. They were already busy cleaning patient rooms, toilets, nurses' stations, break rooms, and halls. Having to bring their own linens up from the linen room in the basement to the linen stations upstairs put additional burdens on their limited time. This extra task took between 1/2 hour and 60 minutes for each department, time they didn't have to do a task that wasn't on their job descriptions.

They complained but were not heard. "Just work faster," was the solution proposed by Turdex. That was the common solution to every complaint regarding overworking conditions. It required no work or understanding from an incompetent, cruel, and disinterested manager. "Thanks," thought the housekeepers, with appropriate undeniable sarcasm. And then he complained they weren't getting their work done.

At the end of that meeting, after Turdex had left, Flush asked Juyn if they could meet alone. She consented and set up a time and date. The following Tuesday afternoon, Flush came to her office with a significant award he'd received.

The previous HR Director, Liseanne O'Donnell, who'd been much friendlier to employees and respected Flush's unique contributions, had held an annual awards ceremony called *Values in Action*. This was before Diggery Wealth came in and cancelled all awards. There were five categories of consideration, and about a dozen employees each year were recognized. Most nominees were doctors, nurses, CNAs, and managers. It was rare for anyone from EVS to be recognized. But Flush was nominated for all five categories: Collaboration, Dignity, Excellence, Justice and Stewardship.

Liseanne, having observed Flush's many original contributions over many years and his success relating to patients and visitors, extremely rare among other porters, recognized these with this award. He was proud of this and had hung the plaque on the wall of his living room.

He showed it to Juyn, who was unaware of Flush's award. Flush hoped it would earn him some support with this new HR director, who seemed mostly overwhelmed and uncomfortable, still learning the HR ropes. She looked at the plaque, paused, and said, "This was before my time. It means nothing to me." Flush left, disappointed, with the feel of a noose tightening around his increasingly exposed neck.

***

The following Monday saw Flush, Turdex, Luna, and Juyn Lancaster meeting in the linen room. It soon became obvious that Turdex's par system was the same way Luna had delivered linen for many years. At Turdex's command, she described how she loaded the delivery wagon with a certain number of flat sheets, contour sheets, bath blankets, an assortment of different gowns, diapers, pajamas, blue pads, towels, wash clothes, and a few other items. She showed Flush where each item went on which shelf in the wagon.

Flush asked Turdex, "How is this your new par system?"

"This is the system that works, and everyone must use it. Period. I can't have people running around doing crazy things and getting complaints. Just pay attention and learn."

This was unnecessary, as Flush had been taught this several months ago and rejected it as inefficient. There was nothing "par" about it. Turdex just wanted it to look like it was his idea. Flush and Juyn saw through that, but Juyn's hands were self-tied, and Flush pretended to pay attention. He remained silently out of trouble for most of the next hour, occasionally looking at Juyn, who always looked away.

After the wagon was loaded, Turdex gave a speech, telling Luna to take a picture of the loaded wagon. This picture would then be placed in the notebook so "anyone can duplicate this par system process." He went on to proclaim the necessity of systems that could be duplicated (he was very proud that he'd mastered that big word and used it repeatedly in this lecture) so new hires could learn it fast. With every job, he wanted to cut back on training, so "this duplicable system is a big improvement. Anyone can follow the picture."

Once the wagon was loaded, the four of them set off down the hall towards the Emergency Department, which was also on the basement floor. It took them about two minutes to get there. I was porter that day and happened to be in ED pulling soiled linen. I was able to witness the following unpleasant transaction.

The ED was now secured with two large doors in the hall that swung open when certain people, all registered staff members, put their index finger on a pad to be read and approved. Then the doors opened and they were allowed to enter. This security was new, about one year old, and not necessary before.

Turdex approached the station and put his index finger on the pad. Nothing happened. Irritated, he tried his thumb. Still nothing. Then he tried the index finger of his other hand. No reaction from the doors, stubbornly closed tight. "Dammit! Nothing works around here!" He turned to Luna. "You do it."

She put her finger on the pad and it opened immediately. They entered the ED in silence.

Except for Turdex (we all enjoyed his failure and frustration), this fingerprinting entry was usually not a problem if you weren't wearing gloves. Linen delivery didn't require gloves. But us porters did, so I always tore the fingertip off one glove whenever I came to doors that could only be opened this way.

In the last few years, the administration had instituted many locked doors around the hospital, opened with keys, punch codes, or fingerprints. I think the recent terrorist attacks by deluded lone-wolf Americans or Islamic extremist jihadis (violating the Qu'ran by committing suicide) have had a paranoid effect on many hospitals and places open to the public. But an attack could happen. Even at little old NCMH. Remember Rudy's lockdown? Except Rudy's finger would open every door.

One of three linen stations in the ED was in the hall between two large rooms that held patients on beds. Luna drove the electric motorized wagon (actually, she walked alongside it with her finger on the "forward button") opposite the station, leaving a space of about three feet between them. This was enough to work in and didn't leave much distance to move the various linens. We all did it the same way.

Luna unloaded the flat sheets onto the middle shelf where they belonged. Then she took out from her jacket pocket a small yellow pad of paper, Post-its, and wrote *ED; 45fs* on it.

"What's that?" asked Turdex, perturbed.

"It's the number of flat sheets I delivered today," answered Luna.

"No. I don't want you writing on those tiny papers anymore," directed Turdex. It surprised Flush and me that Turdex would disagree with his favorite, Luna. Still, Flush was glad to see their discord, pleased that he wasn't the only one with Turdex problems.

"Well, how am I going to record the deliveries?"

"You'll have to write them in the notebook. Doing it on those tiny yellow papers means you have to copy the information into the book later. That wastes time and risks making a mistake. And you could lose those papers."

Luna, a little irked, said, "I've been doing it this way for about 20 years and never made a mistake."

"You'll just have to change. No more yellow pads. Go back to the linen room and get the notebook."

While Luna returned to the linen room, Flush said, "Please look at Frank's spreadsheet recording system. It's simple to learn and easy to use." It wasn't in Flush's nature to remain silent when a problem's solution was readily available.

"No. I've seen it and don't like it. The colors are confusing."

One of the better features of my spreadsheet was the colors. Each horizontal row was a different color so the eyes could go across the page and stay in the same row. This avoided problems and made data entry more accurate. So, Turdex's objection was counterproductive. About four months before, he had only looked at it for five seconds, rejecting it because Luna didn't like it and had said so to him. Luna had inspected it for four seconds before rejecting it because it was my idea. And she and Fude had quickly rebuffed all my ideas without any consideration. Linen was their territory; no male intruder was coming in there and making suggestions, even if they were improvements!

While Luna was gone for three uncomfortable minutes, we waited in silence. I left for one minute to get a drink. Turdex was so angry and distracted he didn't notice my presence, not doing my porter job. But I was interested in this training, too, so maybe needed to be there.

When Luna returned with the notebook, she turned to the page for Emergency Department, found the row for flat sheets, and wrote "45" in the column for Monday.

This notebook was very clumsy and difficult to use while moving around the hospital to 22 different locations, each with a separate page. To use it, one had to find a flat place to put the notebook, sometimes unavailable in the hallways where linen went, then find the page for the location where you had just arrived. Then you had to write the correct number (e.g., 45 flat sheets) in the correct row under the correct day. Each page had room to write the deliveries for that department for seven days. Once you got used to this tedious process, it wasn't difficult; just time-consuming and annoying. My spreadsheet had all the same information on one page (that day's sheet) that Turdex's notebook had on 22 pages. And mine was on an easily stored clipboard that hung on a hook on the front of the wagon. But we couldn't use it now.

Dumb.

Luna began moving each set of linens from her wagon to the shelves in the ED station, writing down the quantities of each type. She talked while she made the routine transfers, explaining where each separate group went on which shelf at a normal pace, something she (and Flush and I) had done many times.

When she was halfway done, Turdex interrupted her. "Let me show you." Turdex charged into the cramped space between the wagon and linen station; Luna exited, moderately miffed but saying nothing. She looked surprised since he'd never done it before.

Turdex began rapidly shifting blue pads from the wagon to the station. Then contour sheets. Then towels. Then wash clothes. He moved at a frantic pace that would make a juggler look like a house plant.

He didn't understand (or seem to care) that the locations in the linen station for each linen item were specific and organized; everything had its assigned place on the shelves, which he ignored. Otherwise, it's hard for nurses in a hurry to find the exact linen they need. He just stacked the linen anywhere there was an empty space. And he didn't bother to write down the quantities of each item he delivered. He really did about half the job poorly, but, in his defense, he only took half as long.

We all watched in amazement, afraid to interfere. Luna was shocked by his misplaced casualness and relaxed disorder, but nothing surprised me. Flush was smiling, realizing Turdex was making a fool of himself. Juyn observed in silent disapproval. Only Turdex thought it was a good teaching moment.

When the shelves were full and could hold no more, he stood up and said, "That's the way it should be done. It shouldn't take five minutes. Two minutes is about right. I have an important appointment at eight. Luna can take over from here."

Then he left hurriedly. We all watched him walk down the hall and try to activate the security doors with his finger. It didn't work again, so he reversed course and walked into and through the Emergency Department. We were relieved by his exit.

Juyn said, "Well, I've seen enough." Then, to Flush, "I hope you can figure this out. I'm not needed here anymore, and I have a busy day." With that, she left, too.

Luna was upset but said nothing. She began rearranging the linen on the shelves, counting them, and entering the numbers into Turdex's book. It took her a long time to correct his errors; she was visibly shaken and irritated, barely concealing her anger with troubled silence. With any other people, she would have expressed vigorous disapproval, but not to Flush or me. She didn't want to interfere with the good relationship that many months of brown-nosing had earned her. And she didn't want us to observe the strain in their relationship. But we saw it clearly, pleased that another employee had problems with that despot. General Turdex had put his foot down, but it went through thinning ice.

Luna walked Flush through her inefficient system, which Flush knew and had rejected, and Flush pretended to be ok with it. At lunch, Luna said, "I have other work to do. You can take over from here." After lunch, Flush did the job Luna's way and used Turdex's notebook. Afterwards, Flush said it took at least an hour longer than if he'd done it the way I'd taught him. It was a wasted day, but Turdex was triumphant, having imposed his will on Flush.

Flush saw that Turdex's slow notebook system of recording all the different linens at each of the 22 linen stations was clumsy and difficult. He knew that Turdex and Luna weren't working on weekends, so he felt safe using my simple spreadsheet on weekends. However, to be cautious, Flush always took the notebook along in the wagon, just in case Turdex popped in for a surprise inspection.

Flush also took advantage of the weekend "shield from Turdex" and delivered the same way as before Turdex made the scene about "par level deliveries."

***

Things went smoothly for several weeks. Flush did linen our way on weekends without getting caught since Turdex was off work, and I had little trouble with Turdex while being porter during the week. He'd occasionally snoop around and look into the blue wagon to see if any blue linen bags were touching clear trash bags, a totally unnecessary segregation required by nobody but him. Evidently, his company, Errormake, and Bossella's company, Crawful, agreed on that pointless segregation of bags. Once, he caught me mixing them and scolded me in the hall in front of a nurse, but I weathered that small storm and mostly stayed away from him.

Then, on a Friday, Flush got another rude, demanding message on his home answering machine. It was Turdex: "There's been another complaint. Be in HR next Monday at 1 PM and bring a union rep. You're going to need it this time. And you're cancelled for

453

work this weekend. No one does linen, and it's your fault."

Again, Flush was stressed, not knowing what he'd done wrong this time. He called Juyn Lancaster in HR and asked her what the complaint was. She said a technician in Cardio Pulmonary had complained that he'd used a chair (previously occupied by a possibly contagious patient) to transport bath blankets. Immediately, Flush remembered the incident and admitted his mistake to Juyn, as he had previously done to the complaining technician, with an apology.

The next Monday, Flush and me, as his union rep, were in HR. We got there before Turdex, who was usually late and rushing. Flush was apologetic with Juyn and readily admitted his mistake. Since he had done so with the tech and Juyn, he wondered why this meeting was necessary and why he was again taken off his usual weekend job delivering linen. Juyn had no answer except to say it was Turdex's decision, out of her control. We could tell from her diplomatic response that she agreed with Flush. She was getting tired of the continuous meetings with many EVS employees over minor offenses that should have been dealt with elsewhere, probably in Turdex's office. It was becoming obvious that Turdex lacked the managerial skills to control his vassals without the threats of HR discipline.

Turdex entered and sat quickly at the round table. These meetings were becoming frequent and uncomfortable for Flush. I hated them, too.

"You made a big mistake a week ago, which endangered the health of a patient." This was a lie; no patient had been endangered. "We can't have this sort of neglect by you." Turdex was proud and triumphant, having poor Flush squirming in defense.

"Yes, I made a mistake. I had to deliver about 40 bath blankets from the wagon in the hall to the warming cabinet inside Cardio Pulmonary. I saw an empty wheelchair there, and since it was a weekend and very slow, with only one technician and one patient, I loaded it with 20 bath blankets. The tech saw and told me the wheelchair had been used by a possibly contagious patient. I unloaded the now contaminated blankets into the soiled linen hamper and got a new load, which I carried in my arms to the warmer. It was stupid of me. I should have asked her before I used the wheelchair. I've used wheelchairs before to deliver linens, so didn't think anything about it, but it was my error. I apologized to her. I won't do it again. There was no damage done. Nobody got sick from my mistake. I'm sorry."

He was genuinely contrite. I knew Flush to be conscientious, and he would never do anything intentionally to spread germs. In fact, just the opposite. He was probably the most germ-conscious employee in our department. He had gotten a little careless, committing an error that could happen to anyone.

Turdex pounced. "That's right! It won't happen again. We are discontinuing weekend deliveries of linen, starting now. The weekend housekeepers will have to do their own deliveries. You'll have to do something else on weekends now. I can't trust you anymore with linen."

"This was a small mistake that was corrected. No harm was done. We shouldn't cancel linen because of that."

"I make the calls around here. Besides, we save money with no weekend delivery."

"Well, I can do porter on weekends then."

"We'll see. I have other jobs for you. Every per diem must learn every job. That goes for you, too. So get ready to scrub." With that, this contentious meeting was over.

Flush was crushed. The grind of working as a per diem, with no defense against a despotic leadership with a personal ax to grind (on Flush's good-natured soul), was wearing him down.

I was beginning to re-evaluate my opinion of Juyn, whose new job in HR was more difficult than I'd previously seen. She was a decent person in a job that required, as she saw it, insensitivity and an abandonment of her natural integrity and kindness. Somehow, she thought she couldn't intervene between managers and employees, so when managers made cruel mistakes, Juyn sat in silence. This was totally different from the approach her predecessor, Liseanne, had employed, with more success. I concluded that some decent people in managerial positions will sacrifice their values for money.

***

The "one size fits all" policy, enacted by Turdex for the first time in EVS history, in which all per diems must learn every job, might have worked with the four new, young, recent per diem hires. They were people in their early twenties who badly needed jobs, wanted as many hours as possible, and were physically able to do every job. However, with his sciatica and 74 years, it didn't work for Flush.

The next day, Flush emailed Juyn the following letter. He also cc'ed it to me as his union rep.

Hi Juyn,

Thank you for understanding my mistake and accepting my apology and being forgiving in our meeting yesterday. Your input was encouraging.

However, I continue to believe that Turdex doesn't support me (and many others in EVS) and has damaged the morale in EVS. Many of us are discouraged by his tyrannical decisions, favoritism, and his rude, inconsiderate way of relating to us. He disrespects us, never supports us, and his militaristic attitude is insulting. Your response that "He can do that," while technically correct, ignores the bigger issue of **should** he do that. Has he no accountability?

As regards the weekend porter position, it's clear that:

1. We need two porters for 16 hours every day. The job done by the porter is indispensable. Our CEO can take off for two weeks and the hospital will do fine. But if no one did the porter job for two days, there would be many complaints (smell, germ spread, overflow of mess, etc.). If it went three days, the state would shut us down. It's a very necessary, though often disrespected, job.

2. With over six years' experience as porter and huge seniority among per diems, I deserve, more than any other candidate, the weekend porter position. Most people want weekends off; my wanting to work weekends is advantageous. Turdex could schedule it the same way he schedules other positions on a regular basis. It would be ok if he has to schedule me on alternating weekends.

3. On weekends, the porter job is usually a little slow for me. I sometimes have an hour of downtime. I would be happy to deliver some linen during this time, which would solve some of the problems created by the absence of a linen person on weekends. Other porters are not trained in linen, so can't help the way I can.

4. Turdex, who dislikes me and will do anything to oppose me, will dance all around this obvious solution, knowing full well that he has to schedule someone for the weekend porter job but won't commit to me. He can give the job to another per diem, who has been here one month, but not to me. This is another example of the rampant favoritism he displays. He's a well-dressed, counterproductive phony, and I hope the administration recognizes it.

*I sincerely hope you, and others, will **take a good look at the EVS Employee Surveys.** I'm sure they will give strong evidence of the low morale in EVS produced by Dora and Turdex. This information should be paramount when choosing a new manager for EVS. Now, we have two people doing a job that one person has always done in the past. Turdex and Dora are each doing half a job and doing it very poorly. If it takes two of them* *now, how could one of them do it when ErrorMake leaves?*

We employees do all the work and deserve a voice in the choice of our new boss. We will be seriously impacted by your choice. Happy workers perform better and do more work than disgruntled, distrusting workers. Some of us are tired of the stress they've brought and the lack of support we're getting. If we hate our jobs (but need the money) can you expect us to care and excel?

Thanks for your consideration.

***

The next weekend, Flush was assigned to learn housekeeping in the Emergency Department. "Thanks a lot" (you bastards). His reasonable request to do porter on weekends was denied. His email to Juyn accomplished nothing. I never saw Flush so depressed.

ER was never boring, as there was a continuous flow of patients going in and out. Also, some mental patients (51-50s) were in small rooms that had to be continuously monitored by security guards (nice guys) to prevent escape. The docs, nurses, and supporting staff were terrific, caring professionals who cooperated and treated us EVS employees with respect and appreciation. They were all busy most of the time but knew Flush well and found time to joke with him occasionally, which they appreciated. There was almost no humor in ER, so they welcomed Flush's unusual approach to work, bringing a healthy escape from the serious business of temperatures, blood pressures, MRI readings, splints, and bandages. And extensive medical records, produced by all medical staff, hunched over keyboards far more than over patients.

Parts of the housekeeping work were fine for Flush. He could empty the trash, wipe the higher surfaces, sweep and mop the floors, and most of the other duties of the job. But parts were painful. He was expected to clean low areas in and around toilets and sinks, under beds, and the low parts of gurneys. Beds and gurneys, which raised and lowered, had many mechanisms and were hard to clean without bending, stooping, and squatting, which aggravated his sciatica.

He told this to Turdex, but his response was, "Too bad. Just tough it out. We can't show any favorites just because you're old."

The next day, recovering from a sore lower back and leg, Flush realized he needed help. He went to his personal doctor, a very kind PA (physician assistant) who knew of his sciatic condition, verified years earlier by X-rays. She wasn't connected with the hospital; she worked for a primary care physician in town. She wrote a note asking for relief from certain types of work that needed squatting for more than a minute at a time. Flush took the note to the Employee Health nurse, Louise Humffers. This nurse, a usually sweet woman in a bureaucratic job, asked for clarification. Evidently, the note wasn't specific in describing Flush's limitations.

Flush went again to the PA and asked for another note, this time specifying problems when "squatting, bending, stooping, crouching, and hunkering down." Again, this was rejected by the Employee Health nurse, after consulting with her superiors, as being "Too general."

Finally, Flush went again to his PA for another note. She was getting impatient, understandably, but wrote another note. These three visits were all charged to our hospital insurance company. Flush was also assigned a prescription for citalopram, a drug that reduced stress.

With this third note, it was decided to hold an "accommodation meeting." This was held in HR with Juyn Lancaster (who was tired of all of Flush's appearances), Louise Humffers, in charge of this accommodation, Flush, Turdex, and me, as a union representative.

The meeting began with a semi-apology from Louise Humffers, who stated she had consulted with the hospital's expert on employee accommodations. He/she (they wouldn't identify this expert) said Flush could do all jobs, but when he had to work in low positions, he was to call for help from other workers.

This may have been legal under contract law but was totally impractical and unworkable in this case. As approximately 20-30% of all housekeeping jobs were working down low, such as in every bathroom, Flush would have to call for help every hour. Other housekeepers didn't have this time to spare, doing his job. If asked, they were sure to be resentful and refuse. Both Flush and I made this point repeatedly at the meeting but were told by Turdex, "It's legal. You have to do it." Juyn, manifesting her usual managerial leadership with expected problem-solving capability, was as useful as wings on a fire hydrant. She shrugged her shoulders, saying nonverbally, "Oh well." That passed for management at NCMH.

Once again, Turdex's stranglehold was tightening, making Flush's employment more precarious. Flush cared too much about doing a job well, particularly a job that could jeopardize patients' health. And he knew this accommodating solution wouldn't work in the real world, even though it was acceptable on paper, produced by indifferent desk jockeys with zero hands-on experience cleaning a variety of rooms. The mystery person who determined this accommodation never considered its workability, disregarding the inevitable stress it placed on other housekeepers, ultimately leading to their refusal to comply. Great way to introduce poison into an already stressful situation. Who cared about janitors anyway? Easily replaced.

This "solution" would also produce ill feelings between other housekeepers and Flush, which was probably Turdex's objective. And make Flush the enemy of any housekeeper on his shift. Very dumb. Divide and conquer, a manager's favorite strategy. Keep 'em squabbling amongst themselves so they won't collaborate and complain about poor management.

Flush again mentioned his expertise and experience delivering linen, a job that went undone on weekends since Turdex canceled linen delivery. Nobody cared to remedy this omission that offended all housekeepers on weekends since they had to do that job themselves in addition to cleaning 18 patient rooms, restrooms, and nurses' stations.

Flush mentioned his need for citalopram, stating he had never before needed any medication for stress. Louise Humffers, an Employee Health nurse, apologized sincerely, recognizing the problem while saying it was out of her control. She was just following orders from higher up. She had known Flush for years and sympathized with him since she, too, suffered from sciatica and knew its limitations. She wanted a different solution but was powerless to require a real remedy.

Flush, knowing it was hopeless but still thinking his job might survive, agreed to try it with the enthusiasm of a cat for a bath, a pig for a barbecue, and a snail for tar.

The following Saturday, Flush began work as a housekeeper in 2 North. With no training in that area, he was expected to clean 18 rooms, 18 bathrooms, a large nurses' station, and the nurses' breakroom. Good luck. He didn't have any keys and had to get another housekeeper to show him which keys he'd need and the combination to the 2 North break room. He tried, with very limited success, while irritating housekeepers when asking for help with lower cleanings. One of the two housekeepers he asked for help refused—"I don't have time!" The other spent 30 seconds, did nothing and left angrily. Everyone knew it was a stupid, unworkable solution.

Flush managed about 1/2 the job before his eight-hour shift was over. Half the rooms were uncleaned that day. Nobody worked to train him in this new job in a new location. Both housekeepers asked for help were irritated at Flush, and showed it. Very uncomfortable and unnecessary.

***

At this time, Dora had come back to work after her maternity leave was over. She had been out for four months, long enough for Turdex to solidify his position as *de facto* manager, even though Dora had the higher title.

Both Dora and Turdex had been hired by ErrorMake, and so they were outside the reach of the hospital administration. However, ErrorMake's contract was about to expire, and it was announced that it would not be renewed. Even though the first year with ErrorMake under Brock Chill was successful and happy, one year led by Crawful and another by ErrorMake were disastrous, so the hospital would take over, again, the hiring of EVS and Dietary manager(s). This was very good news for all the EVS staff, except Dora and Turdex, whose jobs were suddenly up for grabs.

This hiring process lasted about two months, during which there were many rumors: ("Dora's got it;" "Turdex will move to Dietary;" "A new guy from San Francisco will take over;" "Turdex will adopt Dora's baby by another man;" "Dora is transgender;" "Turdex is having an affair with a sexy female vice president, so keeping his job"). We all wanted a change, so welcomed the new process, thinking the administration would make a correction and get us some competent management.

Not to be. After two months of tension and mystery, we were told that Dora would be leaving, but Turdex was rehired. Another man with EVS managerial experience at another hospital would replace Dora. We all hoped this new guy would be able to restrain Turdex, something Dora couldn't do. We were hopeful this new guy would be strong and able to reinstall respect, kindness, and honest cooperation into our EVS leadership. We were wrong, hopes being only hopes, having no influence on fate's sometimes ugly product.

The new guy was a recently retired manager, 68 years old, who was brought in from another Diggery Wealth hospital (out of desperation). He had no need for the job and no desire to oversee anything. Named Rychael (we were told to call him Rick) Matise, he attended meetings, said very little, acted bored most of the time, made few decisions, refused to control Turdex's excesses, and waited for his final retirement, which came shortly. Flush tried to meet him five times, one on one, to present his position regarding the per diem job, but each time Rychael made an excuse. Usually, Juyn Lancaster had forbade their meeting.

The entire EVS staff, all 30 of us, observed again that having two people to run the department was unprecedented and a huge waste of money. One person had always done it before. Why two now? This was an admittance that these two were weak leaders, unable to do a one-person job alone.

Flush was never able to meet with Rick. Unlike previous management, meeting with the new boss was impossible, with few exceptions for recipients of favoritism, like Luna Irkley. And Flush had learned the futility of meeting with Turdex, who had the flexibility of religious extremists and great hostility towards Flush.

Frustrated, Flush started writing more emails. As he said several times, he wrote more persuasively than he spoke. When speaking under pressure, as happened in HR, he sometimes forgot to mention a cogent argument.

He sent the following email to HR Director Juyn Lancaster, newly hired director of EVS Rychael Matisse, Labor Union Director Carie Martina, NCMH CEO Betsy Socutesome, and me. It read:

ONE SIZE FITS ALL--OR DOES IT?

Turdex Darkhart, the new assistant manager for EVS, has recently instituted a new policy forcing every per diem to learn every job that EVS does. I believe this one-size-fits-all is inappropriate, in many cases, at NCMH.

Expecting all doctors to perform every procedure is unworkable and bound to produce failure and rebellion. We wouldn't ask every nurse to have all of the same skills and do every job in every department. Same with technologists. They are not subjected to one size fits all.

In many other contexts, one size fits all is totally inappropriate and destructive. Parents of several children know that 14-year-olds have different needs and interests than 4-year-olds. Serving them both the same quantities of food and the same bedtimes will fail. Boys and girls are often treated differently.

*And in many other contexts, such as civilians in a hospital, one-size-fits-all needs to be **very flexible** if this strategy is to succeed. Turdex's rigid demand that all per diems learn every EVS job is impractical, even if it makes sense theoretically. In practice, it won't work and there's no reason to insist that all be subjected. It's unrealistically theoretical, and I'm one of the victims.*

I am 74 years old; all other per diems are in their 20s. I've been working at SNMH over 13 years. Other per diems are new hires. I am looking for fewer hours; other per diems are looking for more hours and full-time, permanent jobs. It makes sense for these young per diems to learn several EVS jobs, making them more hirable when full-time jobs become available. It also makes them more useful as substitutes. Learning every job, for me, is expensive, unnecessary, and counterproductive. I have different goals, skills, and needs from the other per diems.

Until recently, as a per diem, I did linen delivery every weekend, the two days that Luna Irkley, the regular linen person, was off. As a per diem, I was happily given a regular weekend job I knew and liked. But a week ago, to save money, they discontinued linen delivery on weekends. Now that linen no longer exists on weekends, why can't I do the same thing with porter?

*I have six years of experience, full-time, as a porter. Hospitals need two porters, AM and PM, seven days a week. There is a vacancy on alternating weekends for the day porter position. **I would be perfect for that position and it's all I'm asking for.***

In addition, on weekends, I often have a spare hour since porter work on weekends is slower for several reasons. During this extra time, <u>I have done, and will do, some of the linen deliveries that</u>

are not done now for those two days. If I don't do this, the housekeepers must do it, taking away from their time to do their assigned housekeeping jobs. Often, they are already overworked and understaffed, so adding linen to their chores produces stress and animosity for them. Ask any weekend housekeeper.

Last weekend and this coming weekend, Turdex has me training to learn the housekeeping job. This job requires a lot of bending and stooping to clean low areas on gurneys, toilets, floors, and shelves. This provokes my sciatic condition, which causes pain in my right leg. It's a poor fit for me. There are several other new young per diems who could be trained for the housekeeping job.

Forcing someone to do jobs he doesn't know and dislikes, which endangers his health, when unnecessary, is poor management, lowering respect and morale. This is true when a viable alternative is available and needed, which is the case with me and weekend porter. Training someone in a new job is expensive, requiring twice as much manpower as usual. I don't need any training in porter or linen. You'd be getting 1 1/2 jobs done if you will take my request. And you'd have a happy employee (me) instead of a *disgruntled one. And happy housekeepers, spared of the additional task of doing their own linen. It's a win-win-win-win-win.*

Per diems are humans, different from each other. Good management considers those differences. At some point, the opinions of employees should be considered. Sometimes, good management supports the employees who do the work. Previous EVS managers would have solved this easy problem without stress. There's an obvious solution if flexibility is employed. Turdex Darkhart will be successful in his new job if he relaxes his rigidity. So will I.

Despite this email suggesting possible success, Flush had all but given up on Turdex. He wanted to end his polemic on a high note to impress the upper echelon of his optimistic positivity. In reality, he was depressed by the whole affair.

Making matters worse, he received the following email from Juyn:

Jerry,

This issue has gone on long enough via email. The emails, in many ways, express your opinion, which you have a right to do, but are also very disrespectful. I am recommending that the leadership of Sierra Nevada no longer engage in this type of email communication with you.

Juyn.

Instead of addressing the issues mentioned in his email, Juyn ignored them. Consistent with previous behavior, the admin refused a fair consideration of facts, instead resorting to dictatorial decisions that ignored employees. They didn't care about us, and it was becoming obvious.

The last four months of his job as a per diem were very depressing for Flush. Every weekend job was cancelled by Turdex for a variety of unnecessary reasons. Upper management stepped aside and watched the massacre. He worked two days in four months, which were painful, exacerbating his sciatica while doing a housekeeping job for which he was ill-suited.

Finally, seeing no possible solution, he went to Juyn's office and offered to quit if it could be arranged so he could collect unemployment for six months. Juyn agreed, which resulted in NCMH losing a fine employee. Toxicity running through the company culture had caused another painful result. An institution designed to bring health was bringing disease.

My experience with Dr. Glasser's *Choice Theory*, introduced by our last competent boss, Brock Chill, taught me an axiom that applied to all relationships. It said that coercion was only acceptable when both people benefit. Otherwise, coercion was counterproductive. That was certainly true in this case.

David lost; Goliath won. It was that simple.

With no fanfare, Flush emptied his locker on a Friday. Rudy had been told of Flush's departure and was brokenhearted. The two of them had continued solving Sudoku puzzles together for over a year during their lunch breaks. Their collaborative meetings were very therapeutic for Rudy and gave Flush confirmation of his teaching and Sudoku's psychological benefits.

As Flush was saying a few "goodbyes" to EVS staff, Rudy rushed into the break room, relieved to catch Flush on his way out. "I have a going away present for you." He handed a rapidly wrapped package to Flush.

Flush, surprised, said, "I didn't expect anything, but thanks," as he unwrapped the package. Inside was a top-of-the-line slingshot, the metal kind with a brace that covered the forearm, allowing for a more powerful shot.

"I thought about giving you one of my guns, but I knew you wouldn't want it. So maybe you can use this for self-defense sometime."

"Fantastic," said Flush sincerely. "I'll use it for fun. Thanks." He hugged Rudy, probably the only affection Rudy had received in forty years other than his wife.

Chapter 19: The Fourteenth Strikeout

One year after leaving NCMH, Flush saw a notice in the local newspaper. The Spiritual Care Department at NCMH was soliciting volunteers to assist the non-denominational chaplain. Volunteers would be trained to visit interested patients, offering comfort to a wide spectrum of religious or spiritual beliefs. Some patients might be dying, but most not, and just want comfort from a friendly and skilled stranger.

This department employed one person, a new chaplain named Barry Maford, whose job was recruiting, training, and scheduling volunteers to work 3-4 hours each week and making assigned rounds to welcome patients. These volunteers were almost always seniors and retirees with maturity from life experiences, empathy, and open-mindedness that works well for anything called "Spiritual Care." They were trained to never impose their own personal religious beliefs; they did best when supporting the patients 'beliefs.

Flush always felt empathy for all patients, knowing they all wanted to go home and disliked being stuck in the hospital despite realizing they had to stay and were lucky to have competent medical care to save or improve their lives. Over fourteen years, Flush intentionally developed the capacity to approach strangers and quickly establish a rapport most of the time. He learned this while realizing that his job in the hospital offered an ideal opportunity to develop this invaluable social skill that contributed to a fuller life. He often said his job was a very hands-on graduate-level course in personal human communication.

This made this Spiritual Care volunteer opportunity a good fit for him, in Flush's appraisal. He called NCMH, asked for the chaplain's office, and was connected to Barry Maford. He introduced himself and submitted his offer to take the training and become a volunteer. Barry was very friendly, receptive, and happy to talk.

Flush told Barry that he wasn't religious in any particular denomination but believed humans had souls that went somewhere after death and that there was a God that ran things, mostly outside human understanding.

Barry said he would email Flush the date of the first training session.

After hanging up, Flush felt comfortable and trusted Barry's judgement. After some thought, Flush sent the following essay to Barry. Flush had written it for his blog but felt he best reveal his beliefs to Barry lest he get into an uncomfortable and insupportable position.

I know about this because Flush cc-ed it to me.

FROM ATHEIST TO THEIST (c)

I was raised in an American Protestant family. My parents, though not particularly religious, almost never went to church while observing Christian holidays (Christmas and Easter) like everyone else in their circle of friends. But in my teens, I became an atheist and remained so, unquestioning, for about 50 years, coming to that conclusion from a scientific education and orientation. I needed more than faith.

However, in the past five years, I've begun to question my apostasy, probably an activity taken by many seniors facing impending death. I'm in good health now and don't expect my passing anytime soon. Nonetheless, I've become more philosophical lately, so the question of the existence of a higher power, called God, is interesting and germane, if not definitively answerable. I am not a theological scholar nor a student of comparative religions.

In exploring this question, I did not give scripture any consideration. These books (Bible, Quran, Torah, etc.) were written by humans many years ago when humans had many fallacious opinions. I doubt the authors were divinely inspired, as claimed, so I needed evidence from other sources.

As an aside, I'm convinced that God has no gender. People referring to God as "He," which is usually done by Christians, Jews, and Muslims, is a mistake. Why would God have a gender? Gender is only needed if there is procreation, but whom would God procreate with? If God is a he, does he have male genitalia? Why would God need to have sex? I suspect they give God maleness because Jesus, Mohammed, Abraham, Moses, etc., were males, and religious books were all written by men, so they are naturally biased in that direction.

Atheists argue that a loving God would not allow frequent bad things to happen to good, innocent people, so there must be no God. They reason that a loving, caring God could/would not behave so hypocritically. This is a strong argument unless the God that exists is hands-off, allowing humans and nature to behave unimpeded, without intervention. That's certainly God's inherent constitution and intention.

What if God is a tough-love kind of God who allows humans to make their own mistakes without rescuing us in order for us to learn a bigger lesson? What if innocent babies die and millions perish from war and disease so that we humans find the remedy, maybe hundreds of years from now? "But what about millions dying from natural disasters?" you might ask, with justification. Maybe there's a lesson to be learned there, too, like don't live in a flood plain or downhill from an active volcano or on an earthquake fault. Or maybe that's God's way to combat an unsupportable population explosion.

There are five pieces of evidence that, for me, indicate the existence of an indifferent God. These are not proof; they are only evidential in strength. I find that evidence in the world around me. Four of the five are based on the unique nature of humanity. The fifth will begin my explanation. It's frequently challenged by a few astronomers, with only statistics to back them up.

1) Earth is undisputedly unique for its quantity and variety of life. We have millions of life forms here that do not exist anywhere else that we have discovered, and astronomers have been searching for many years. There are billions of stars, planets, and moons that, to our knowledge, possess no life. Yes, Earth could have developed this way by some strange accident millions of years ago, but is that the only possible explanation? And if so, why nowhere else on those billions of rocks out in space? People say we will find other civilizations, probably more advanced than ours, but until there is substantial evidence, I see that as only a hypothesis, science fiction that sells books and movies to our active imaginations. My scientific orientation says: "Bring me proof, not a statistical possibility." Could a God have created Earth as an experiment, inhabiting it with life as disparate as clams are to eagles are to elephants are to

butterflies are to humans? With a huge variety of plant life?

2) Humans have many attributes that differentiate us from all other life forms. The most unique is our brain, which allows us to create many advancements. Our brains have given us languages, allowing us to communicate with each other in a variety of means, from speech to writing. We have symbols (traffic lights, wedding rings, pictures, applause, etc.) that we humans understand, but lesser animals don't. Our brains give us the power to create technology that has given us planes that can fly farther and faster than birds, submarines that can dive deeper and longer and faster than whales, bulldozers stronger than elephants, and cars faster than cheetahs. We have television, radio, telephones, and the internet that allow us to communicate with others at great distances. We have major institutions that treat us for disease and accidents, entertain us, educate us, ensure our protection from other harmful humans, and make it possible to travel great distances safely for a reasonable cost. Our brains give us music and humor, characteristics other lesser species don't have. Art, in its many forms, is unique to humans. We are continuously creating new things that result from our brain power, usually, improvements in processes or objects that allow us more or better accomplishments.

How is it that we have such a huge superiority over the next smartest species, the apes? Why such a gap in ability? I don't dispute evolution, but it doesn't go far enough. Evolution leaves a huge gap, which it cannot explain. Could we have developed this huge disparity as a result of the touch of God, which imbued us with these unchallenged skills? This explanation makes more sense to me than that explained by evolution without the intervention of God.

3) In addition to our obviously superior brain power, humans are imbued with a characteristic I'll call bonding (it could be called love). There are millions of examples of bonding between humans and between humans and other species. Bonding between us drives us in many ways. This bonding is the power that motivates great acts of sacrifice for others, risking our lives to save others, often strangers. Bonding causes adopted children to search for their birth parents. Bonding causes us to establish complicated institutions such as hospitals where "teams" of medical specialists work together to help sick and injured humans (usually

strangers) recover, aware the rescued will leave and probably lose contact with the rescuers. Bonding between humans is the cause of charities and generosities that help others. We give millions to help victims of disasters (Haiti, Bangladesh, Darfur, Houston, Florida, etc.) because of this bonding. Many people adopt animals in shelters, and many of us place great value on our pets. Other species don't have pets, relationships that exist for no practical purposes (food, work, material for clothing) but deliver special bonding between humans and dogs, cats, etc.

No other species bond to the extent that we humans do. Oh sure, there are a few examples of birds that mate for life. And we all have seen pictures of groups of elephants that seem to mourn the death of a fallen member. But if my dog encountered his parents, instead of reacting in the loving way most of us do with our parents, he would sniff their butts and move on with no acknowledgement of any relationship.

Yes, I am aware of the many cruelties that humans do to each other. These are real and undeniable and cannot be minimized. But the other side of the same coin is the love and bonding we have that far exceeds that demonstrated by other species.

How did we acquire this characteristic? Evolution doesn't explain it. Other species (sharks and cockroaches) have survived for millions of years without this bonding. Could this bonding, or love, have been implanted in us humans by the touch of a God? I can't ignore this possibility, and my rational side now sees this as a real probability.

4) Another unique characteristic of humans is the universal existence of morality. Unlike other species, we have a sense of right and wrong, values that neutralize the prevailing thought in the animal kingdom that <u>might makes right</u>. Most of us have consciences that tell us (often too subtlety) when we've done wrong. Religions are usually the basis of morality; Earth's many religions all condemn murder, rape, theft, and cruelty to the weak. Yes, once again, I don't deny the frequent violations of morality by humans, who sometimes succumb to cruelty. But the fact that we have morality and formalized systems that punish violators makes us humans different and superior to all other species, which have no such morality and operate according to their instincts.

5) *Observing human behavior and mental characteristics, we see a huge variety. Physically, we differ from each other, also, with a few of us being seven feet tall and others only four feet tall; some of us weighing, as adults, 800 pounds and others weighing only 70 pounds. But other species (birds, dogs, fish) have as much variety in physical attributes as size and color. So, our physical variety is not unique to humans.*

But we are unique when we consider behaviors. Some humans are athletes and some are intellectuals. Some are religious, while others are atheists. Some are fundamentalist Christians, while others are extreme jihadist Muslims, and others are live-and-let-live Buddhists. Some are cruel and some are kind. Some are ditch diggers and some are surgeons. Some live in the Arctic, while others live in deserts on the equator. Some have four wives, while others have none. Some live in enormous mansions, while others live in portable crude tents.

No other species have this wide variety of behaviors. Could these choices of behavior been created in humans by the touch of God? I think this explanation is probable. Yes, nature and evolution could have created these variations, since weather and resources and geography differ so much on Earth. But is that the only possible explanation? I don't think so.

Looking hard enough, one can find exceptions to everything I've written above. There are examples among other species of these aforementioned characteristics. But these exceptions and examples are so slim in comparison that they cannot refute the uniqueness and wealth of humans in many ways.

This makes me think that God probably had a hand in creating humans, making us so special, able to control many aspects of events on Earth, and giving us the power to determine the future of our existence here. Five hundred years from now, will humans have improved all life conditions on Earth, or will we have destroyed life, including ourselves? Along with our physical evolution, will we humans have evolved cognitively, with better thinking and understanding? Will we humans develop morally, with more golden rule behavior and less right-makes-right dominance?

I suspect God is watching us, but giving us the power to make these determinations, hopefully, collectively behaving more productively and less destructively.

The next day, Barry sent the following email to Flush.

Thank you, Flush,

It was great to hear some of your thoughts and catch a glimpse of your journey. I look forward to getting to know you better. To be continued!

Have a great day!

Chaplain Barry.

This encouraged Flush, though he wasn't surprised, having felt comfortable on the phone with the new chaplain. He began developing strong feelings about this future opportunity to positively impact the lives of people who needed help. He responded quickly.

Hi Barry,

Thanks for your response. I assume this doesn't disqualify me from becoming a spiritual care volunteer. Please let me know when/where the next class will begin. I think I'd like to participate as a volunteer.

Flush Malone.

Chaplain Barry responded positively.

Flush,

I'll let you know when I get the dates set. No, that doesn't disqualify you.

Chaplain Barry.

Nothing happened for seven weeks, but Barry had said it might be a while before they started. Flush was confident and patient. Then he received the following email from Barry's female boss, an original scowl crow named Leery Smellman. She had two titles: Patient Experience Manager and Mission Integration Interim Manager.

This woman took herself seriously and marched with the established rhythm that defined scowl crows, saying without words, "Leave me alone. I'm not interested in any petty thing you have to say." At first, I said, "Good Morning," but was met with silence with the warmth of a frozen moose dropping, so I stopped. After a few months, the scowl crows were easily spotted.

Flush,

Thank you for your interest in spiritual care training, however, at this time, we are unable to extend an offer for you to register for this training.

I am hopeful you will be able to find other venues to share your time and interests.

Leery Smellman.

(2 titles here)

Flush was shocked. Then he remembered the very poor decisions made by earlier managers and concluded that nothing had changed. He sat on it for a day and then decided to call Chaplain Barry. Chaplain Barry was polite but politically safe, saying nothing that might jeopardize his job. He said he was sorry, but the decision came from above him. And he identified Lerry Smellman as his boss.

Flush asked him if Leery had seen the essay he'd sent. Barry was noncommital; he didn't directly answer that question, which was asked twice. Both times, Barry advised Flush to call Leery.

Flush remembered Leery from before and, though he barely knew her, was sure she was a certain scowl crow with the charm of a cactus. He called her and left a message on her answering machine. He asked her to call him back and left his phone number. He was polite, but his tone suggested the pursuit of answers he deserved.

After callously leaving Flush in suspense, Leery called back two days later, at about 4:25 PM. Flush asked why his application had been rejected. Leery mumbled things that made little sense, including, "We're not accepting any current or past employees in Spiritual Care now."

"Why is that?"

"You're not the only one. I have to tell another ex-employee the same thing."

"You probably don't know this, but I became very good at making friends with patients. I practiced it a lot when I went into the rooms to collect the blue bags. I think that's one of the capacities that makes a good Spiritual Care volunteer."

"We just feel like there's too much chance of a poor outcome—you might not understand new changes—things are different now from when you were here."

"I felt empathy for patients. They all wanted to go home, and many were lonely for friends and uncomfortable there. Sometimes, I was their only friend."

"I'm sorry, but I know you'll find another chance to achieve fulfillment."

"Is this something personal?"

"Oh no! Spiritual Care has been disorganized for 20 years (this was a lie, ignoring the five inspired years that Jonah Perspirman was in charge), and we're finally bringing some order to the confusion. I think you should volunteer at another facility. You know Hospice is always looking for volunteers. I'm off work at 4:30, so I have to go now. Good Luck." She hung up.

Again, NCMH's "Humankindness" was false and insincere. Again, the totally subjective narrowness of the NCMH administration made a decision that served neither the public nor the employees. Flush was a victim of stupid judgments made by people who didn't deserve the power given to them.

Chapter 20: A Hollywood Ending

Every event in the preceding 19 chapters was based on real occurrences. I may have embellished a bit, but that was all true as I saw it.

This last chapter never happened, but it could if Hollywood decided to make a movie of this novel, which would suit me quite well. I might make enough money to quit this job, which I no longer enjoy, four years after Flush's forced retirement. I know the true ending (which you just read) wouldn't be as crowd-pleasing as this fictional conclusion. Here's the spectacular, fictional, Hollywood-pleasing ending.

And this last chapter describes an event that is, unfortunately, happening now regularly in the United States and rarely in other countries with enough sense to outlaw most guns. We do everything to prevent most countries from developing nuclear weapons, which would give a crazy leader the ability to kill millions if he (probably a man) decided to use his weapon offensively and drop the first bomb. However, on a smaller but much more deadly scale, we refuse to outlaw military-grade rifles while making them available to every wacko in America. It only takes one disturbed young man with an AR-15 to kill many strangers. These mass killers are always angry loners, like Rudy, who reach a point of desperation. Frustrated by a lifetime of feeling powerless, having easily accessed assault rifles, and desperately needing 15 minutes of power and fame, they tell themselves, "What the hell! I'm going out in a flame of glory. I hate my life and have nothing to live for, so what's to lose?" And soon, the damage is done; many innocent strangers lie dead in a church, synagogue, school, supermarket, party, or street of a parade.

Our politicians have been bought by the NRA (thanks to Citizens United) to promote the nonsense that "guns don't kill people, people kill people." They fail to acknowledge the obvious truth that both guns and people kill people, and without guns, people would kill far fewer people. And the fear and hate in the US would be reduced. These elected officials lack the courage and integrity to pass laws that would make buying assault rifles illegal. So the mayhem continues while the cowards shrug their shoulders and offer no better remedy than ineffective thoughts and prayers. Even God is disgusted, I suspect.

I was working on a Sunday morning and was out on the San-i-Pack dock unloading the bags from my first round. Suddenly, I heard a loud BANG coming from a mysterious source and location. I stopped unloading, totally surprised and unsure of this unexpected shock. There was a brief pause, about three or four seconds, and then two more BANGs, coming from close and above, I now determined. I looked at the windows on the second floor, but all were solidly closed, picture windows unable to be opened.

Above them was the heliport, the rooftop where a helicopter landed when delivering ill patients or picking them up to take to another hospital better equipped to serve a patient beyond our capabilities. Helicopters used this landing spot about three or four times per week. Whenever they came or went, there was tremendous noise and wind down in the San-i-Pack area where we porters dropped our collected dross. Sometimes, the wind blew our wagons off the loading dock onto the pavement six feet below.

This heliport was the highest roof of the hospital. It was the highest roof within twenty-five miles. It was secure, with very few people having access. An elevator with one door was the only way to get there by land. Transporters pushing gurneys on and off helicopters with very sick patients were the only users, accompanied by medical professionals, mostly nurses or EMTs, who rode the helicopters. From the heliport, one could see parking lots on three sides of the hospital. And a freeway, which ran near and below the hospital, could also be seen from this high point of our small community.

I ran into the linen room, which was just inside the back door. Scared, I grabbed the phone and dialed 911. It was answered immediately.

"Emergency. Can I help you?"

In panic, I said, "There's been gunshots at NCMH. I think they came from the roof—probably the heliport. Not sure."

"Have there been injuries?"

"I don't know. There were three shots."

Then BANG! BANG! BANG! BANG!

"There it is again!" I yelled. "Did you hear it?"

"Yes, I did. We're sending help now. Stay on the phone."

"No. I can't. I need to tell others in the hospital. Get here quick. Be careful. I think he's on the roof and can see in several directions. Bye. Gotta go."

I ran to the ER and screamed, "There's been a shooting from the roof. I heard seven or eight shots. I think from the heliport."

The ER doc in charge said, "We heard it and are going into 'alarm mode 'now."

Just then, Steve, a security guard, came running in, shouting, "Three people are wounded in the east parking lot. They're on the ground. I tried to get to them, but he shot at me and missed. We need a truck to block his shots. That's the only way to reach them."

From this point on, the usually controlled, professional activities in our busy ER descended into loud, frightened mayhem. The calm professionals, trained for many serious emergencies, were not prepared for this level of lethal, non-medical threat. The tension and noise, occasionally punctuated by gunfire from above, totally altered the tone and quality of the mostly quiet ER that we all knew and were confident in. Police sirens outside began slowly increasing, some getting closer, announcing a very unusual event to us and the surrounding neighborhoods. The three patients in the ER, none seriously ill, were quickly moved to a safe wing and then mostly ignored. One got out of his bed, wandered into the main room, where we all discussed options, and was told to get back in bed. He did, reluctantly, curious for details.

Someone must have contacted the central desk because an announcement was broadcast over the PA system throughout the hospital: "Attention! May I have your attention. Everyone proceed to lockdown positions. Secure yourselves behind locked doors. There is a shooter. This is a real emergency. Secure yourselves immediately. Lockdown now! Call 411 if you see trouble." By now, I was sure the shooter was on the roof and not roving the halls, but the announcement didn't give that information.

Then, Mike, the head of security, came in. "Who's on the roof? How many shooters are there?" We all paused.

I was the closest witness. "I heard about eight shots. Probably one or two guys up there. No way to see from anywhere without being shot at."

During the next fifteen minutes, there were sporadic bursts of gunfire about every twenty seconds. They went in several directions, giving the initial assumption that more than one shooter was responsible. During this time, about five pedestrians were shot in two hospital parking lots, three more in another parking lot, and caused six car crashes on the freeway, with a driver in one car and a passenger in another wounded. And probably fifty or more bullet holes in eight more cars driving calmly in that peaceful neighborhood. The shooter wasn't particular about quarry. Oddly, he never shot at the six houses, plainly visible and close by.

Also, during those fifteen minutes, our local and state police, with at least thirty sirens blaring from all directions, close and up to thirty miles away, were able to close the few roads near NCMH that were vulnerable and receiving unexpected destructive, even lethal attention. The state highway patrol, police from two towns and the county all coordinated very well to shut down all outdoor movement and minimize the deaths surrounding the hospital.

Soon, after I ran to the ER, three police cars stopped outside under a drive-thru roof. Six policemen ran into the ER. They started asking questions. We didn't know much. Then, while outside under the ER entrance roof, we heard about six more shots, with small spacing between each. We couldn't tell which direction they were going. But we all knew they were from the heliport.

While there, we heard a call coming into one of the police cars. "There's been a crash on the freeway. Looks like a car was shot and crashed into another car."

The policeman in charge, Captain Hawkins, the only ER doc on duty, and the head of security discussed how to rescue the three wounded (maybe dead) in the parking lot. Captain Hawkins asked if we had any armor-proof vehicles they could use to rescue the victims in the parking lot. "I doubt it" and "I don't think so" were the responses.

Captain Hawkins dialed a number on his phone and said, "How soon can you get our MRAP ready and over to the hospital? We need it ASAP. There's been a shooting and it can save lives, but you got'ta get it here fast." He listened to the answer. "OK. There's no time to waste. People are bleeding out and we can't get to them without getting shot. Hurry!" I later learned an MRAP was a retired military vehicle from Iraq, the MRAP standing for Mine Resistent-Ambush Protected. It was a "gift" from the US Department of Defense. It originally cost $730,000, a very solid piece of indestructible machinery.

I grabbed a phone and called Flush. "Hello," he answered, surprised to get a call from the hospital ER. "Flush, there's been a shooting from the heliport."

"What?"

"I can't explain now. What's the name and number of your friend with the drone—the one with a camera?"

"That's Bill Stevenson. Wait. I'll get his number." There was a pause. "It's 265-2682."

"Thanks. Gotta go," I hung up.

To Capt. Hawkins, I said, "An acquaintance of mine has a drone with a camera. He could fly it here and take pictures of the roof. We could learn how many shooters. Maybe even who they are."

"Great. Call him and get him here. We need that information."

I called Bill, explained the situation, and requested he come immediately. "Don't take the freeway near the hospital. He's shooting cars there. Come to the ER entrance. He can't see us here from the heliport."

"OK. I need to change the batteries in the drone and get dressed, but I'll be there (BANG! BANG! BANG! BANG! BANG!—-five shots in quick succession interrupted us) (unintelligible) about 20 or 25 minutes."

Hawkins told two of his sergeants to go to the second floor, where they could see the freeway and report back to him. Hawkins was starting to use me, realizing I had knowledge of people and the layout of the whole hospital. He told me to take them to the best viewing place.

Together, we went to a large window in the hallway on the second floor outside ATC (Ambulatory Treatment Center) that overlooked the freeway about 100 yards away. We saw a car upside down that had crashed into a side railing. Its windshield was shot and shattered. We couldn't see inside. Two more cars, one with the driver's side window shot out and the driver slumped, having crashed into each other, were blocking northbound traffic. Three cars, unable to advance forward, were backing up, aware they were under fire from somewhere unknown. Police cars, about a 1/2 mile away, were gathering to stop more northbound traffic from advancing towards the hospital.

During the seven minutes I spent with these two officers, I was relieved by their kind professionalism. A little older than me, both nice guys not disposed to push their badges in a domineering way towards civilians. It was my first close encounter with the law, other than getting my driver's license at the DMV. I was encouraged that our local police were competent and we were in good hands. They also spoke highly of Hawkins, their boss. That, too, was supportive; the good news, I wouldn't presume otherwise.

We noticed two police cars stopping traffic on the southbound lanes about 1/2 mile north of us. Fortunately, no cars had been hit coming from that direction, and none were in those two southbound lanes. To the left, on an overpass, for the first five minutes, cars were driving unimpeded, unaware of their danger. None were hit. That was the only good news. But police soon arrived and stopped that traffic, too.

Within fifteen minutes of the start of the shooting, all traffic and pedestrians within sight of the hospital had been stopped. None were left as targets. So, the shooter began methodically hitting parked cars in four parking lots nearby. Then he saw a golf cart on the country club course about 1/2 mile away. He shot and the two men inside scurried for cover behind a tree.

Then the shooter noticed part of a community college building was visible through the forest about a half mile away. Several bullets hit the side; several more broke two windows. The shooter was running out of targets.

On a hill about 1/4 mile across the freeway, slightly lower than the hospital, was a large lumber yard with a parking lot. Three cop cars had gathered there and surrounded three wounded people lying on the pavement. As we watched, the windshield of one of the cop cars shattered. The cop inside got out from the passenger side and ran safely for cover. We reported all this to Hawkins. We didn't have to tell Hawkins that the hospital stood on a hill, the highest point within a mile. Nobody could shoot down from any building higher than the heliport. It was very defensible. The shooter(s) was safe.

There were sirens on cop cars coming from all directions. People for miles around were becoming aware of some immense danger, a rare occurrence in our normally quiet small town. By then, Hawkins had closed all surrounding streets and highways. The siren noise was deafening and very stress producing. We could barely talk. It certainly warned the citizenry. I wondered if it was a police strategy to overwhelm the shooter(s).

I left the two policemen by the window and returned to the ER, which had become the central control of the improvised effort to mitigate the destruction and eventually overcome this lethal threat.

Hawkins turned to the head of security, Mike, and asked, "How can we get onto the heliport?"

"There's only one elevator. Almost nobody has a key. I do. But it opens immediately onto the heliport, so anybody going there would probably get shot when the door opens. It's a very secure location—defensible—for a shooter. There's no stairway up there."

Then Hawkins asked, "Can you get me a blueprint of that area? It will help us decide our next move."

Mike said he'd look into it, but it might take a while since all the managers were home. "I wouldn't know where to look without their help. I'll call someone and get them to come to find it."

He called Dalton Takeman, the Plant Operations manager, who had all the blueprints, explaining the emergency. Takeman was annoyed to be disturbed on his day off. He said he'd be there. "It'll take awhile. I'll have to shave and shower first."

"Hurry! This can't wait!"

"Who is this? Don't tell me what to do!" Takeman hung up.

I immediately called Flush again. "Did you say you were meeting with Barry Maford this morning?" This was about six months following Flush's departure. He was trying to become a Spiritual Care volunteer. Maford was the chaplain.

"Yeah, but I guess that's cancelled now. Let me know what's happening. I probably shouldn't come."

"That's right. Don't come. Cars are getting shot at."

Just then, a nurse ran in and said two people were wounded—maybe dead—in the north parking lot. By this time, about twenty-five people of every job title were in the ER. As it was a Sunday, the admins and supes weren't there. But they were called at home and some came within a half hour. Soon, security guards were posted at both ER entrances, restricting entrance to necessary, appropriate people.

Hawkins commanded his lieutenant to take a megaphone outside and try to talk the shooter(s) into surrendering. Suddenly, all sirens were silent, to the great relief of everyone. The lieutenant, who had taken de-escalation training in a course called "Lone Wolf Interception and Control," over a megaphone made a constant demand, delivered in a firm, steady, polite manner, telling the shooter(s) he was surrounded, could not escape, and put down his gun and surrender.

We heard a voice yell back, "Fuck you! I'd rather die than surrender to you communist bastards!" I thought I recognized something familiar about the voice, but I wasn't sure.

In a calm, commanding tone, the megaphoning lieutenant continued to try to persuade him to surrender between gun volleys, occasionally prompting some cursing from the angry rooftop. "Go to hell!" and

"Now I'm in charge!" and "It's 200 against one and you punks still can't take me. Give up before I kill all you dipshit lib-tards!"

Finally, Takeman showed up with a bundle of blueprints. He arrived an hour after being called, properly attired for a professional meeting with the press. He was obviously peeved.

By that time, several reporters from the two local radio stations and newspaper, with photographers, were milling around, interviewing (even me!) and taking notes. The radio stations were broadcasting this momentous news minutes after it happened. The public access TV station of volunteers was gathering and coordinating an appearance that was slow to happen. Sacramento TV reporters were on their way. This was probably the biggest event to hit this area since the Gold Rush (not too recently). The media knew it. All this arriving media was restricted to the ER waiting room or outside the ER entrance under a protective canopy.

Takeman and Hawkins spread the blueprints out on a bed in a back room. They chose one that showed the entire complex. From that, they discerned that the view from the 3rd story heliport of surrounding parking lots was obstructed by the extensive two-story buildings of hospital wings surrounding the heliport. But there was a clear shot east, west, and part of north. Anyone in those directions was very vulnerable. So were cars parked there. This made sense, as people in the lot towards Building 4, which was north-east, were the first to be hit. And the freeway below was also eastwards of the heliport. The road and golf course on the north side were also targets, where several cars were hit and crashed. An apartment complex to the distant north became the shooter's favorite victim after all cars were stopped on surrounding roads and freeway, and most of the 244 cars in the parking lots were becoming colorful Swiss cheese on wheels.

About this time, Bill Stevenson arrived with his drone. He showed it to Captain Hawkins, who was pleased. "Now we can see who our enemy is. Where do you need to be to send it up above the rooftop?"

"I need to be outside but not visible to the shooters. The drone is quiet, so hopefully, they won't see it." At this time, we didn't know how many shooters there were.

Hawkins said, "Go outside under the ER driveway roof. They can't see you from there. Can you control it from there?"

"I'll have to try it, but it might be OK." Together, Bill and Hawkins went outside to launch the drone. The control panel had a small screen that showed the picture the drone was taking. Bill could control the drone and camera from the ground. It was an amazing piece of technology that would play an important role in our efforts. Bill sent it up and had it hover from a short distance. Bill suggested he position it in front of the sun in the east, over the freeway, so the shooter couldn't see it.

After some experimentation, Bill decided that his best place on the ground, direct line to the drone but safe from gunfire above, was next to a small industrial building that housed the large generator. It was safe; controlling the drone and camera was effective.

Everyone wanted to look at the small screen, but Hawkins motioned everyone but Bill away. The surrounding cops, nurses, and docs, all curious, stepped back a few paces. We were safe and out of the shooter's sight.

The camera on the drone at first showed an empty rooftop. Then, as Bill maneuvered the angle, they saw a large American flag, 3' by 5', taped hurriedly cattywampus to the side of the elevator. This partially solved a mystery, eliminating an extremist Muslim jihadist as the attacker. Then, on the small screen, we saw one man dressed in camouflage, wearing a black cowboy hat, kneeling beside the three-foot-high eastern wall surrounding the heliport. He was unseen from the ground. He was holding a rifle. As the camera zoomed in, they could see it was an assault rifle with a large magazine. By maneuvering the camera, they saw two more high-powered military rifles and several magazines leaning against different sides of the low wall surrounding the heliport. This wall provided protection for the shooter. The camera could see his every move. So far, the shooter didn't see the drone. As the camera panned around the roof, we learned there was only one shooter. It provided the information necessary to win the battle. More good news among a lot of bad.

Hawkins asked employees to look at the screen to see if they could recognize the shooter. Several nurses and I watched closely but were unable to identify him, his large hat covering his face when viewed from above.

"Can you lower the drone a little so we can see his face better?" asked Hawkins. As Bill lowered the drone, which was still about 100 yards from the heliport, the shooter saw it and started shooting to bring it down. He missed. Then Bill started moving it quickly, side to side, up and down, but it lost its ability to focus, so the shooter was only visible occasionally. He stopped shooting at it. Bill sent the drone back up into the sun, making it hard for the shooter to see. It could be almost steady and functioning when there, and the shooter didn't shoot at it. He also gathered another gun and moved to the north edge of the heliport, where he could see a large parking lot that was beginning to fill with cop cars. No people were vulnerable, so he kept up a steady barrage, shattering windows in every car and truck in the parking area.

Hawkins told three cops to get tear gas rifles ready. When they returned minutes later, they started lobbing tear gas onto the roof. There was a slight wind, about 5 MPH, so the tear gas dispersed in about a minute. When the gas cleared, we saw, on the drone's screen, the shooter lying face down with a scarf covering his face. When he could, he stood up in the middle of the roof, ran to the other side, knelt behind the short wall, and began shooting cars in the lumber yard parking lot and those wrecked on the freeway. Two of those cars still had people inside. They'd stayed there, safe but terrified, for about an hour after being shot at, with broken windows. We couldn't tell how many people were there and were injured.

As we watched the drone picture, we saw the shooter running between the three walls, picking up a different assault rifle he had placed there, and shooting many shots. Then he'd put the rifle down, run to a different wall, and shoot again with a different assault rifle. He could terrify three different directions and seem like more than one shooter.

Just then, Flush appeared outside the ER. "What are you doing here?" I asked, surprised.

"It's being covered by local radio. I thought I recognized his voice. It sounded like Rudy."

"I thought of him, too. Could it be him?"

"I'm pretty sure I saw his truck in the north lot. Let's go look."

They didn't need me in the ER, so Flush and I entered the hospital and ran quickly toward a point where we could see the north lot. As we ran, we saw nobody in the halls, but we knocked on the 1 South break room door. There was no answer. I knocked again. "Go away. We can't open the door. Go away. We're ok here. Leave us alone." The panicked voice, trembling with fear, was not reassuring.

"Ok. It's safe out here now, but you should stay there until the 'All Clear" is announced."

"Don't worry about us. We'll stay here for as long as it takes."

Flush and I left.

When we got to the other side of Building 1, we saw a beat-up Ford 150, rusty and blue, in the north lot. It was the only one without broken windows. The other seventeen cars and trucks were shattered glass boxes. Three police cars were also victims of the attack.

Flush asked, "Is that Rudy's truck? I think it's the only one without damage."

"Yes, it sure looks like it," I answered.

"That answers the enigma," replied Flush. "It's Rudy. Something happened to set him off. I've been afraid of this for years."

We talked as we went quickly back to the ER on the south side of Building 1. I said, "I saw him on Thursday. He seemed the same as always. Said he was going hunting. I asked him, 'For what?' He mumbled something and walked away. I couldn't understand."

When we got there, the cops were shooting a third round of tear gas. On Bill's drone camera, we saw it worked for about a minute, putting Rudy on the floor face down before dissipating. When he stood up, his hat fell off. Bill took a quick photo. When Flush and I saw it, we were sure it was Rudy.

Flush, about Rudy's only friend, thought he might be able to talk Rudy down. He approached Capt. Hawkins. "I know this guy. He's a very distraught, neurotic employee here. We were sort of friends a while ago. Can I try to talk to him on the megaphone?"

"Let me think about it," was Hawkins' terse reply.

I dragged Flush aside. "I don't usually give you advice, but you need to be careful. He could kill you."

"I know. But maybe I could at least talk to him."

"Ok. But you're not thinking of going up there, are you?"

"Hell no. No way. I'm no hero."

We were two hours into the standoff, and Hawkins was showing frustrated impatience and anger at his impotence. It wasn't the kind of professional calm we see in the movies. He was still a small-town cop with zero training or experience for this level of derangement. I couldn't blame him. He was holding things together, sort of, and getting little help from the hospital staff.

By then, the county cops had brought their huge, heavily armored, 12-ton MRAP, a refugee from the Iraq war. Designed to withstand a landmine, it had been unused for about four years, sitting in some police warehouse, unneeded. It was driven to the three parking lots and used to shield EMTs, who picked up wounded and dead. At that time, there were two dead and six bleeding victims to be retrieved. When it arrived with the wounded, the ER docs and nurses earned their salaries, tending to the wounded as they were trained to do. Then, the MRAP went down the freeway to retrieve the eight frightened people from the shot-up and wrecked cars. One was dead, either from a gunshot or an accident.

Hawkins cried out, "Where's the guy who knows the shooter? Where is he? Get him over here! Now!"

Flush immediately responded. "I've known him for about eight years. We worked together in EVS. I taught him Sudoku, which he loves. I don't guarantee anything, but I might be able to mollify him a little. "

Immediately, Takeman interrupted and dragged Hawkins into a side area. We could see them arguing with dramatic hand and arm expressions. There was shouting from Takeman. "He's crazy. He got fired from here. He'll just make things worse! He treats Soduku like a religion. It's a dangerous cult! Don't give him any voice here! He'll really screw things up. He's crazy! He's probably in cahoots with the shooter. They're friends—both are troublemakers!"

From Hawkins, "How could it get worse? We have few options."

Then Takeman again. "Let me talk to him. I know him. He'll listen to me."

"Your anger is all wrong. You'll just make it worse."

Takeman responded, "Listen. This is my hospital. I give the orders now. This is my responsibility. I'm in charge here until the CEO gets here."

"When is he getting here?" asked Hawkins.

"The CEO is a she. She's in San Francisco at a weekend corporate meeting. We called her about this. She's driving back and will be here in about three hours."

"So what do you expect us to do? Wait three hours? Give me her phone number."

"I'm sorry. I'm under very strict orders to never give out her private number."

"This is an extreme emergency. I need to speak with her immediately. We can't wait for three hours."

"No. I could lose my job. I can't give it to you."

"Well, then, we have more than one problem. Do you want me to withdraw from here with all my men? Cause that's what you're provoking by your lack of cooperation."

"No, of course not. Just stay here and keep doing what you've been doing. Just let me talk to him. He always listens to me."

"I'm going against my instincts and training, but I'll give you one minute. But calm down. Your anger won't work." They went outside, where Hawkins took the megaphone from the lieutenant and handed it to Takeman.

Takeman took three deep breaths and started shouting, but nothing was amplified. Hawkins showed him to pull the trigger on the megaphone. Takeman pulled the trigger and launched into a militaristic, domineering exhortation, totally frustrated, "Rudy! Rudy! We know it's you. Stop this immediately! You're going to get killed! This is Dalton Takeman, your boss. If you don't stop now, I'll fire you! Come down immediately! Throw your weapons down, NOW!"

BANG! BANG! BANG! BANG!

Laughter from the roof. "Come up and get me, you coward! You're the bastard who makes my life miserable! Fuck you and all the nazi communists you work for. Leave us workers alone. We do the real work. For you! Fuck you, you stuck-up Antifa bastard! I stand with the 2nd Amendment!"

Hawkins demanded the megaphone from Takeman. "Yeah. You were great." His sarcasm was obvious.

From the roof: "I have the Second Amendment on my side. You can't have my guns. I have Freedom of Speech."

Then Hawkins said in a forced friendly voice, "Rudy. This is Captain Hawkins. I want to help you. But you got'ta help me. What do you want? What can I do for you?"

Long pause. No gunshots.

"I want to talk to Trump. Put the president on the line."

"We can't do that. He's not here."

"I like Donald Trump. I'll do what he says."

"I wish I could, but I can't get him. He's in Washington, DC, or someplace. Maybe Florida."

One of the security guards noticed, hanging from the overpass 1/2 mile away, was a large sign that read "TRUMP 2020." We wondered how it got there since police were supposed to stop people from crossing that overpass. Later, we wondered if it was coordinated with the shooter.

About that time, Turdex came and started milling around in the driveway under the roof outside the ER. One of the local radio stations was interviewing him, at his request. Then he went to Hawkins and asked to speak with Rudy on the megaphone.

Hawkins: "Who are you?"

"I'm the guy's boss. I know him well. He'll do what I tell him."

Hawkins: "How many bosses does he have? I thought that Takeman guy was his boss."

Turdex: "He's a higher-up boss. I'm Rudy's immediate boss. Just give me 20 seconds."

Hawkins: "What do you plan to say?"

Turdex: "I'll tell him to give up. He'll do it. He always does what I tell him to do."

Hawkins (very frustrated): "Ok. But make it quick."

Turdex, with megaphone: "Rudy, this is Turdex. You're fired! I cleaned out your locker. What do you want me to do with all that junk?"

Rudy: "Shove it up your stuck-up army ass, you snotty bastard! And take this with it." Bang! Bang! Bang! Bang! Followed by Rudy's triumphant laughter. "And cut off that girly blond ponytail you have. It sheds lice and disease all over the hospital!" More laughter. Bang! Bang! Bang!

Turdex, with more than a hint of intentional cruelty in his tone: "Rudy, you have one last paycheck coming. But you won't be around to spend it. You're going to die up there. Where should I send it?" The snarl in his voice was as tangible as a kick in the groin.

Hawkins, to Turdex: "All right. That's enough. Give me that megaphone. You're making it worse." The lieutenant wrestled the megaphone from Turdex's despotic hands.

Irritated, Hawkins motioned Turdex aside for a (semi) private conversation. "What do you mean talking like that? That's the opposite of what you should say. We don't want to kill him and we don't want him to think he's going to die. What kind of boss are you?"

Turdex: "You don't understand this guy. You have to be tough with him. That's what works!"

Hawkins: "I see why he hates you. If you treat your other employees that way, I bet they all hate you. Get out of here. If you don't leave, I'll have you arrested for obstruction."

Turdex slinked away, shame on his humiliated face, lame in his embarrassed gait.

Hawkins, his lieutenant, and another cop huddled, alone, totally plan-less, to discuss options. Talking didn't seem to work, but there weren't any other options short of calling in a military helicopter, a solution not high on anyone's list. It might get shot down and would definitely escalate the damage to the hospital.

After a pause, Hawkins announced on the megaphone, "Here's a friend of yours. His name is Flush."

"Yeah! Fantastic! Let me talk to him. Send him up." Rudy sounded different, anger gone, excited, maybe friendly.

Takeman, embarrassed and outraged, stormed back inside the ER. He then launched into a shouting tirade. "I'm not responsible for this debacle! I'll see that Hawkins gets fired. He can't override my command. He'll pay, big time! I'm supposed to be in control here. It's my hospital!"

Hawkins told Flush to stop before he started talking. Then Hawkins got into his patrol car and made two short but important phone calls. Ten minutes later, he exited the car and asked to see Takeman, who was inside, still disrupting progress. Takeman came out and faced Hawkins, who said, "I've just spoken with my chief and the governor's office. They both said it was an extreme emergency. My office supersedes yours. I'm in charge now. I appreciate your help, but if you continue to mouth off, out of control, I'll have no choice but to have you escorted off the premises. Do you understand?"

This shut Takeman up. It was his first defeat after eleven years of total tyrannical domination. About five minutes later, I saw him in the ER waiting room being interviewed live on Sacramento TV by a reporter. Salty Dalty was raving, semi-coherent, claiming the police were amateurs, didn't understand medicine (like he did?), and shouldn't be trusted. He said the hospital was not responsible for any deaths or injuries. He claimed he talked to a Diggery Wealth counselor who totally absolved the hospital and corporation of all responsibility. "If law enforcement wants to be in charge, so be it, but all problems are theirs. And so far, they've only made matters worse." And on and on, until the reporter claimed to have to cut to a commercial.

By this time, 2 1/2 hours after the shooting began, two other cameramen from major TV stations down in Sacramento had set up cameras in secure positions in the secure driveway outside the ER waiting room and were recording most of the action on the ground. They also recorded some shaky shots from the drone. They competed with each other for interviews with a few police, doctors, hospital security, and anybody else willing to talk and give an opinion, which came in a variety of suggestions and objections. Salty Dalty's interview was easily the most dramatic for its anger and volume and outrageous non-stop prattling.

Hawkins told Flush to continue. Flush took the megaphone. "Hey Rudy, it's me, Flush. You still doing Sudokus?"

"Yeah. Everyday. I'm gettin 'pretty good. Do you have any now?"

"I do, but I need a guarantee I'll be safe if I come up."

"Flush, I know you live in a house near here, so I didn't shoot at any houses nearby. You're about the only person I'd never shoot."

"Ok, I trust you. We're still friends. I have a big puzzle in my car. I'll get it if you want. We can do it together."

Me, interrupting, to Flush on the ground outside, under cover. "Are you crazy? He could kill you or take you hostage."

Roofed Rudy: "Great. I'd like that. I'll wait."

Flush again, "You got'ta promise you won't hurt me. You got'ta put down the guns when I'm up there. Promise?"

"Of course, Flush. I'd never hurt you. You're the best friend I have. Now."

Both Flush and I wondered why he qualified it with "Now." Flush gave me his keys and told me to go to his car, get the puzzle and markers, and bring them back. Surprisingly, he also told me to bring his dog, Panda, a sweet, long-haired terrier mix that everyone loved. Panda had short legs, a long, chubby body, and a very cute face.

To Rudy: "Ok, Frank will go to my car to get the puzzle and a marker. I'll be up soon."

"Be sure to put the leash on her," Flush told me.

Then Hawkins spoke to Flush. "Are you sure about this? I'm taking a big chance letting you do this. I definitely don't want you to get hurt."

Flush: "I can tell from his tone of voice that he's ok. We have an unusual friendship, but he needs me now. I can tell."

Hawkins: "What is this Sodukee? (mispronunciation) What's it good for?"

Flush dug into his back pocket and pulled out a business card about Sudoku. He handed it to Hawkins. "I teach it to kids here in schools. It trains logical thinking."

Hawkins, suspicious but curious, read the card carefully. Flush could see interest in his face.

Flush said, "Sometime—not now—I'd be happy to show you how it's done. Just give me 20 minutes—maybe 30. You might like it.

It's not a cult. It's in our daily newspaper every day."

Hawkins: "I'll get back to you on that. Let's see how this goes."

Flush to Hawkins: "It's a small puzzle. It does many things, but for Rudy, it allows him to make order out of chaos. It gives him control when he feels he has none. It gives him confidence. It's a low-tech tool to train brain gain. It satisfies a major gap in Rudy's psychological needs. It gives him power and I give him belonging. Both make a big difference to him. His daily life gives him little of either. He needs power and belonging to feel whole. They're what he craves. We've built up mutual trust over our lessons. It's the only reason I'm willing to try this. He trusts me and I think I can trust him. And I know he loves Sudoku. Maybe more than I do."

There was a long pause. Hawkins was impressed, feeling more comfortable now with his decision to give Flush the reins of this potentially wild bucking stallion.

Flush excused himself from Hawkins and megaphoned Rudy: "Frank is getting the puzzle from my car, and a surprise. I'll be up in a few minutes. Can I trust you to not shoot me?"

"Absolutely, Flush. I'm real glad you came. I'd never harm you. You're the only person who understands me."

Flush: "Ok, just wait. I'll be up when I get the puzzle."

Rudy: "Flush, did you notice I didn't shoot any houses? I know you live somewhere near here and I didn't want to hurt your house." Rudy's repetition was, in this case, confirmation of his sincere respect for Flush. It reaffirmed in Flush's mind his safety.

While I was gone, Flush spoke with Capt. Hawkins. "I need you to guarantee you and your men won't interfere. You won't intrude on us other than to watch with the drone. I'm sure I'll be safe. I know Rudy. He won't shoot me. But If you or your police try anything, I think Rudy will react very badly and I might get killed. Will you promise you won't come up there while I'm there with Rudy? If you won't promise, I won't go."

"You have my word. You're doing something we can't do. I appreciate your help and hope you're right about trusting this madman. I just insist you at least wear a bulletproof vest under your shirt. We can't protect you. I just hope you know what you're doing. He seems to like you. And I pray for you. God bless you for this."

Actually, while Flush was still working, two years ago, before quitting and spending time with Rudy doing Sudokus together, Flush told me that Rudy was mostly still a mystery to him. He had empathy for Rudy but was never sure of Rudy's temperament or next move. Still, Sudoku seemed to calm Rudy down and make him more reasonable. Flush seemed about 90% sure he'd be safe. He knew, as we all did that Rudy liked and trusted nobody, so his relationship with Rudy was very rare, if not unique. Of course, there was that unknown 10%.

Hawkins gave Flush the bulletproof vest and helped him put it on. It didn't show under Flush's jacket and shirt.

When I returned with the puzzle and marker and Panda, Flush, with the megaphone, said to Rudy, "I have the puzzle now. I'll come up. I'll be the only one with you on the roof. We'll work the puzzle together like we used to do."

"Ok. Come on up. I promise you'll be safe."

Flush, six armed police, and Hawkins prepared to go up to the second-floor elevator together. Flush asked if I could come too. Hawkins hesitated and then asked, "What for?"

Flush said, "I'd just feel more comfortable if he was nearby. He's a close friend and knows Rudy, too."

"We almost never take civilians into potential danger," Hawkins replied, "but if he promises to stay back out of the way, he can come. I might be crazy to trust you." He was looking at me. "Bad enough, I'm allowing the dog to go."

"Don't worry. I'll stay out of your way," I said.

So, I was included and had no intention of joining Flush on the roof. I didn't share Flush's confidence in Rudy's stability and promise of safety. I was scared for Flush and would have prayed for him were I the praying sort. It was very scary.

When we got to the second floor, outside the elevator, I saw two security guards and two policemen who had been stationed there for hours in case Rudy decided to come down. They were safe and saw no action, but their position had been smart and added security.

Nobody knew what to expect. Rudy was unpredictable and dangerous. Everyone feared he'd rove the hospital, shooting hundreds of shots everywhere. He knew the layout much better than the police did and had three assault rifles. Fortunately, he never came down off the roof, where he knew he was safe and in command. Rudy's power on the roof with three rifles was an extremely unique experience for him.

On the second floor, outside the elevator, before Flush opened the elevator door to enter, Hawkins handed Flush a cell phone. "This is connected to my phone. You need to hide it in your jacket and keep it on so we can hear what's happening in case there's trouble. Do you understand?"

Flush nodded. "Yes. And I need you to promise again there will be no shots fired unless he fires first. And you won't come up there as long as I'm up there and there's no danger. And you and your men will not harm Rudy if he surrenders. He's not big, and without a gun, he's not dangerous. If I can talk him down, you must treat him gently. Handcuff him in front, not in the back. "

"You have my word. Hear that, gentlemen?" Hawkins asked the six police. "Cuff him in front." They all nodded affirmatively. They were beginning to show in their faces a respect for Flush I had never seen from cops before.

Hawkins asked Flush, "Do you want a pistol? We can hide it on you."

There was a long pause while Flush considered this unexpected (though justified) option. "No. I wouldn't use it right. It would just cause trouble. He's much better with guns than I am. Thanks, but I better not."

I said to Flush, "You can always back out, but this is your last chance."

"No. I feel good about this. I may not get him down, but he won't shoot me. I'm sure of that. And I think Panda will calm him down. Maybe. Let's hope." He pushed the elevator button. The door opened. Flush and Panda stepped in.

While the seven armed police and I waited below on the second floor, Flush, Sudoku puzzle and marker in hand, Panda on a leash, went up alone in the elevator. Mike, head security, had given the elevator key to Flush.

Hawkins said to his men and me, "We need absolute silence. Any noise here will be heard up there." We all nodded assent. He put his cell phone on speaker, so we all could hear their dialogue.

Bill was still on the ground outside the ER, operating the camera on the drone. He had just replaced the battery in the drone, so it was good for at least 20 minutes. He was in phone contact with another policeman who was around the corner from us on the second floor. If the drone showed any imminent violence on the roof, Bill could report it to Hawkins 'police, and they could intervene in about ten seconds, the time it would take to deliver police up one floor to the roof.

When the elevator door opened onto the heliport, Flush stayed inside, holding the enlarged Sudoku, rolled up. Rudy, 20 feet away, greeted Flush with a smile. He was still holding a rifle. "Rudy, I'm alone and unarmed. You have to put down the gun."

Rudy was standing in the middle of the heliport, unseen from the ground. Only the drone could see him. Rudy slowly put the gun at his feet, stood up, and said, with obvious sincerity, "I'm glad to see you. I was hoping you'd come. Oh, who's that?" He pointed to Panda.

"This is Panda. I thought you'd want to meet her."

"Oh yes!"

Flush hesitated but then came slowly out of the elevator a few feet. He was justifiably unsure of this perilous situation. The elevator door closed behind him. He told me later he started to regret his audacity for a moment. But there was no turning back now.

"So what's going on? What happened?"

"Jenny left me. I went hunting Friday afternoon, and when I came home Saturday, she was gone."

"Maybe she'll come back."

"No. All her clothes and stuff were gone. Both her suitcases gone. The house felt so empty. I know she's gone back to the Philippines."

"That's expensive. Did she have money to buy a ticket?"

"We had about $900 hidden in a drawer. It was gone when I looked."

"Did she say anything before you went hunting? Did you have a fight?"

"Oh no. I loved her and treated her real good. I never said a cross word. She was my whole life."

"Can you think of anything that might have set her off?"

"She wanted a baby. We both did. We tried for years, but it never happened. I guess she just got tired of waiting. She was 33 years old and thought her time was running out. Maybe that was it."

"Yeah, that was probably it. It wasn't your fault. Sometimes, women are difficult. I've been there."

"Most women are hard to understand."

Flush agreed. "That's why I never got married after my wife died. I dated but got my heart broken twice. I know now it was a serious depression, though I didn't realize it then. Both times, I was depressed for about a year."

"Yeah. I think I have depression now. So I'm here. I didn't know what else to do. I just had to take it out on somebody. The world is cruel to me. Can I hold Panda?"

"Sure. She's very friendly to everyone."

They both sat on the rooftop, facing each other. Flush handed Panda to Rudy, who held Panda on his lap affectionately. Panda reciprocated, licking Rudy's hand.

"Did you ever consider adoption? Some couples solve their problem that way."

"We talked about it once…but got into a fight and couldn't agree. I dreamed about being adopted when I was a kid, so I was open to the idea. But I didn't want an

American baby. Americans are really fucked, and I didn't want a pure American kid. But she wanted an American boy. She thought he'd have the best chance to succeed. They have different ideas in the Philippines. So adoption never came up again. Now I wish I gave in."

"Well, let's do this Sudoku together. We haven't done one together since I left. Like old times. It'll be fun." Flush unrolled the enlarged 2' by 2' puzzle and put it on the roof floor between them.

"I got Jenny doing Sudokus. She let me teach her. I've gotten good at it. I do about 4 or 5 every day. It helps me relax. Jenny was learning real good. We had fun together. I'd do anything to get Jenny back." He said this as though there were few things they enjoyed together.

They started solving the intermediate puzzle. Flush was impressed by Rudy's sophisticated approach, finding solutions that required a more knowledgeable recognition of elusive patterns. This was what made these puzzles harder than beginning puzzles. Whenever one found a solution to a small cell, he'd mention it to the other and show the proof. They'd worked this way many times before, during lunches, when Flush still had a job there. They worked quietly. Rudy subconsciously petted Panda, who was good at showing the love that Rudy desperately needed then (and always).

Then Flush broke their concentration. "You know, you have a decision to make. This is all your call. You're in charge here. It's your life, so you decide. What are you going to do?"

"I don't know. Let's just keep doing the Sudoku, for now. I'm so confused about everything. I can't decide yet."

"Ok. Take your time. But you're in charge of this."

"You know, when I got home yesterday, I knew something was wrong. I saw the puzzle book Jenny and I did together. She tore out the last ten pages and took them with her. Just like she took my heart." He could barely speak. He was choking up, almost in tears.

"You were good at teaching her Sudoku. You made a good impression on her."

"I wish her mother thought so. She hated me. Never did approve. But her dad came to live with us a while. He was ok. Nice guy. My age. But then he left last year."

There was a long silence while they worked on the puzzle.

Then Rudy asked, "What do you think I should do?"

"I think you should give up. Otherwise, there's no good escape. Too many police. Trump can't help you."

"What will happen? Will I go to jail?"

"Either that or a mental institution, which would be better. I don't know. But they have this place surrounded. You'll never escape. And you're running out of targets. No one's moving within a mile of here. The cops shut everything down."

"I'm just so dammed tired of always feeling weak, laughed at, always angry, powerless! Well, I ain't powerless now! I bet they're not laughing at me now."

"I know. Sometimes, people are cruel. They were cruel to me, too. But not like they treated you."

They worked the puzzle in silence for about five more minutes. Rudy found a hidden triple, which solved a cell. Flush was impressed. "Wow. I didn't see that. You've gotten really good at this."

"What would you do?" asked Rudy, trusting Flush's judgement.

"I'd give up. At least I'd be alive and still have a future. I know it feels bad now, but you'll get over Jenny in a year or so. You could still have a life. Unless you give up, you'll never get off this roof alive. They got you outnumbered."

"But in jail...prison even..., without Jenny, would be real hard for me. I don't know that it's worth it. I really miss her already. We all got to die sometime. Maybe this is my time."

"I know. But we all recover from losses. I did, and you will, too. God will forgive what you've done today. It's your decision. You're in charge of what happens from here. Live or die, it's your call. You're in control of this. Nobody else. You've learned a lot about Sudoku. You could teach it to people wherever you end up. They need it the same way you did. You could help lots of lost souls. Think about it."

They worked on the puzzle quietly again. Rudy found a solution. "What's that?" asked Flush.

"That's a finned X-wing." He pointed it out to Flush.

"Wow! I didn't see that. You're probably better than me now."

"I've never taught anything before. I couldn't ever teach Sudoku—to prisoners! No way!"

"You taught it to Jenny, didn't you?"

"Yes...but...that was Jenny. She wanted to learn."

"Prisoners are trapped, with no place to go and not much to do. Most of 'em are bored. Half of them would love to learn a puzzle that occupies and stretches their minds. They might like you...a lot. And learning Sudoku would give them confidence."

"That makes sense, but me? Why don't you teach them?"

"I'm not going to be stuck there."

"Oh yeah." He got silent in thought. They worked the puzzle quietly.

Flush interrupted the silence. "Like everything we do, the first time you teach a class will be scary; that's normal, and you'll fumble some. The second time, you'll fumble again, but not as much. And it won't be as scary. Like everything we do, the more you teach a small—maybe five prisoners—class of Sudoku, the easier it will be. After a month, it won't be scary anymore. You'll win; just keep going and be stronger than the scary. Then you're in charge, and scary loses his power to stop you. You win!"

Rudy interrupted. "I just don't know if I can do it the first time. I've never seen a Sudoku class before. How can I teach it?"

"If they let me, and I'd love to do it, I could teach a few classes with you watching, so you'll have a better idea of how to teach Sudoku. Together, we could make a big contribution to prison reform. Raising self-esteem has to be good for prisoners. And you'd be very good at it since you love Sudoku and see its emotional value."

Rudy again. "You make it sound so easy, but I can't see myself in front of a class. I used to skip classes all the time in school."

Flush continued, "You know, the most important thing about teaching is loving your subject. If you love your subject, the rest will eventually take care of itself. Teachers make mistakes all the time, generally at first, but most teachers, if they love their subject, get real good. Students see that and love them. I know that's true."

There was a long pause in their conversation. Both men concentrated on the puzzle. Flush found a solution, a remote, uncommon pattern that yielded an answer to one cell. "Wow!" from Rudy. "That was almost invisible. How'd you see that?"

"Sometimes I surprise myself. Just like you will do when you become the first prisoner to teach Sudoku to other prisoners. Gradually, after watching me, you'll become a very strong teacher. It will become very important to you. The most important part of your life. Surprise yourself—do it—and a year from now, you will thank me. And many of your students will thank you. And I'll do what I can to convince the prison administration and the court to let you teach it. I promise. Cause I love Sudoku, too. "

That brought a proud smile to Rudy's usually distraught face. "Ok. I've decided. I'm gon'na give up. Will you go with me?"

"As far as they'll let me. The police promised me they wouldn't hurt you. You sure?"

"Yeah, I'm sure. Let's go before I change my mind and chicken out. I don't want to die yet. I guess I want to live."

They stood up slowly and walked to the elevator door. Rudy carried Panda in his arms. Suddenly, Rudy handed Panda back to Flush, turned, and ran back to the puzzle that was left on the heliport floor. So was his rifle. He picked up the puzzle and walked back to Flush. "We haven't finished it yet."

THE END

About the Book's Name

Flush and I had many discussions to name this book, which we both liked. My first suggestion was "The Peristalsis of NCMH." Peristalsis described our job moving trash through and out of NCMH, which stands for Northern California Memorial Hospital, the altered name of our employer. But Flush thought it was too obscure, too elite, and too esoteric, so would reduce sales and chance of publication. And he didn't like the acronym, which is totally unknown.

He suggested "David's Rock" as a title, a referral to the Old Testament battle between David and Goliath. It did describe our low position as underdogs in the blue-collared level of the hierarchy and made the book the "rock" that brought down a clumsy, cruel, and huge opponent. It optimistically predicts our victory over the hospital's Goliath. And I was the hurler, David.

Flush considered himself an "underdog on a short leash" and a "whistle-blower without a whistle." He thinks that if this book succeeds, it could be the stone that felled Goliath. Or it would at least wake administrators up. I feel the same way, but so far, Goliath stands.

I liked this title at first, but upon reflection, I considered it was too religious, if correctly understood, and easily misunderstood. Would today's audience recognize the biblical reference? It would work for most of Flush's generation, but we millennials aren't so religious.

So together, Flush and I came up with the current title, "Our Angry Hospital."

It was simple, clear, and easily understood, so good communication, as Flush always recommended. And it made the point that wonderful institutions, like hospitals that employ many terrific healers, save many lives, and improve many others, can also go wrong with poor management that makes ruinous decisions. Employees are the hearts and souls of hospitals. They shouldn't be ignored. Doing so is ailing.

Even hospitals can be ailing, and many ailments are non-medical.

About the Author

With two college degrees (BA and MA) and a precarious financial situation, at age 62, Jerry Martin took a job as an attendant (janitor) in a local hospital in a small town in the Sierra Nevada foothills in northern California. He intended to work there for about 3 months until he found a job more suitable to his training and interests. However, he found attributes of this manual labor job appealing and worked there for 14 years, one of 850 employees.

During this time, his department, Environmental Services, comprising female housekeepers and male janitors, went through 10 different managers. Also, a large corporation bought this hospital, and management went from local to San Francisco, which resulted in more authoritarian decision-making motivated by profit and far less friendly, to the disadvantage of the workforce. He witnessed many events that comprise the plot of this book, describing frequent blue-collar vs.

white-collar battles. Most managers and administrators employed leadership styles of dysfunctional power over rather than functional power with. Morale suffered on most levels, and many seasoned professionals took early retirement. The work environment became unpleasant, and many nursing positions were filled by inexperienced recent college graduates who were paid less, saving the corporation from higher salaries.

Martin has published two non-fiction books on education, *Why and How Sudoku in Schools* and *Active Video*. Now single and retired, he has become a dedicated proponent of raising Sudoku from merely a pastime to a powerful and practical training 'tool' for developing logical, emotional, and social intelligence in children, seniors, and jail inmates.